THE THEORY OF FUNCTIONS OF REAL VARIABLES

INTERNATIONAL SERIES IN
PURE AND APPLIED MATHEMATICS

William Ted Martin and E. H. Spanier
CONSULTING EDITORS

AHLFORS · Complex Analysis
BELLMAN · Stability Theory of Differential Equations
BUCK · Advanced Calculus
CODDINGTON AND LEVINSON · Theory of Ordinary Differential Equations
DETTMAN · Mathematical Methods in Physics and Engineering
EPSTEIN · Partial Differential Equations
GOLOMB AND SHANKS · Elements of Ordinary Differential Equations
GRAVES · The Theory of Functions of Real Variables
GREENSPAN · Introduction to Partial Differential Equations
GRIFFIN · Elementary Theory of Numbers
HAMMING · Numerical Methods for Scientists and Engineers
HILDEBRAND · Introduction to Numerical Analysis
HOUSEHOLDER · Principles of Numerical Analysis
LASS · Elements of Pure and Applied Mathematics
LASS · Vector and Tensor Analysis
LEPAGE · Complex Variables and the Laplace Transform for Engineers
NEHARI · Conformal Mapping
NEWELL · Vector Analysis
ROSSER · Logic for Mathematicians
RUDIN · Principles of Mathematical Analysis
SAATY AND BRAM · Nonlinear Mathematics
SIMMONS · Introduction to Topology and Modern Analysis
SNEDDON · Elements of Partial Differential Equations
SNEDDON · Fourier Transforms
STOLL · Linear Algebra and Matrix Theory
STRUBLE · Nonlinear Differential Equations
WEINSTOCK · Calculus of Variations
WEISS · Algebraic Number Theory

THE THEORY OF FUNCTIONS OF REAL VARIABLES

LAWRENCE M. GRAVES
Professor of Mathematics
University of Chicago

Second Edition

McGRAW-HILL BOOK COMPANY, INC.

New York Toronto London

1956

THE THEORY OF FUNCTIONS OF REAL VARIABLES

Library of Congress Catalog Card Number 55-11565

V

24145

THE MAPLE PRESS COMPANY, YORK, PA.

PREFACE

Modern mathematics has tended to emphasize more and more the abstract point of view because of its economy and power and the light it throws on special cases. To guide the student more adequately in this direction, two new chapters have been added in this edition: Chap. XIII on the general theory of sets and relations and Chap. XIV on the properties of abstract metric spaces. A properly prepared student may go immediately to these chapters after a brief look at Chap. I. But since many students can appreciate a general theory only after a thorough examination of more familiar special systems, the first twelve chapters are retained essentially as they appeared in the first edition. The notions of continuity, derivative, and the Riemann integral, familiar from the calculus, are studied here in connection with the more general notions of semicontinuity, derivates, and the Lebesgue integral. The reader is guided toward the abstract point of view by the study of several postulate systems in Chap. II and by the study of several function spaces in Chaps. VII, X, XI, and XII.

Since mathematical proofs are deductive in nature, a brief exposition of some of the fundamental concepts and methods of deductive logic is included in Chap. I. Chapter II begins with the postulates of Peano for the natural numbers and outlines a method for constructing the real-number system. It includes the theorem on the embedding of an abstract commutative semigroup in a group and the theorem on the completion of a linearly ordered system by means of Dedekind cuts. Chapter V includes a generalization of the theorem of the mean to nondifferentiable functions and a careful treatment of total differentials of any order for functions of several variables. Chapter VIII contains some theorems on the extent of the domain of functions defined implicitly and a theorem on the existence of fixed points for continuous transformations. In Chap. IX are some theorems on the extent of the domain of solutions of ordinary differential equations. The Lebesgue integral is introduced in Chap. X by the method of F. Riesz, which is preferred by the author because it leads directly to the fundamental theorems on approximation and convergence. Thus the reader may learn about the main features of the Lebesgue integral from the first six sections of Chap. X. Some miscellaneous formulas and theorems connected with Lebesgue integrals are collected in Chap. XI. A large part of Chaps. X and XI is immediately interpretable for the Lebesgue-Stieltjes integral of functions of several variables, the exceptions being marked with a dagger. The classical Stieltjes integral for functions of one variable is discussed in Chap. XII, and additional properties of the Lebesgue-Stieltjes integral are developed. A large number of convergence theorems are collected in Chaps. XI and XII. In view of the material in Chaps. X to XII, the treatment of Riemann integrals in Chap. VI may seem unnecessary. However, the Riemann integral is a strictly elementary concept of the calculus, and the treatment given it in Chap. VI introduces the student to ideas that are useful in developing the integrals of Lebesgue and Stieltjes. The careful study of uniform convergence in Chap. VII is needed to prepare the student to understand the more general types of convergence associated with the Lebesgue integral. The fundamental theorem of Moore on interchange of order of limits is used repeatedly in later chapters. Chapter XIII includes a careful study of ordinal and cardinal numbers, using the definition of ordinals introduced by von Neumann. It also treats the axiom of choice and the several commonly used propositions which are equivalent to it.

Selections from the book may be used as bases for a variety of courses. For example, Chaps. I to VII, with portions of Chaps. VIII and IX, form a substantial introduction to the classical theory of functions of real variables. Chapters III to VII may be used for a shorter course. A course on fundamental concepts of mathematics may be based on Chaps. I, II, and XIII. Chapter XIV may serve as an introduction to abstract topology. Chapter X may be used for a short course on the Lebesgue integral of functions of one variable, with the measure $m(i)$ of an interval interpreted as its length. Part of Chap. XII may be read independently of the rest as an exposition of the Stieltjes integral. A more extended course on the Lebesgue-

Stieltjes integral may be based on Chaps. X, XI, and XII, with $m(i)$ as a general-measure function. The theory is developed here in such a way that the student who has mastered it will readily understand its generalizations to abstract spaces.

For some of the theorems the proofs are only sketched or are omitted entirely. The completion of these proofs is an important exercise for the reader, but may require some guidance from an instructor. In addition, many of the chapters contain lists of exercises, of varying degrees of difficulty.

At the end of each chapter selected references are given relating to the content of that chapter. The student should form the habit of making use of some of these references. Numbers in square brackets are used in the text to indicate references from these lists.

For the sake of coherence, the two new chapters contain some repetitions of material. For reasons explained in the text, they also introduce a few notations and definitions which are inconsistent with those used in the earlier chapters.

The author acknowledges his indebtedness to many books and authors. It would be impossible to state this indebtedness in detail, and in fact little attempt is made to give a historical account or to give credit to sources. However, the profound influence of Professors G. A. Bliss and E. H. Moore will no doubt be obvious to many who read these pages.

Special acknowledgments are due to Professors R. W. Barnard, W. T. Reid, and E. H. Spanier for valuable criticisms and suggestions. Professor Spanier also contributed many of the exercises in Chaps. XIII and XIV.

LAWRENCE M. GRAVES

CONTENTS

Preface v

CHAPTER I. INTRODUCTION

1. The Purpose of an Introductory Course in the Theory of Functions 1
2. Fundamental Logical Notions 2
3. The Class Calculus 7
4. Relations and Functions 11
5. Résumé of the Symbols for Logical Connectives 12
6. Remarks on Various Bases for Logic 14
   References 15

CHAPTER II. THE REAL NUMBER SYSTEM

1. Introduction 17
2. The Natural Numbers 18
3. Groups and Semigroups 23
4. The Embedding of a Semigroup in a Group 24
5. The Positive Rational Numbers 26
6. Linearly Ordered Sets 27
7. Dedekind Cuts 28
8. Construction of the Real Number System 29
9. Properties Characterizing the Real Number System 33
10. Additional Properties of the Real Number System 35
    References 39

CHAPTER III. POINT SETS

1. Space of k Dimensions 40
2. Examples of Point Sets 41
3. Operations on Aggregates 42
4. Some Fundamental Definitions and Theorems of Point-set Theory 43
5. Sequences of Points, and the Weierstrass-Bolzano Theorem . . 49
6. The Heine-Borel Theorem 51
   References 52

CHAPTER IV. FUNCTIONS AND THEIR LIMITS. PROPERTIES OF CONTINUOUS FUNCTIONS

1. Introduction 54
2. Upper and Lower Bounds and Limits of Functions 56
3. Continuous and Semicontinuous Functions 63
   References 68

CHAPTER V. FUNDAMENTAL THEOREMS ON DIFFERENTIATION

1. Functions of One Variable 69
2. Differentiation of Functions of Several Variables 75
3. Indeterminate Forms 81
References 84

CHAPTER VI. THE RIEMANN INTEGRAL

1. Conditions for the Existence of the Integral. 85
2. The Fundamental Theorem of Integral Calculus 90
3. Further Properties of the Integral. 94
References 97

CHAPTER VII. UNIFORM CONVERGENCE

1. The Cauchy Condition for Uniform Convergence 98
2. Interchange of Order in Repeated Limits 100
3. Infinite Series 107
4. The Space of Continuous Functions 116
5. Discontinuous Functions 126
References 132

CHAPTER VIII. FUNCTIONS DEFINED IMPLICITLY

1. Introduction 134
2. Solutions Defined near an Initial Solution 135
3. Maximal Sheets of Solutions 141
4. An Extended Implicit Function Theorem 144
5. Implicit Function Theorems without Differentiability. 145
References 150

CHAPTER IX. ORDINARY DIFFERENTIAL EQUATIONS

1. Conditions Ensuring the Existence of Solutions. 151
2. Special Properties of Linear Homogeneous Differential Equations 161
3. An Embedding Theorem, and the Differentiability of Solutions . 163
4. First Integrals. 168
5. Equations in the Form $F(x, y, y') = 0$ 170
References 172

CHAPTER X. THE LEBESGUE INTEGRAL

1. Introduction 173
2. Point Sets and Functions of Intervals 174
3. Definition and Properties of the Integral. 180
4. Measurable Sets and Functions 195
5. Differentiation of Functions of One Variable 201
6. The Fundamental Theorem of Integral Calculus 207
7. Rectifiable Curves 211
References 214

CHAPTER XI. THE LEBESGUE INTEGRAL

1. Differentiation with Respect to a Parameter 215
2. Fubini's Theorem on Reduction of Multiple to Repeated Integrals 215
3. Integration by Parts 220
4. Change of Variables. 221
5. Integrals over Unbounded Domains 227
6. Invariance of Lebesgue Integrals and Lebesgue Measure of Sets under Motion 230
7. Mean Value Theorems 230
8. The Inequalities of Schwarz, Hölder, and Minkowski 232
9. A Criterion for Uniform Absolute Continuity 235
10. Modes of Convergence 236
11. Orthonormal Systems in the Space $\mathfrak{L}_2$ 247
12. Additional Theorems on Differentiation 252
13. Integral Means 254
References 259

CHAPTER XII. THE STIELTJES INTEGRAL

1. Definitions and First Properties 260
2. Functions of Bounded Variation 267
3. Further Definitions and Relations between Integrals 269
4. Convergence Theorems. 281
5. Linear Continuous Operations on the Space $\mathfrak{C}$ 292
6. Remarks on Improper, Multiple, and Repeated Stieltjes Integrals 295
References 296

CHAPTER XIII. THE THEORY OF SETS AND TRANSFINITE NUMBERS

1. Introduction 297
2. The Algebra of Sets. 297
3. Relations and Functions 300
4. Partial Ordering. 304
5. Ordinal and Cardinal Numbers 308
6. Explicit Definition of Ordinal Numbers 311
7. The Natural Numbers 314
8. Finite Cardinals and the Alephs 316
9. Algebra of Ordinals and Cardinals 317
10. The Axiom of Choice and Zorn's Lemma. 321
11. Algebra of Ordinals and Cardinals (*Continued*) 327
References 333

CHAPTER XIV. METRIC SPACES

1. Introduction 335
2. Definition of Metric Spaces 335
3. Spheres, Neighborhoods, Open Sets, and Closed Sets 339
4. Convergence and Continuity of Functions, Homeomorphisms, and Topological Properties 341

5. Complete Spaces 346
6. Connected Sets 351
7. Separable Spaces 354
8. Compact Spaces and Sets 356
9. Category of Sets 365
References 370

Index 371

CHAPTER I

INTRODUCTION

1. The Purpose of an Introductory Course in the Theory of Functions.—The following chapters are written with a threefold purpose in mind. The first is to afford the student a survey of the field of analysis from its foundations. Modern analysis is based on the system of natural numbers and its properties. In Chap. II is outlined a method for constructing the real number system and for proving its properties on the basis of the properties of the system of natural numbers. The second purpose is to review the fundamental concepts and theorems of the calculus. The reader is supposed to have reached the stage where he can understand precise statements of these fundamental concepts and rigorous proofs of the theorems. In the following chapters are included some theorems for which fallacious or incomplete proofs are frequently given in elementary calculus texts. The third purpose is to acquaint the student with the theorems and the methods of investigation that are fundamental for modern research in analysis. These theorems and methods are frequently used also in other branches of mathematics and in the applications of mathematics.

It should be emphasized that mathematics is concerned with ideas and concepts rather than with symbols. Symbols are tools for the transference of ideas from one mind to another. Concepts become meaningful through observation of the laws according to which they are used. This introductory chapter is concerned with certain fundamental notions of logic and of the calculus of classes. It will be understood better after the student has become familiar with the use of these concepts in the later chapters. Consequently it is recommended that after a bird's-eye view of the contents of Chap. I, the student should pass on to a study of Chap. II, returning to Chap. I from time to time as occasion arises.

Numbers in brackets refer to the list of references at the end of the chapter.

2. Fundamental Logical Notions.—Logic is largely concerned with the study of the laws governing the use of logical connectives or operators which apply to statements to form more complex statements.[1] The situation is quite analogous to elementary algebra, which is concerned with the laws governing the operations of addition, multiplication, etc., as applied to numbers.

As undefined operations on statements, whose meaning is generally understood, we may take **negation, conjunction,** and **alternation.** If p and q denote statements, the negation of p is denoted by $-p$ (or sometimes by $\sim p$, or by p'). The conjunction of p and q is denoted by $p.q$, read "p and q." The alternation of p and q is denoted by $p \vee q$, read "p or q." We wish to consider these operations independently of the truth or falsity of the statements p and q. To make the meaning of $p \vee q$ completely unambiguous it is perhaps necessary to remark that the statement $p \vee q$ is true when p and q are both true as well as when only one of them is true.

Other logical connectives or operators may be defined in terms of those already given. The conditional is denoted as follows: $p \supset q$, which may be read "p only if q," or "if p then q." This is defined to mean

$$-p \vee q.$$

Thus of the following four conditional statements:

(2:1)	If $1 < 2$, then $3 < 4$,
(2:2)	If $2 < 1$, then $3 < 4$,
(2:3)	If $1 < 2$, then $4 < 3$,
(2:4)	If $2 < 1$, then $4 < 3$,

only (2:3) is false, while the other three are true. The words "implies" and "implication" have not been used in the above discussion because they have been used by different authors with different meanings and have given rise to some controversy and misunderstanding.

It should be noted that the symbols or formulas

$$p \vee q \qquad \text{and} \qquad p \supset q$$

[1] In what follows, the words "statement," "proposition," and "sentence" are considered as synonymous. Some writers on logic prefer one, some another. Quine [2] defines statements as those sentences which are true and those which are false.

etc., are not themselves statements. They become statements only when specific statements are substituted for the symbols p and q, *i.e.*, when p and q are taken to stand for specific statements. The same is true of

$$-(p . -p), \tag{2:5}$$

$$p \vee -p. \tag{2:6}$$

However, we may form statements from (2:5) and from (2:6) in another way by prefixing the words "Whatever statement p is, . . . ," or "For every statement p, ..." The statements formed in this way happen to be true in both these cases. Irrespective of their truth or falsity, they are said to be formed from (2:5) and (2:6) by application of the **universal quantifier** and are frequently written as follows:

$$(p) . -(p . -p), \tag{2:7}$$

$$(p) . p \vee -p. \tag{2:8}$$

The variable p in (2:5) and (2:6) is called a **real** or **free** variable, while in (2:7) and (2:8) it is said to be **apparent** or **bound.** There is some question as to whether in the use of the universal quantifier, the variable that is bound by it may be allowed to stand for any entity whatever. The use of the notion of the "class of all entities whatever" leads to contradictions if no safeguards are set up. Different types of safeguards have been proposed by various workers in logic. However, it is clear that if p is replaced in (2:5) or (2:6) by the number 3 or by the concept *fright*, the result is not a statement. In the formulas (2:7) and (2:8) the universal quantifier refers implicitly to the class of all statements p. In mathematical practice it turns out that whenever the universal quantifier occurs it may always be taken to refer to some specific class of objects, which is generally recognized to be sufficiently well determined to be the subject of discourse. This class should be explicitly indicated whenever its nature is not sufficiently obvious from the context. The method of procedure just indicated seems to be a practical way of avoiding the paradoxes. It is desirable to use specific classes as the subjects of discourse but, since it is always possible to imagine new objects which are not members of a given class, no such class can be regarded as *the* universal class. For the same reason the objection may well be raised that the class of all statements

p, referred to above, is not a well-determined class. In many ways a pragmatic approach to mathematics seems preferable to that of the modern logicians and is in practice adopted by most mathematicians, either consciously or unconsciously. The work of the logicians is none the less valuable and interesting.

Another logical operator of importance is the biconditional, for which we use one of the notations: $p \sim q$, or $p \equiv q$. This is to be read "p if and only if q," and is defined to mean

$$p \supset q \cdot q \supset p.$$

We shall use the symbol "$\sim$" for this operator except in definitions, where the other symbol "$\equiv$" will be used, with the symbol whose use is being defined placed to the left of the sign.

The following important logical laws relate to the various operators we have been discussing. They hold for all statements p, q, and s. For convenience the symbol for the universal quantifier is omitted in stating these laws. This omission is quite frequently practiced in mathematical writing and will cause no confusion.

(2:9) $$(p.q) \sim (q.p).$$
(2:10) $$(p \vee q) \sim (q \vee p).$$
(2:11) $$(p \sim q) \sim (q \sim p).$$
(2:12) $$-(-p) \sim p.$$
(2:13) $$-(p. -p).$$
(2:14) $$p \vee -p.$$
(2:15) $$-(p.q) \sim (-p \vee -q).$$
(2:16) $$-(p \vee q) \sim (-p. -q).$$
(2:17) $$(p \supset q) \sim (-q \supset -p).$$
(2:18) $$-(p \supset q) \sim (p. -q).$$
(2:19) $$(p \vee q) \vee s \sim p \vee (q \vee s).$$
(2:20) $$(p.q).s \sim p.(q.s).$$
(2:21) $$(p \vee q).s \sim (p.s) \vee (q.s).$$
(2:22) $$(p.q) \vee s \sim (p \vee s).(q \vee s).$$

The first three, (2:9), (2:10), and (2:11), state properties of **symmetry** for ., $\vee$, and $\sim$, *i.e.*, they are commutative laws; (2:12) is the law of **double negation**; (2:13) is the law of **contradiction**; (2:14) is the law of the **excluded middle**; (2:15) and (2:16) are called **de Morgan's laws**; (2:17) is the law of **contraposition** for the conditional; (2:19) and (2:20) are **associative** laws; and (2:21) and (2:22) are **distributive** laws. Note that we are here asserting these statements to be true. The assertion or denial of a statement is a statement about a statement, and so differs from such an operation as the negation of a statement, which transforms a statement into another statement. Thus

"Jones is ill" is false,

differs from

$-$(Jones is ill).

For the study of logic and its structure, it is interesting to note that all the operators we have been discussing may be defined in terms of a single operator, called "joint denial," which is denoted by $(p \downarrow q)$, read "neither p nor q."[1] The three operators that we have previously taken as primitive may be defined in terms of this new operator as follows:

(2:23) $$-p \equiv (p \downarrow p).$$
(2:24) $$(p.q) \equiv (-p \downarrow -q).$$
(2:25) $$(p \vee q) \equiv -(p \downarrow q).$$

On the basis of these definitions the law of the excluded middle becomes a formal consequence of the laws of double negation and of contradiction. The meaning of the operator ($\downarrow$) may be defined by means of a **truth table,** giving the truth value of the statement $(p \downarrow q)$ in terms of the truth values of p and q, as follows. Here "T" stands for "true" and "F" for "false."

p	q	$(p \downarrow q)$
T	T	F
F	T	F
T	F	F
F	F	T

Thus all the logical operators so far mentioned, except the universal quantifier, are definable by means of truth tables, and the relations between them may be derived by means of truth tables, so that if we use the definitions (2:23) to (2:25) above, all the logical laws (2:9) to (2:22) are implicitly contained in the truth-table definition of ($\downarrow$).

A system which could perhaps be called a system of logic can be constructed on the basis of a truth table with three or more

[1] See, for example, Quine [3], pp. 45*ff*.

kinds of entries. In such a system more types of operators present themselves for consideration.[1]

Another quantifier of frequent occurrence is the **existential quantifier.** If $q(x)$ is a statement form or "propositional function" involving a variable x, the symbol

$$\exists x \ni q(x) \tag{2:26}$$

is read "there exists x such that $q(x)$." The symbol $\exists$ is read "there exists" and the symbol $\ni$ is read "such that." The symbol $\ni$ may be used also in other situations to connect a property or a statement to an entity. It is interesting to note that the existential quantifier may be defined in terms of the universal quantifier and the operation of negation. That is, in terms of symbols, the formula (2:26) may be defined to mean

$$-[(x).-q(x)]. \tag{2:27}$$

It is important to be familiar with this relation between (2:26) and (2:27), especially in connection with the making of indirect proofs. Formulas (2:15) to (2:18) are also frequently used in the making of indirect proofs.

It has already been mentioned that the symbol for the universal quantifier will sometimes be omitted. Where it is necessary to indicate this operator, we shall adopt the convention that it is implicit in the conditional and the biconditional. Thus in stating the commutative law for addition we shall write

$$a + b = b + a.$$

This always refers to the elements a and b of a particular class $\mathfrak{M}$ of numbers. In the strict notation of logic this commutative law is written

$$(a).(b).a\epsilon\mathfrak{M} \,.\, b\epsilon\mathfrak{M} \supset a + b = b + a,$$

where the symbol "$a\epsilon\mathfrak{M}$" means "a is a member of $\mathfrak{M}$." Since we are taking the universal quantifier always to refer to a specific class, the initial symbols "$(a).(b)$" may as well be omitted. The statement

$$a\epsilon\mathfrak{M} \,.\, b\epsilon\mathfrak{M} \supset a + b = b + a$$

[1] See, for example, Lewis and Langford [7], pp. 213–234; Bennett and Baylis [4], p. 278.

may be regarded as a relation of implication between two properties. It may be true or false, depending on the meaning assigned to "$\mathfrak{M}$" and "+." This notion of implication is not the same as any of the notions of material implication, strict implication, or logical implication. A discussion of these notions is not essential for our purposes and will be omitted.

Treatises on logic usually include a formal analysis of the relation of class membership, symbolized by "ϵ," and the relation of identity, symbolized by "=." This formal analysis sets forth the rules applicable to these relations, but the intuitive understanding of the meaning of these notions remains fundamental for reasoning. Some writers on mathematics do not use the symbol "=" for identity, but define the meaning of the symbol by means of postulates. In the present work this symbol will be used only to indicate the relation of identity, that is, "$a = b$" means that a and b are symbols standing for the same thing.

3. The Class Calculus.—The meaning of the notions of a class and of class membership will be taken as commonly understood. These notions are fundamental in logic and mathematics. The terms "set," "collection," "family," and "aggregate" will ordinarily be understood to be synonymous with "class." Classes are frequently defined by means of the properties possessed by their elements, *i.e.*, by means of propositional functions. If $q(x)$ denotes a propositional function or statement form involving the variable x, such a definition of a class may be given the following form: The class A is defined to consist of all those elements x such that $q(x)$ is true. The unguarded use of such definitions leads to paradoxes, as in the case of the following: The class A consists of all those classes x such that x is not a member of x. We shall avoid such difficulties by refraining from using the unrestricted variable, that is, in using the form of definition now being discussed, we shall restrict the variable x to range over a definite preassigned class U. The class A defined in this way is then a well-defined subclass of U, provided the statement form $q(x)$ is properly constructed. The use of good judgment in determining when a statement form is acceptable in defining a class seems to be unavoidable. Thus the class of all x who are living humans and have blue eyes is not well determined for mathematical purposes, although the property in question is a practically useful one as an aid to identification. One difficulty lies in drawing the boundary line between blue eyes and gray, and another lies in determining which people are living at any particular instant, since people are continually being born and dying.

Other methods of defining classes are of course needed and will be met in the following chapters. For instance, it is usually admitted that the class of all subclasses of a given class forms a well-defined class.

Parallel to the operations on statements previously discussed are certain operations on classes. The **sum** of two classes A and B is a class $A + B$ consisting of those elements which are members of A or of B. The **complement** cA relative to a "universal" class U of a subclass A of U consists of those elements of U which are not members of A. If the subclass A is identical with U itself, its complement cA cannot have any members. It is convenient to postulate one definite class, called the **null class,** having no members, and to agree that it shall be considered as a subclass of every class. We shall denote the null class by the symbol Λ, or sometimes by 0. Thus if U is the universal class of a given discussion, $cU = \Lambda$. The **difference** $A - B$ of two classes A and B consists of those members of A which are not members of B. Such a difference may of course reduce to the null class. The **product** AB of A and B consists of those elements which are members of both A and B. Sums and products of classes obviously obey the usual commutative and associative laws of algebra. Moreover, there are two distributive laws:

(3:1) $$A(B + C) = AB + AC.$$

(3:2) $$A + BC = (A + B)(A + C).$$

Care must be taken with the operation of taking the difference, because it does not obey the usual laws of algebra relating to subtraction.

The operations of taking sums and products of sets may be extended in an obvious way to quite arbitrary collections of sets. Thus if $\{A_\alpha\}$ denotes a collection of classes distinguished by the different values taken by the index α, the sum of the classes A_α, denoted by $\sum A_\alpha$, consists of all elements x such that there exists an α such that x is a member of A_α. The product, denoted by $\prod A_\alpha$, consists of all elements x that are simultaneously members of all the classes A_α. When the definitions are phrased in this way, there is no question of proving commutative or associative laws.

The Cartesian product $P \times Q$ of two classes P and Q consists of all ordered pairs (p, q) of which the first element p is a member of P and the second element q is a member of Q.

The relation

$$A \text{ is a subclass of } B$$

is indicated by one of the notations

$$A \subset B \qquad \text{or} \qquad B \supset A.$$

As previously indicated, there is a close connection between the operations on classes and the logical operations on statements. Let U be a class of elements x, and let P, Q, and R consist of those elements x of U for which the statements $p(x)$, $q(x)$, and $r(x)$, respectively, are true. In the following symbolic statements we adhere to the convention already mentioned that the universal quantifier is implicit in the conditional and the biconditional. If

$$r(x) \sim p(x) \vee q(x)$$

is true, then $R = P + Q$. If

$$r(x) \sim p(x).q(x)$$

is true, then $R = PQ$. If

$$r(x) \sim -p(x)$$

is true, then $R = cP$. If

(3:3) $$x \supset p(x)$$

is true, then $P = U$. If

(3:4) $$\exists x \ni -p(x)$$

is true, then $cP \neq \Lambda$. As was indicated in the preceding section, the statements (3:3) and (3:4) are the negatives of each other. This simple principle is an important one and frequently needs to be applied several times in an indirect proof. If

$$p(x) \supset q(x)$$

is true, then $P \subset Q$. The laws

$$ccP = P, \tag{3:5}$$

$$PcP = \Lambda, \tag{3:6}$$

$$P + cP = U, \tag{3:7}$$

$$c(PQ) = cP + cQ, \tag{3:8}$$

$$c(P + Q) = (cP)(cQ), \tag{3:9}$$

$$P \subset Q \sim cQ \subset cP, \tag{3:10}$$

correspond, respectively, to the laws (2:12), (2:13), (2:14), (2:15), (2:16), and (2:17) of Sec. 2.

The notion of a class of counters is fundamental for mathematics and may be set up formally in the following way. Let the null class be denoted by 0, the class whose sole element is 0 by $\{0\}$, the class whose sole element is $\{0\}$ by $\{\{0\}\}$, and so on. The counter class C is the class $[0, \{0\}, \{\{0\}\}, \ldots]$. It may be defined as the product of all classes B having the following two properties:

(i) The null set 0 is a member of B;

(ii) If a is a member of B, the class $\{a\}$, whose sole element is a, is also a member of B.

The existence of a class B having the properties (i) and (ii) is an assumption, called the **axiom of infinity.** The counter class C has a number of familiar properties which will be discussed in Chap. II. The elements of C may be considered as representing the natural numbers. A satisfactory definition of the natural numbers seems to be as elusive as a definition of space or time. We can however readily set down the laws according to which we use the natural numbers, just as we set down rules for measuring space and time.

At this point mention should be made of a logical assumption, known as the "axiom of Zermelo," the "axiom of choice," or the "multiplicative axiom," which enters into many mathematical proofs. One form of its statement is as follows:

For every family of nonnull classes A_α, no two of which have an element in common, there is a class B which has exactly one element in common with each class A_α.

A few parts of analysis have been reconstructed by some writers so as to avoid the use of this assumption. For many proofs it is sufficient to assume its validity when only a denumerable infinity of classes A_α are considered.

4. Relations and Functions.—There are many instances of relations occurring in mathematics. An important example is the order relation between real numbers, denoted by "$<$." If the class of real numbers is denoted by R, then $<$ is a relation on RR. It is called a "binary" relation because it involves pairs of elements. Just as a property may be regarded as consisting of the class of elements having that property, so a relation may be regarded as consisting of the class of ordered pairs for which the relation holds true. Thus the relation $<$ between real numbers consists of the points in the xy-plane lying above the line $x = y$. In general a binary relation on PQ is a subset of the Cartesian product $P \times Q$.

A ternary relation consists of a class of ordered triples of elements. An example is the geometric relation of collinearity. This relation has properties of symmetry which mean that the order of the elements is not significant. A ternary relation on PQR may be regarded as a binary relation on SR, where S is the Cartesian product $P \times Q$.

If we admit to consideration multiple-valued functions, as it is frequently convenient to do, a function is nothing more nor less than a relation. The only difference is in the notation, terminology, and emphasis. For example, a relation on PQ may be written in the functional notation as simply

$$(f(p)|p \text{ in } P),$$

where it is understood that $f(p)$ stands for the set of all the elements in Q to which p bears the given relation. If P and Q both consist of all the real numbers and the relation is $<$, then $f(p)$ is the set of all numbers $q > p$. The subset P_0 of P consisting of all those elements p for which $f(p) \neq \Lambda$ is called the **domain** of the function f. The **range** of f is the set $Q_0 = \sum f(p)$. When the set $f(p)$ is singular or null for every p, the function f is said to be **single-valued.** The **inverse function** f^{-1} of f is the relation obtained by reversing the order in the pairs for f. Thus the domain of f^{-1} is the range of f, and vice versa. For example, if for each p, $f(p)$ is the set of all numbers $q > p$, then $f^{-1}(q)$ is the set of all numbers $p < q$. If $f(p) = \sin p$, where the domain is the set of all real numbers, then the range is the interval $-1 \leqq q \leqq 1$, while, for the inverse function $\sin^{-1} q$, the domain is the interval $-1 \leqq q \leqq 1$ and the range is the set of all real numbers. When both f and f^{-1} are single-valued, the function establishes a **one-to-one correspondence** between P_0 and Q_0. A single-valued function having domain P and range contained in Q is frequently referred to as "a function on P to Q."

5. Résumé of the Symbols for Logical Connectives.—The following list of logical symbols and their readings will be useful for reference:

$\vee$	or
.	and
$-$	not
$\supset$	only if, if . . . then . . .
$\sim$	if and only if
$\equiv$	is defined to mean
$\exists$	there exists
$\exists \vert$	there exists uniquely
$\ni$	such that
ϵ	is a member of
$\subset$	is a subset of (between classes).

The reader has no doubt observed that in the more complex logical statements, brackets are frequently needed. In most circumstances it is desirable to replace the brackets by a system of dots, for greater ease in reading and writing the notation. The more inclusive brackets are indicated by the larger number of dots. The symbols $\supset$ and $\sim$ will always be accompanied by dots on both sides. The same will be true for the symbol $\equiv$ except when it is used in defining the symbol for an entity or a class. The symbol $\ni$ will ordinarily be accompanied by dots on the right only. The symbols $\supset$, $\sim$, $\equiv$, and $\vee$ are regarded as superior to the symbol $\ni$ having the same or a fewer number of dots, while "and," which is symbolized by dots only, is inferior to all other symbols accompanied by the same or a greater number of dots. A few examples will make the clear. Thus if R denotes the class of real numbers, the statement

$$\exists y \ni\cdot\, y \epsilon R \,.\, y^2 < x$$

is interpreted to mean "there exists y such that [y is in R and $y^2 < x$]." The statement as a whole expresses a property of the element x. It may form a part of a more complex statement, such as the following:

$$(5{:}1)\quad x \ni : x\epsilon R : \exists y \ni \cdot\, y\epsilon R \,.\, y^2 < x : \supset : z\epsilon R \cdot\supset\cdot\, x > -z^2.$$

Here the universal quantifier is understood to apply to each of the variables x and z, and the class R over which they range is explicitly indicated. The statement (5:1) written out explicitly with brackets reads: "for every x, (if $\{x$ is in R and there exists y such that [y is in R and $y^2 < x$]$\}$ then $\{$for every z [if z is in R then $x > -z^2$]$\}$)." If all the letters are understood to stand for real numbers, the statement (5:1) may be compressed as follows:

$$(5{:}2)\qquad x \ni : \exists y \ni \cdot\, y^2 < x : \supset : z \cdot\supset\cdot\, x > -z^2.$$

This may be read as follows: "if x is such that there exists y such that $y^2 < x$, then for every z, $x > -z^2$." The same meaning may also be conveyed with a different construction, as follows:

$$(5{:}3)\qquad x.z : \supset : \exists y \ni \cdot\, y^2 < x \cdot\supset\cdot\, x > -z^2.$$

If $f(x)$ is a real-valued function of the real variable x, the definition of the property of continuity of f at a point b may be written as follows, if P is used to denote the subclass of R consisting of the positive numbers:

$$(5{:}4)\quad e\epsilon P : \supset : \exists d \ni : d\epsilon P : x\epsilon R.\, |x - b| < d \cdot\supset\cdot\, |f(x) - f(b)| < e.$$

The dots are used to indicate the following bracketing:

$$e\epsilon P \supset \{\exists d \ni [d\epsilon P.\{[x\epsilon R.\, |x - b| < d] \supset |f(x) - f(b)| < e\}]\}.$$

The negative of the statement (5:4) is

$$(5{:}5)\quad \exists e \ni : e\epsilon P : d\epsilon P \cdot\supset\cdot\, \exists x \ni \cdot\, x\epsilon R.\, |x - b| < d.\, |f(x) - f(b)| \nless e.$$

The statement (5:4) is ordinarily abbreviated as follows:

$$(5{:}6)\quad e > 0 : \supset : \exists d > 0 \ni : |x - b| < d \cdot\supset\cdot\, |f(x) - f(b)| < e.$$

EXERCISES

Write the negative of each of the following statements in a form in which no logical connective appears on the right of a symbol for negation. The symbols x, y, and z are understood to stand for numbers of a class M for which an operation of multiplication and an order relation are defined.

1. $x \cdot \supset \cdot \exists y < x$.
2. $x \,.\, y \cdot \supset \cdot xy = yx$.
3. $x \,.\, y \cdot \supset \cdot \exists z \ni \cdot xz = y$.
4. $\exists x \ni : y \cdot \supset \cdot xy = x$.
5. $\exists z \ni : xy = z \cdot \supset \cdot x = z \vee y = z$.
6. $x \neq y \cdot \supset \cdot x < y \vee y < x$.
7. $x < y \cdot \supset \cdot \exists z \ni \cdot x < z \,.\, z < y$.

***6. Remarks on Various Bases for Logic.**—In the preceding sections occasional hints have been given of the problems of modern logic. There is no general agreement on the best solution for these problems. In fact mathematical logic is a field in which controversy is still both possible and profitable.

Some of the problems are raised by the paradoxes that occur in the general theory of classes and of propositions. These paradoxes arise from the consideration of unrestricted variables, the universal class, statements that refer to themselves, and classes that are members of themselves. It seems clear that a statement that refers to itself is not a sensible statement, and so should be excluded from discourse. Also the members of a class must be themselves well-determined before the class containing them as members can be specified, so that it does not make sense to speak of a class that is a member of itself. When any given class of entities is presented for consideration, it is thereupon possible to conceive of a new entity not present in the given class. This ability of the human mind continually to create new concepts indicates that the concept of a universal class containing all entities is not a useful one. In any particular theory, mathematics deals with fixed classes, and the results have been satisfactory to most people.

Many workers in logic would differ from the "common-sense" point of view expressed above. For example, Quine (see [3], pages 163–166) seems to prefer the following criteria of acceptability of a system of logic: (1) it should preserve the unrestricted variable and the universal class; (2) it should be as simple and general as possible while still containing rules that prevent paradoxes from entering the system. Although Quine's rules in

[3] are not sufficient to keep out paradoxes, they do prevent some entities from being members of classes. Moreover, they seem to make the meaning of the notion of class membership somewhat different from that ordinarily assigned to it. Russell proposed a theory of types as a means of keeping out the paradoxes. His theory has been widely discussed but has not been found universally acceptable.

The intuitionist school, led by Brouwer and Weyl, maintains that many of the processes of reasoning commonly used by mathematicians are lacking in justification. For example, it is admitted that one can conceive of as many natural numbers as one wishes and that consideration of these numbers is justifiable. But objection is raised to the consideration of the class of all conceivable or possible natural numbers as a definite closed system. (See Weyl [11], pages 246–249.) Objection is also raised to the use of infinite logical sums and products and to the consideration of the class of all subclasses of a given infinite class. These concepts are fundamental for the construction of the continuum of real numbers, and so for much of modern mathematics. Thus they have at least a pragmatic justification. But for the intuitionists their logical justification is lacking.

An explicit axiomatic basis for the theory of classes as commonly used by mathematicians was formulated by Zermelo (see [12]; also Fraenkel [9], Chap. 5, pages 268*ff.*; Quine [3], pages 163–166). In this basis there is no fixed universal class. The use of infinite classes and of infinite processes is justified by the pragmatic criterion that these concepts have proved useful in exploring and understanding the world of thought and also the world of sense. It is nevertheless interesting and valuable to see what can be done with a more cautious procedure and a more critical point of view.

REFERENCES

1. Tarski, *Introduction to Logic*, 1941.
2. Quine, *Elementary Logic*, 1941.
3. Quine, *Mathematical Logic*, 1940.
4. Bennett and Baylis, *Formal Logic*, 1939.
5. Whitehead and Russell, *Principia Mathematica*.
6. Russell, *Principles of Mathematics*, 2d Ed., 1937.
7. Lewis and Langford, *Symbolic Logic*, 1932.
8. Hilbert und Ackermann, *Grundzüge der theoretischen Logik*, 2d Ed., 1938.

9. Fraenkel, *Einleitung in die Mengenlehre,* 3d Ed., 1928.
10. Brouwer, "Intuitionism and Formalism," *Bulletin of the American Mathematical Society,* Vol. 20 (1913), pp. 81–96.
11. Weyl, "Consistency in Mathematics," *The Rice Institute Pamphlet,* Vol. 16 (1929), pp. 245–265.
12. Zermelo, "Grundlagen der Mengenlehre," *Mathematische Annalen,* Vol. 65 (1908), pp. 261–281.

Tarski [1] and Quine [2] give useful introductions to the ideas and methods of modern logic. Although Quine's treatise [3] involves a contradiction, its first three chapters form an extremely clear and acceptable textbook on the subjects they cover. Much space in Bennett and Baylis [4] is taken up with a discussion of classical logic and with ingenious exercises in deduction. However, this work gives a fairly good exposition of the ideas and methods of modern logic in its latter part. Whitehead and Russell's *Principia* [5] is a monumental work, intended to exhibit how the various branches of mathematics may be built up out of purely logical notions. Russell's *Principles* [6] is an earlier work. The reader should note in the introduction to its second edition the author's outline of how his stand on various problems of logic has changed. The system of strict implication is explained at length in Lewis and Langford [7], and the formalist point of view in logic is expounded in Hilbert and Ackermann [8]. Quine [3] gives a useful bibliography on logic including a reference to the more complete bibliography by Church.

CHAPTER II

THE REAL NUMBER SYSTEM

1. Introduction.—In this chapter we shall show how the real number system may be constructed and its properties proved on the basis of assumed properties characterizing the system of natural numbers (positive integers). The process used in the following pages is not the only one that may be followed in constructing the real number system. Other methods are explained in the references given at the end of the chapter. The properties of the real number system proved in Secs. 2 to 9 are summarized in Sec. 9. These properties form a categorical set, in the sense that any two systems that satisfy them are simply isomorphic. For mathematical purposes, then, the real number system is simply a system having the properties set forth in Sec. 9. The reader who so desires may omit most of Secs. 2 to 8, since the properties of Sec. 9 form a logical basis for all the remainder of the theory. In Secs. 2 to 8 we gain assurance of the existence of the real number system, since most of us are satisfied with the abstraction we call a natural number, and with the properties of the natural numbers listed in Sec. 2. Moreover in the process we discover the logical relationship of the various systems: natural numbers, fractions, and real numbers.

As the notion of simple isomorphism occurs frequently in this chapter, we define it here for several types of systems. Let $\mathfrak{M}$ and $\mathfrak{M}'$ be two classes of elements, and let s be a function on $\mathfrak{M}$ to $\mathfrak{M}$, f be a function on $\mathfrak{M}\mathfrak{M}$ to $\mathfrak{M}$, and $<$ be a relation on $\mathfrak{M}\mathfrak{M}$, while s', f', and $<'$ denote corresponding functions and a relation for $\mathfrak{M}'$. Then (*a*) $(\mathfrak{M}, s)$, (*b*) $(\mathfrak{M}, f)$, (*c*) $(\mathfrak{M}, <)$ are, respectively, simply isomorphic to (*a*) $(\mathfrak{M}', s')$, (*b*) $(\mathfrak{M}', f')$, (*c*) $(\mathfrak{M}', <')$ in case there is for each case a one-to-one correspondence between $\mathfrak{M}$ and $\mathfrak{M}'$ such that (*a*) $s(m)$ corresponds to $s'(m')$, (*b*) $f(m, n)$ corresponds to $f'(m', n')$, (*c*) $m < n$ if and only if $m' <' n'$, where m corresponds to m' and n to n' under the correspondence appropriate to the case in question. A system $(\mathfrak{M}, s, f, <)$ is simply isomorphic to a system $(\mathfrak{M}', s', f', <')$ in case the correspondence can be set up in such a way that the three conditions hold simultaneously. This indicates how simple isomorphism is defined for other types of systems.

2. The Natural Numbers.—We assume the existence of a system $(\mathfrak{M}, s)$, where $\mathfrak{M}$ is a class of elements $m, n, \ldots$, and $s(m)$ may be called the successor of m, having the following properties:

P1. s is a function on $\mathfrak{M}$ to $\mathfrak{M}$; that is, to each m in $\mathfrak{M}$ corresponds a uniquely determined element $s(m)$ in $\mathfrak{M}$.

P2. $\exists m_0 \ni: m \cdot \supset \cdot s(m) \neq m_0$; that is, there is an element m_0 in $\mathfrak{M}$ which is not the successor $s(m)$ of an element of $\mathfrak{M}$. If we let $s\mathfrak{M}_0$ denote the set of all functional values $s(m)$ corresponding to elements m of the set $\mathfrak{M}_0$, this statement may also be written as follows: $\mathfrak{M} - s\mathfrak{M} \neq \Lambda$.

P3. $s(m) = s(n) \cdot \supset \cdot m = n$; that is, there is at most one element of $\mathfrak{M}$ having a given element of $\mathfrak{M}$ as its successor.

P4. $\mathfrak{M}_0 \subset \mathfrak{M}. s\mathfrak{M}_0 \subset \mathfrak{M}_0 . \mathfrak{M}_0[\mathfrak{M} - s\mathfrak{M}] \neq \Lambda \cdot \supset \cdot \mathfrak{M}_0 = \mathfrak{M}$; that is, if $\mathfrak{M}_0$ is a subclass of $\mathfrak{M}$ which contains the successor of each of its elements, and which furthermore contains an element m_0 satisfying P2, then $\mathfrak{M}_0$ is the whole of $\mathfrak{M}$.

These postulates are essentially due to Peano. The fourth property is the basis for all proofs by mathematical induction. The counter class C discussed in Sec. 3 of Chap. I, with $s(m) \equiv \{m\}$, is an example of a system having these properties.

The following three additional properties are immediate consequences of the Peano postulates:

P5. $\mathfrak{M}_0 \subset \mathfrak{M} . \mathfrak{M}_0 \neq \Lambda \cdot \supset \cdot \mathfrak{M}_0 - s\mathfrak{M}_0 \neq \Lambda$; that is, every nonnull subclass $\mathfrak{M}_0$ of $\mathfrak{M}$ contains at least one element that is not the successor of an element of $\mathfrak{M}_0$.

P6. The class $\mathfrak{M} - s\mathfrak{M}$ contains only one element m_0.

P7. $m \cdot \supset \cdot m \neq s(m)$.

To prove P5, suppose $\mathfrak{M}_0 - s\mathfrak{M}_0 = \Lambda$, so that $\mathfrak{M}_0 \subset s\mathfrak{M}_0$, and let $\mathfrak{M}_1 = \mathfrak{M} - \mathfrak{M}_0$. Then $\mathfrak{M}_1 \supset \mathfrak{M} - s\mathfrak{M}$. By P3, $s\mathfrak{M}_0$ and $s\mathfrak{M}_1$ have no elements in common, so that $\mathfrak{M}_1 \supset s\mathfrak{M}_1$. Hence by P4, $\mathfrak{M}_1 = \mathfrak{M}$, and $\mathfrak{M}_0 = \Lambda$, which contradicts the hypothesis. To prove P6, let m_0 be an element of $\mathfrak{M} - s\mathfrak{M}$, and set $\mathfrak{M}_0 = \{m_0\} + s\mathfrak{M}$. Then $s\mathfrak{M}_0 \subset \mathfrak{M}_0$, so that $\mathfrak{M}_0 = \mathfrak{M}$ by P4, and hence m_0 is the only element of $\mathfrak{M}$ which is not in $s\mathfrak{M}$. To prove P7, let $\mathfrak{M}_0 = [\text{all } m \ni\cdot\ s(m) \neq m]$. Then $\mathfrak{M}_0$ contains the element m_0 described in P2, and $s(m) \neq m \cdot\supset\cdot s(s(m)) \neq s(m)$ by P3. Hence $s\mathfrak{M}_0 \subset \mathfrak{M}_0$, and $\mathfrak{M}_0 = \mathfrak{M}$ by P4.

It is easily seen that any two systems satisfying P1 to P4 are simply isomorphic, so that these four postulates form a categorical set. It may also be proved that P1, P5, and P6 imply P2, P3, and P4, so that the principle of mathematical induction may be regarded as a theorem if one so desires.

It is instructive to note examples where one or more of the preceding properties fails to hold. In each of the following examples $\mathfrak{M} = [m]$ is a class of numbers, and $s(m) = m + 1$ except where otherwise specified.

A. $\mathfrak{M} = [1, 2, 3]$. P1 fails, since $s(3)$ is not in $\mathfrak{M}$.
B. $\mathfrak{M} = [1, 2, 3]$, with $s(3) = 1$. P2 and P5 fail.
C. $\mathfrak{M} = [1, 2, 3]$, with $s(3) = 2$. P3 and P5 fail.
D. $\mathfrak{M} = [1, 2, 3]$, with $s(3) = 3$. P3, P5, and P7 fail.
E. $\mathfrak{M} = [1, 2, 3, 4, \cdots, \frac{3}{2}, \frac{5}{2}, \cdots]$. P4 and P6 fail.
F. $\mathfrak{M} = [\frac{1}{2}, 1, 2, 3, 4, \cdots]$, with $s(\frac{1}{2}) = 2$. P3, P4, and P6 fail.

In a system $(\mathfrak{M}, s)$ having the properties P1 to P4, operations of addition and multiplication and a relation of order may be defined. We proceed first to define addition by requiring it to satisfy the following condition:

(2:1) $p \,.\, m \cdot\supset\cdot p + m_0 = s(p) \,.\, p + s(m) = s(p + m)$.

It will be noted that with this definition of addition, the element m_0 behaves as 1, whereas in the counter class C the first element is the null class 0. In succeeding sections it is convenient to defer the introduction of zero as long as possible.

The operation of addition has the following properties:

M1. $+$ is on $\mathfrak{M}\mathfrak{M}$ to $\mathfrak{M}$; that is, for each p and m in $\mathfrak{M}$ there is a uniquely determined element $p + m$ in $\mathfrak{M}$.
M2. $+$ is associative; that is, $m \,.\, n \,.\, p \cdot\supset\cdot (m + n) + p = m + (n + p)$.
M3. $+$ is commutative; that is, $m \,.\, p \cdot\supset\cdot m + p = p + m$.
M4. $m \,.\, p \cdot\supset\cdot p \neq m + p$.
M5. $m \neq p :\supset: \exists q \ni\cdot m + q = p \cdot\vee\cdot \exists n \ni\cdot m = p + n$.

M6. $m + n = m + p \cdot \supset \cdot n = p$; that is, the result of subtraction is unique.

To prove the uniqueness in M1, suppose $+$ and $\oplus$ are operations satisfying (2:1), and for a fixed p, let $\mathfrak{M}_0 = [\text{all } m \ni\cdot p + m = p \oplus m]$. Then m_0 is in $\mathfrak{M}_0$ and, if m is in $\mathfrak{M}_0$, $p + s(m) = s(p + m) = s(p \oplus m) = p \oplus s(m)$, so that $s(m)$ is in $\mathfrak{M}_0$. Thus $\mathfrak{M}_0 = \mathfrak{M}$ by P4. To show the existence of an operation $+$ having the property (2:1), let $\mathfrak{M}_1$ denote the class of all elements p for which there exists an operation $+$ such that $p + m_0 = s(p)$, and $p + s(m) = s(p + m)$ for every m. To show m_0 is in $\mathfrak{M}_1$ we may take $m_0 + m = s(m)$. Then $m_0 + s(m) = s(s(m)) = s(m_0 + m)$. If p is in $\mathfrak{M}_1$, we may set $s(p) + m \equiv s(p + m)$. Then $s(p) + m_0 = s(p + m_0) = s(s(p))$, $s(p) + s(m) = s(p + s(m)) = s(s(p + m)) = s(s(p) + m)$. Hence $s(p)$ is also in $\mathfrak{M}_1$, and $\mathfrak{M}_1 = \mathfrak{M}$ by P4. Note that in the course of proving M1 we have proved that

$$(2{:}2) \qquad p.m \cdot \supset \cdot s(p) + m = p + s(m).$$

To prove the associative law M2, let m and n be fixed and let $\mathfrak{M}_0 \equiv [\text{all } p \ni\cdot (m + n) + p = m + (n + p)]$. Then m_0 is in $\mathfrak{M}_0$ since $(m + n) + m_0 = s(m + n) = m + s(n) = m + (n + m_0)$. If p is in $\mathfrak{M}_0$, $(m + n) + s(p) = s((m + n) + p) = s(m + (n + p)) = m + s(n + p) = m + (n + s(p))$. Thus $\mathfrak{M}_0 = \mathfrak{M}$ by P4.

The proof of the commutative law M3 requires a double application of P4. We first prove by use of (2:2) that the class $\mathfrak{M}_p \equiv [\text{all } m \ni\cdot p + m = m + p]$ has the property that $s\mathfrak{M}_p \subset \mathfrak{M}_p$. Next, it is obvious that $\mathfrak{M}_{m_0}$ contains m_0, so that $\mathfrak{M}_{m_0} = \mathfrak{M}$ by P4. Thus m_0 is in every $\mathfrak{M}_p$, and $\mathfrak{M}_p = \mathfrak{M}$ by another application of P4.

To prove M4, let $\mathfrak{M}_0 \equiv [\text{all } p \ni\cdot p \neq m + p]$. Since $m_0 \neq s(m) = m + m_0$, m_0 is in $\mathfrak{M}_0$. By P3, $s\mathfrak{M}_0 \subset \mathfrak{M}_0$, and thus $\mathfrak{M}_0 = \mathfrak{M}$ by P4.

In considering the property M5, we shall let p be a fixed element of $\mathfrak{M}$, and set $\mathfrak{M}_1 = \{p\}$, $\mathfrak{M}_2 = [\text{all } m \ni: \exists q \ni\cdot m + q = p]$, $\mathfrak{M}_3 = [\text{all } m \ni: \exists n \ni\cdot m = p + n]$, $\mathfrak{M}_0 = \mathfrak{M}_1 + \mathfrak{M}_2 + \mathfrak{M}_3$. If $p = m_0$, m_0 is in $\mathfrak{M}_1$, and if $p \neq m_0$, $p = s(q) = q + m_0 = m_0 + q$ so that m_0 is in $\mathfrak{M}_2$. If m is in $\mathfrak{M}_1$, then $s(m) = p + m_0$, so that $s(m)$ is in $\mathfrak{M}_3$. If m is in $\mathfrak{M}_2$ and $q = m_0$, then $s(m)$ is in $\mathfrak{M}_1$, but if $q \neq m_0$, $q = s(q_1)$, $p = m + s(q_1) = s(m) + q_1$ by (2:2) and $s(m)$ is in $\mathfrak{M}_2$. Finally, if m is in $\mathfrak{M}_3$, $s(m) = s(p + n) = p + s(n)$ and $s(m)$ is in $\mathfrak{M}_3$. Thus $s\mathfrak{M}_0 \subset \mathfrak{M}_0$ and $\mathfrak{M}_0 = \mathfrak{M}$ by P4. In conclusion we note that no two of the classes $\mathfrak{M}_1$, $\mathfrak{M}_2$, $\mathfrak{M}_3$ can have an element in common, by virtue of M2 and M4.

To prove M6 we may use an indirect proof. Suppose $n \neq p$, $m + n = m + p$. By M5, we may suppose $p = n + q$. Then $m + n = m + (n + q) = (m + n) + q$ by M2, but this contradicts M4.

To define a relation of order in the class $\mathfrak{M}$ we choose the following:

$$(2:3) \qquad m < p \cdot\equiv\cdot \exists q \ni\cdot m + q = p.$$

The next four properties characterize what is called a **linear order.**

M7. $<$ is on $\mathfrak{M}\mathfrak{M}$; that is, for every pair m and p of elements of $\mathfrak{M}$ it is determined whether $m < p$ or not.

M8. $<$ is transitive; that is, $m < n \,.\, n < p \cdot\supset\cdot m < p$.

M9. $m < m$ is true for no element m.

M10. $m \neq p \cdot\supset\cdot m < p \vee p < m$.

In the verification of these properties it will be noted that M8 depends on M2, M9 on M4 and M3, and M10 on M5. For a subclass $\mathfrak{M}_0$ of $\mathfrak{M}$ we shall use the notation $p < \mathfrak{M}_0$ to mean that $p < m$ for every m of $\mathfrak{M}_0$. The relations $\leqq$, $>$, $\geqq$ are defined in the customary way in terms of $<$ and then extended to relations between elements and subclasses. The order just defined in the class of natural numbers has the following additional property:

M11. $\mathfrak{M}_1 \subset \mathfrak{M} \cdot \mathfrak{M}_1 \neq \Lambda \cdot\supset\cdot \exists p$ in $\mathfrak{M}_1 \ni\cdot p \leqq \mathfrak{M}_1$.

An ordered class having the property M11 is said to be **well-ordered.** To prove M11, let $\mathfrak{M}_2 \equiv$ [all $m \leqq \mathfrak{M}_1$]. With the help of M8 and M9 it can be shown that m in $\mathfrak{M}_1 \cdot\supset\cdot s(m)$ not in $\mathfrak{M}_2$. The element m_0 is in $\mathfrak{M}_2$ and, if $s\mathfrak{M}_2 \subset \mathfrak{M}_2$, we would have $\mathfrak{M}_2 = \mathfrak{M}$, by P4. Hence $\exists p$ in $\mathfrak{M}_2 \ni\cdot s(p)$ not in $\mathfrak{M}_2$. But p not in $\mathfrak{M}_1 \cdot\supset\cdot p < \mathfrak{M}_1 \cdot\supset\cdot s(p) \leqq \mathfrak{M}_1$. As this contradicts the defining property of p, we must have p in $\mathfrak{M}_1$.

We are now in a position to make a simple proof of a general theorem justifying definition of functions on $\mathfrak{M}$ by recursion.

THEOREM 1. *Let* $(\mathfrak{M}, s)$ *have the properties* P1 *to* P4, *and let* $\mathfrak{K}$ *be an arbitrary class,* t *a function on* $\mathfrak{K}$ *to* $\mathfrak{K}$, *and* k_0 *a fixed element of* $\mathfrak{K}$. *Then there is a unique function* f *on* $\mathfrak{M}$ *to* $\mathfrak{K}$ *such that* $f(m_0) = k_0$, *and* $f(s(m)) = t(f(m))$ *for every* m *in* $\mathfrak{M}$.

Proof.—For convenience, let $\mathfrak{M}_m = [\text{all } p \leqq m]$. The element m_0 is in every $\mathfrak{M}_m$, since if $m \neq m_0$, $m = s(p) = p + m_0$. From this we readily find that $q < m$ if and only if $s(q) \leqq m$. We shall say that an element m has the property $E(f)$ in case f is a function on $\mathfrak{M}_m$ to $\mathfrak{K}$, $f(m_0) = k_0$, and $q < m \cdot \supset \cdot f(s(q)) = t(f(q))$. Now let m have the property $E(f)$, let n have the property $E(g)$, and suppose $m \leqq n$. Let $\mathfrak{M}_0 = [\text{all } p \leqq m \ni \cdot f(p) = g(p)] + (\mathfrak{M} - \mathfrak{M}_m)$. Then it is easily seen that m_0 is in $\mathfrak{M}_0$ and that $s\mathfrak{M}_0 \subset \mathfrak{M}_0$, so that $\mathfrak{M}_0 = \mathfrak{M}$. Hence f and g are equal on $\mathfrak{M}_m$. Now let $\mathfrak{M}_1$ consist of all elements m for which there exists a function f_m with which m has the property $E(f_m)$. It is obvious that m_0 is in $\mathfrak{M}_1$. For each m in $\mathfrak{M}_1$, set $f* = f_m$ on $\mathfrak{M}_m$, $f*(s(m)) = t(f_m(m))$. Then $s(m)$ has the property $E(f*)$, so that $s\mathfrak{M}_1 \subset \mathfrak{M}_1$, and hence $\mathfrak{M}_1 = \mathfrak{M}$. Since for each m, f_m is already known to be uniquely determined, we obtain the desired function f by setting $f(m) = f_m(m)$.

COROLLARY. *If* h *is a function on* $\mathfrak{M}\mathfrak{K}$ *to* $\mathfrak{K}$, *then there is a unique function* g *on* $\mathfrak{M}$ *to* $\mathfrak{K}$ *such that* $g(m_0) = k_0$, *and* $g(s(m)) = h(m, g(m))$ *for every* m *in* $\mathfrak{M}$.

Proof.—Let $\mathfrak{L} = \mathfrak{M}\mathfrak{K}$, $l_0 = (m_0, k_0)$, $t(m, k) = (s(m), h(m, k))$. Then by the theorem there is a unique function f on $\mathfrak{M}$ to $\mathfrak{L}$ such that $f(m_0) = l_0 = (m_0, k_0)$ and $f(s(m)) = t(f(m))$ for every m. Let $f(m) = (\mu(m), g(m))$. Then $\mu(m_0) = m_0$, $g(m_0) = k_0$, and if $\mu(m) = m$, $f(s(m)) = (s(m), h(m, g(m)))$, so that $\mu(s(m)) = s(m)$, $g(s(m)) = h(m, g(m))$, and thus the desired result follows by P4.

The next theorem justifies a property sometimes used, which is apparently stronger than P4.

THEOREM 2. *Let the subclass* $\mathfrak{M}_0$ *of* $\mathfrak{M}$ *contain* m_0, *and contain* $s(m)$ *whenever* $\mathfrak{M}_m \subset \mathfrak{M}_0$. *Then* $\mathfrak{M}_0 = \mathfrak{M}$.

Proof.—Let $\mathfrak{M}_* \equiv [\text{all } m \ni \cdot \mathfrak{M}_m \subset \mathfrak{M}_0]$. Then m_0 is in $\mathfrak{M}_*$, $s\mathfrak{M}_* \subset \mathfrak{M}_*$, so that $\mathfrak{M}_* = \mathfrak{M}$ by P4. But $\mathfrak{M}_* \subset \mathfrak{M}_0 \subset \mathfrak{M}$, so that $\mathfrak{M}_0 = \mathfrak{M}$.

We define multiplication in $\mathfrak{M}$ as follows: $q \times m_0 = q$, $q \times s(m) = q \times m + q$. Then it is a simple matter to verify the following additional properties of the system $(\mathfrak{M}, s, +, \times, <)$.

M12. $\times$ is on $\mathfrak{M}\mathfrak{M}$ to $\mathfrak{M}$.

M13. $\times$ is distributive with respect to $+$; that is, $m \,.\, p \,.\, q \cdot\!\supset\!\cdot (m + p) \times q = m \times q + p \times q$.

M14. $\times$ is commutative.

M15. $\times$ is associative.

M16. $m \times n = m \times p \cdot\!\supset\!\cdot n = p$.

M17. $m \,.\, n \,.\, p :\supset: m < n \cdot\!\sim\!\cdot m + p < n + p$.

M18. $m \,.\, n \,.\, p :\supset: m < n \cdot\!\sim\!\cdot m \times p < n \times p$.

The property M12 follows at once from Theorem 1, with $\mathfrak{K} = \mathfrak{M}$, $k_0 = q$, and $t(k) = k + q$, and M13 is readily proved by induction, using the associative and commutative laws for $+$. We obtain M14 with the help of M13 and two applications of P4. Note that by virtue of the commutative law it is only necessary to prove the distributive law in the form stated. The property M15 is proved in similar fashion with the help of M13 and M14. An indirect proof similar to the proof of M6 suffices for M16, and M17 and M18 also follow easily from the definitions and the preceding properties.

An an example that falls under the Corollary of Theorem 1, we note that $g(m) = m!$ if $\mathfrak{K} = \mathfrak{M}$, $k_0 = m_0$, $h(m, k) = s(m) \times k$.

In concluding this section we note the following result on isomorphism:

THEOREM 3. *If* $(\mathfrak{M}, s)$ *and* $(\mathfrak{M}', s')$ *are two systems satisfying the postulates* P1 *to* P4, *then the systems* $(\mathfrak{M}, s, +, \times, <)$ *and* $(\mathfrak{M}', s', +', \times', <')$ *are simply isomorphic. Moreover, the correspondence is uniquely determined, and* m_0 *corresponds to* m_0'.

This result may be verified by first proving the isomorphism of the simpler systems $(\mathfrak{M}, s)$ and $(\mathfrak{M}', s')$ and then applying Theorem 1 with the definitions of $+$, $\times$, $<$.

3. Groups and Semigroups.—A **group** is a system $(\mathfrak{G}, *)$ having the following properties:

G1. $*$ is on $\mathfrak{G}\mathfrak{G}$ to $\mathfrak{G}$; that is, to each pair of elements a, b of $\mathfrak{G}$ there corresponds a uniquely determined element $a * b$ of $\mathfrak{G}$.

G2. $a \,.\, b \,.\, c \cdot\!\supset\!\cdot (a * b) * c = a * (b * c)$; that is, the operation $*$ is associative.

$G3_l$. $a \,.\, b \cdot\!\supset\!\cdot \exists c \ni\cdot a * c = b$.

$G3_r$. $a \,.\, b \cdot\!\supset\!\cdot \exists d \ni\cdot d * a = b$.

We shall be interested in the two cases when the operation $*$ is, respectively, addition and multiplication. For the present, the operation $*$ should be thought of purely abstractly.

Every group has also the following properties:

G4. $\exists | u \ni : a \cdot \supset \cdot a * u = u * a = a$; that is, there is a unique unit element u such that for every element a in $\mathfrak{G}$, $a * u = u * a = a$.

G5. $a \cdot \supset \cdot \exists | \bar{a} \ni \cdot a * \bar{a} = \bar{a} * a = u$.

G6$_l$. $a * c = a * d \cdot \supset \cdot c = d$.

G6$_r$. $c * a = d * a \cdot \supset \cdot c = d$.

It is easily seen that the properties G1, G2, G4, and G5 imply G3, so that they might be used as an alternative definition of a group. A system having properties G1, G2, and G6 is called a **semigroup.** A group or semigroup having also the following property G7 is called **commutative** or **Abelian.**

G7. $a \,.\, b \cdot \supset \cdot a * b = b * a$.

It is evident from the properties M1, M2, M3, and M6 of Sec. 2 that the system $(\mathfrak{M}, +)$ forms a commutative semigroup. The system $(\mathfrak{M}, \times)$ also forms a commutative semigroup.

EXERCISE

Let $\mathfrak{G}_1$ = [all positive even integers],
$\mathfrak{G}_2$ = [all positive odd integers],
$\mathfrak{G}_3$ = [all positive and negative even integers and zero],
$\mathfrak{G}_4$ = [all positive and negative odd integers].

Determine which of these classes, with the operation of addition or with the operation of multiplication, forms a group or a semigroup.

4. The Embedding of a Semigroup in a Group.—A fundamental process is that of enlarging a commutative semigroup so as to obtain a group. We assume that $(\mathfrak{G}, *)$ is a system having the properties G1, G2, G6, and G7. First consider the class $\mathfrak{H}$ of all pairs (a, a') of elements of $\mathfrak{G}$.

We introduce an **equivalence relation** $\simeq$ in the class $\mathfrak{H}$, defined by the formula $(a, a') \simeq (b, b') \cdot\equiv\cdot a * b' = a' * b$. By means of the properties G1, G2, G6, and G7 it is easy to verify that the relation $\approx$ is **reflexive,** *i.e.*, always $(a, a') \approx (a, a')$; **symmetric,** *i.e.*, $(a, a') \approx (b, b') \cdot\supset\cdot (b, b') \approx (a, a')$; and **transitive,** *i.e.*, $(a, a') \approx (b, b') \,.\, (b, b') \approx (c, c') \cdot\supset\cdot (a, a') \approx (c, c')$. It is only by virtue of having these three properties that the relation $\approx$ is properly called an "equivalence relation." This equivalence relation divides the class $\mathfrak{H}$ into mutually exclusive subclasses, for which we use the notation $\{a, a'\}$. The symbol $\{a, a'\}$ stands for the class of *all* pairs (b, b') which are equivalent to (a, a'). We denote the class of all $\{a, a'\}$ by the symbol $\mathfrak{J}$. This process of obtaining a class $\mathfrak{J}$ from a class $\mathfrak{H}$ by means of an equivalence relation is sometimes called **identification.** We define an operation $*$ in the class $\mathfrak{J}$ as follows: $\{a, a'\} * \{b, b'\} = \{a * b, a' * b'\}$. In order to show that this operation has the property G1, we need only verify that $(a, a') \approx (c, c') \,.\, (b, b') \approx (d, d') \cdot\supset\cdot (a * b, a' * b') \approx (c * d, c' * d')$. Properties G2 and G7 (the associative and commutative laws) are obvious. To verify property G3 we note that when $\{a, a'\}$ and $\{b, b'\}$ are given, $\{a, a'\} * \{a' * b, a * b'\} = \{b, b'\}$. Thus we have proved that the system $(\mathfrak{J}, *)$ constitutes a commutative group.

The system $(\mathfrak{J}, *)$ is an enlargement of the system $(\mathfrak{G}, *)$ in the sense that it contains a subsystem $(\mathfrak{J}_G, *)$ which is simply isomorphic to $(\mathfrak{G}, *)$. To each element a of $\mathfrak{G}$ corresponds the element $\{a * b, b\}$ of $\mathfrak{J}$, and the correspondence so set up is one-to-one by G6 and G7. It is also easy to verify that $a * c$ corresponds to $\{a * b, b\} * \{c * b, b\}$, and that each class $\{a * b, b\}$ consists only of pairs of the form $(a * d, d)$. The following theorem shows that the extension $(\mathfrak{J}, *)$ of the system $(\mathfrak{G}, *)$ which has been obtained is, in the appropriate sense, the minimum extension that forms a group.

THEOREM 4. *Let* $(\mathfrak{G}, *)$ *be a commutative semigroup,* $(\mathfrak{L}, *)$ *a commutative group, and* $(\mathfrak{L}_G, *)$ *a subsystem of* $(\mathfrak{L}, *)$ *which is simply isomorphic to* $(\mathfrak{G}, *)$. *Then there is a subsystem* $(\mathfrak{L}_J, *)$ *of* $(\mathfrak{L}, *)$ *which contains* $(\mathfrak{L}_G, *)$ *and is simply isomorphic to the extension* $(\mathfrak{J}, *)$ *of* $(\mathfrak{G}, *)$ *to form a group.*

To prove this, let the elements of $\mathfrak{L}$ be denoted by capital letters, and let A, A', B, and B' be the elements of $\mathfrak{L}_G$ corresponding to a, a', b, and b', respectively. To each element $\{a, a'\}$ of $\mathfrak{J}$ corresponds a unique element C of $\mathfrak{L}$ by means of the equation $A = A' * C$, since $a * b' = a' * b$ implies that $A * B' = A' * B$, $A' * C * B' = A' * B$, and finally $C * B' = B$. The class $\mathfrak{L}_J$

consists of all the elements C obtained in this way. It is easily verified that two distinct elements $\{a, a'\}$ and $\{b, b'\}$ of $\mathfrak{J}$ cannot correspond to the same element C of $\mathfrak{L}_J$ and that the correspondence is preserved under the operation $*$. Finally, $\{a * b, b\}$ corresponds to A, so that $\mathfrak{L}_G \subset \mathfrak{L}_J$.

5. The Positive Rational Numbers.—The second step in the historical development of the concept of number was the introduction of fractions. In this section we consider a logical basis for this step. The starting point is the algebraic system $(\mathfrak{M}, s, +, \times, <)$ of the natural numbers, having the properties P1 to P4 and M1 to M18. We now apply the process of Sec. 4 to the semigroup $(\mathfrak{M}, \times)$ to form a group $(\mathfrak{F}, \times)$, whose elements f have the form $\{m, m'\}$. Thus each fraction f consists of a class of pairs of natural numbers.

The next step is to define the operation of addition for the system of fractions. As is customary in algebra, the symbol $\times$ for multiplication is omitted here and in the sequel where no ambiguity can arise. It is easily verified that if $(m, m') \backsimeq (n, n')$ and $(p, p') \backsimeq (q, q')$, then $(mp' + m'p, m'p') \backsimeq (nq' + n'q, n'q')$. From this it follows that, if $f = \{m, m'\}$, $g = \{p, p'\}$, the definition

$$f + g = \{mp' + m'p, m'p'\}$$

yields an operation of addition with the property M1, that is, $+$ is a function on $\mathfrak{F}\mathfrak{F}$ to $\mathfrak{F}$.

The system $(\mathfrak{F}, +, \times)$ has the following properties:

F1. $(\mathfrak{F}, +)$ forms a commutative semigroup.
F2. $(\mathfrak{F}, \times)$ forms a commutative group.
F3. $\times$ is distributive with respect to $+$.
F4. $f \neq g \cdot \supset \cdot \exists h \ni \cdot f = g + h \vee f + h = g$.
F5. There is a unique subset $\mathfrak{F}_M$ of $\mathfrak{F}$ such that the system $(\mathfrak{F}_M, +, \times)$ is simply isomorphic with the system $(\mathfrak{M}, +, \times)$ of Sec. 2. Moreover, the correspondence between $\mathfrak{M}$ and $\mathfrak{F}_M$ is uniquely determined. The units for multiplication in the two systems must correspond.
F6. f in $\mathfrak{F} \cdot \supset \cdot \exists g$ in $\mathfrak{F}_M . \exists h$ in $\mathfrak{F}_M \ni \cdot fg = h$.

To prove property F4, let $f = \{m, m'\}$, $g = \{n, n'\}$. Then $mn' \neq m'n$. By M5, we may suppose for definiteness that $mn' + p = m'n$, where p is properly chosen. It follows that

$\{m, m'\} + \{p, m'n'\} = \{n, n'\}$. The subset $\mathfrak{F}_M$ in F5 consists of those elements f_m of the form $\{m, m_0\}$. It is worth remarking that the property F5 follows logically from the properties F1 to F3 without reference to the definition of the elements of the class $\mathfrak{F}$, provided we assume that $\mathfrak{F}$ has at least two members. To show this, we define $\mathfrak{F}_M$ to be the logical product of all the subclasses $\mathfrak{F}_0$ of $\mathfrak{F}$ having the property that $\mathfrak{F}_0$ contains the unit for multiplication, which we denote by the usual notation 1, and contains $f + 1$ whenever it contains f. To prove F6, we note that if $f = \{m, m'\}$, we may take $g = \{m', m_0\}$, $h = \{m, m_0\}$.

We say that $f < g$ in case $\exists h \ni\cdot f + h = g$. This is formally the same as the corresponding definition for order in the class $\mathfrak{M}$. If $f = \{m, m'\}$, $g = \{n, n'\}$, $f < g \cdot\sim\cdot mn' < m'n$. The following additional properties are logical consequences of F1 to F6 and this definition of order.

F7. $(\mathfrak{F}, <)$ forms a linearly ordered set.
F8. $f . g . h :\supset: f < g \cdot\sim\cdot f + h < g + h$.
F9. $f . g . h :\supset: f < g \cdot\sim\cdot fh < gh$.
F10. $f < g \cdot\supset\cdot \exists h \ni\cdot f < h < g$.
F11. $f . g \cdot\supset\cdot \exists h$ in $\mathfrak{F}_M \ni\cdot f < gh$.

To verify F7, we have to show that the properties M7 to M10 of Sec. 2 hold for the system $(\mathfrak{F}, <)$. M7 and M8 are immediate, and M10 follows from F4. If f and h are such that

$$f + h = f, \tag{5:1}$$

then $f + g + h = f + g$ for every fraction g, and $g + h = g$ by the uniqueness of subtraction (F1 and G6). If we multiply (5:1) by $h^{-1}g$, we have $fh^{-1}g + g = fh^{-1}g$, and hence $h + g = h = g$, and the class $\mathfrak{F}$ reduces to the single element h. But this is impossible by F5. This proves that $f < f$ cannot occur.

Property F10 expresses the fact that the class $\mathfrak{F}$ is **dense** with respect to the relation $<$. To prove it, let $f + e = g$, $e = 2a$, where $2 = 1 + 1$. Then $f < f + a < f + 2a = g$. Property F11 is usually called the **Archimedean property.** It is easily derived from F6 for, if $f_2 f = f_1$, $g_2 g = g_1$, where f_1, f_2, g_1, g_2 are in $\mathfrak{F}_M$, we may take $h = g_2 f_1 + g_2$.

6. Linearly Ordered Sets.—A **linearly ordered set** is a system $(\Omega, <)$ with the properties:

O1. $<$ is a relation on $\Omega\Omega$.
O2. $<$ is transitive.
O3. $v < v$ is true for no element v of Ω.
O4. $v \neq w \cdot \supset \cdot v < w \vee w < v$.

These properties are identical with the properties M7 to M10 of Sec. 2. For convenience we shall as usual use the symbol $w > v$ to mean the same thing as $v < w$. The relation $>$ is dual to the relation $<$. The system $(\Omega, <)$ is said to be **dense** in case it has the additional property

O5. $v < w \cdot \supset \cdot \exists x \ni \cdot v < x < w$.

An element x of Ω is a **lower bound** of a subclass K of Ω in case $x \leqq v$ for every v in K. For this relationship we use the notation $x \leqq K$. The definition of an **upper bound** is dual, that is, has $<$ replaced by $>$. We shall denote by K_l the class of all lower bounds of K, and by K_u the class of all upper bounds. These classes may of course be null. If the class K_l has an upper bound y contained in K_l, then y is called the **greatest lower bound** of K and is denoted by the symbol "g.l.b. K". From the properties O1 to O3 of a linearly ordered set, it follows readily that a set K cannot have more than one greatest lower bound. The definition of the **least upper bound** of K, denoted by the symbol "l.u.b. K," is dual to that of the greatest lower bound. A linearly ordered set Ω is said to have the **Dedekind property,** or to be **complete,** in case every subset K which has a lower bound has a greatest lower bound in Ω. We see at once that a linearly ordered set Ω is complete if and only if every subset K which has an upper bound has a least upper bound in Ω.

7. Dedekind Cuts.—The system $(\mathfrak{N}, <)$ of the natural numbers forms a complete linearly ordered set, but it is not dense. On the other hand the system $(\mathfrak{F}, <)$ of fractions is not complete, although it is dense. It is the purpose of this section to show how to obtain a complete system from a given dense linearly ordered system Ω, by making use of the "Dedekind cuts" in Ω.

A subset A of Ω is said to determine a **Dedekind cut** in Ω in case it has the properties:

D1. $A \neq 0$.
D2. $A \neq \Omega$.

D3. a in A . $a_1 < a \cdot \supset \cdot a_1$ in A.

D4. If l.u.b. A exists, it is not in A.

The condition D4 is equivalent to the following: a in $A \cdot \supset \cdot \exists a_1$ in $A \ni \cdot a_1 > a$. The set complementary to A will be denoted by cA, and the partition of Ω into the two classes A and cA is the Dedekind cut determined by A. For example, a Dedekind cut in the system $\mathfrak{F}$ of positive fractions is determined by the set $A \equiv$ [all $a < 3$], and another cut is determined by the set $B \equiv$ [all $b \ni \cdot b^2 < 3$]. It is slightly more convenient to work with only one of the classes A and cA making up a Dedekind cut. Consequently in the sequel we shall refer to the classes A having the properties D1 to D4 as the Dedekind cuts in Ω.

The class of all cuts in Ω will be denoted by Γ. The relation $<$ is defined for the class Γ by saying that $A < B$ in case $A \underset{\neq}{\subset} B$, that is, A is a subset of B but B is not a subset of A. When $(\Omega, <)$ is a linearly ordered set, it is easy to show that the system $(\Gamma, <)$ constitutes a complete linearly ordered set (unless it is vacuous) and that it is nonvacuous and dense when Ω is dense. For example, if $L = [A_\alpha]$ is a set of cuts having an upper bound, the least upper bound of L is the logical sum of the classes A_α,

$$\text{l.u.b. } L = \sum A_\alpha.$$

The greatest lower bound is not always given directly by the logical product, on account of the requirement D4. Moreover, it is clear that when Ω itself has no lower bound and is dense, the system $(\Gamma, <)$ contains a subsystem $(\Gamma_\Omega, <)$ which is simply isomorphic with $(\Omega, <)$. The elements of Γ_Ω are those cuts A for which l.u.b. A exists in Ω.

When the set Ω is not dense, it is necessary to omit the property D4 in order that each element of Ω may determine a cut. The properties D1 and D2 may also be omitted when there is no question of defining addition and multiplication. Since in Sec. 8 we wish to consider the cuts in the dense system $(\mathfrak{F}, <)$, which has no lower bound and no upper bound, and to define addition and multiplication for them, it is desirable here to assume all the properties D1 to D4.

8. Construction of the Real Number System.—We shall denote the complete dense linearly ordered set composed of the cuts in the system $(\mathfrak{F}, <)$ by $\mathfrak{Q}$. When we have defined the operations of addition and multiplication in $\mathfrak{Q}$, we shall have obtained the system of positive real numbers. Let A and B be two cuts in $\mathfrak{F}$, that is, A and B are two subclasses of $\mathfrak{F}$ having the properties D1 to D4 of Sec. 7. Then $A + B$ is defined to be the class C of all fractions c of the form $a + b$, where a ranges over A and b ranges over B. Likewise AB is defined to be the class D of all fractions d of the form ab. Note that here we are *not* using $A + B$ and AB to denote the logical sum and product of classes. It is now possible to verify that the system $(\mathfrak{Q}, +, \times, <)$ has the following properties. All but the last of these are extensions of corresponding properties of the system $(\mathfrak{F}, +, \times, <)$.

Q1. The set $\mathfrak{Q}$ contains at least two elements.
Q2. $(\mathfrak{Q}, +)$ is a commutative semigroup.
Q3. $(\mathfrak{Q}, \times)$ is a commutative group.
Q4. $\times$ is distributive with respect to $+$.
Q5. $(\mathfrak{Q}, <)$ forms a linearly ordered set.
Q6. $A < B \cdot\sim\cdot \exists C \ni\cdot A + C = B$.
Q7. $(\mathfrak{Q}, <)$ has the Dedekind property.

To prove these properties we need the following lemma, which follows by an indirect proof from the Archimedean property F11.

LEMMA. *For every fraction e and every cut A there is a fraction a in A such that $a + e$ is not in A.*

In verifying that the classes $A + B$ and AB are cuts, we find that the properties D1, D2, and D4 are fairly obvious in both cases. For D3, we note that if $c_1 < a + b$ then $c_1 = a_1 + b_1$, where $a_1 = ac_1/(a + b) < a$, $b_1 = bc_1/(a + b) < b$. Also if $d_1 < ab$, then $d_1 = a_1b_1$, where $a_1 = d_1/b < a$, $b_1 = b$. The commutative and associative laws are obvious. To verify the uniqueness of subtraction, let $A + B = A + C$, and suppose that the class B is a proper subset of C. If c_1 and c_2 are in C and not in B, and $c_2 = c_1 + e$, there is by the lemma an element a_1 of A such that $a_1 + e$ is not in A. Then for every a in A and b in B, $a + b < a_1 + e + c_1 = a_1 + c_2$, so that the number $a_1 + c_2$ is not in $A + B$. This contradiction shows that B cannot be a proper subset of C, and likewise C cannot be a proper subset of B, so that $B = C$.

To show that division is always possible is slightly more troublesome. For given cuts A and C, we shall show that the class B of all fractions c/a' where c is in C and a' is not in A is a cut satisfying the equation $AB = C$. It is plain that B has the properties D1 to D4. The product AB by definition consists of all fractions ac/a', where a is in A, c is in C, and a' is not in A. Thus $a < a'$ and $ac/a' < c$, so that $AB \subset C$. Now let c be an arbitrary fraction in C. Choose a_1 in A, c_1 in C, with c_1 equal to $c + e_1$, and set e equal to a_1e_1/c. By the lemma there is a fraction $a > a_1$ and in A such that $a + e$ is not in A. The fraction $c_2 = ac_1/(a + e)$ is obviously in AB. Thus it is apparent that

$$cac_1 = cc_2a + cc_2e = cc_2a + c_2a_1e_1 < cc_2a + c_2ae_1 = c_2ac_1,$$

and hence $c < c_2$ and $C \subset AB$.

To prove the distributive law we note first that the class $(A + B)C \subset AC + BC$, since the first class consists of all fractions of the form $ac + bc$, while the second consists of all fractions of the form $ac_1 + bc_2$. If $c_1 < c_2$, $a_1 \equiv ac_1/c_2 < a$, and so a_1 is in A. Hence $ac_1 + bc_2 = a_1c_2 + bc_2$, which is a member of $(A + B)C$.

For property Q6, we define the class C to be the class of all fractions of the form $b - a'$, where $a' < b$ and a' and b are in B but not in A. It is easily seen that C determines a cut and that $A + C \leqq B$. To prove $B \leqq A + C$, we note first that, if b is in A, we may choose b_1 and b_2 in B but not in A so that $b_1 < b_2$ and $b_2 - b_1 < b$, and then set $a = b - (b_2 - b_1)$. If b is in B but not in A, there is a fraction $b_1 > b$ and in B, and by the lemma there is a fraction a in A such that $a' = a + b_1 - b$ is not in A. But $a' < b_1$, so a' is in B, and $a + b_1 - a' = b$. To prove the converse we note that for every c in C there exists by the lemma a fraction a in A such that $a + c$ is not in A, although it must be in B. Hence $A < B$.

As the final step in the construction of the real number system, we extend the semigroup $(\mathfrak{Q}, +)$ to form a group $(\mathfrak{R}, +)$, according to the process outlined in Sec. 4, and then define the operation of multiplication and the order relation in $\mathfrak{R}$ as follows. Let the elements of $\mathfrak{R}$, which are classes of equivalent pairs of cuts, be denoted by Greek letters, and let $\alpha = \{A, A'\}$, $\beta = \{B, B'\}$, and so on. Then by definition $\alpha\beta = \{AB + A'B', AB' + A'B\}$, and $\alpha < \beta$ in case $\exists(A, A')$ in α. $\exists(B, B')$ in $\beta \ni\cdot A + B' < A' + B$. It will be necessary of course to verify that the operation of multiplication is a single-valued function of the two factors, as stated in property R3 of Sec. 9.

Let us note that, if $A = A' + C$, and the pairs (A, A') and (B, B') are both members of the same real number α, then $B = B' + C$, and conversely. This shows that there is a one-to-one correspondence between the numbers C and the numbers $\alpha = \{A, A'\}$ for which $A > A'$. We shall indicate this correspondence symbolically by $\alpha \cong C$. In the same way there is a one-to-one correspondence between the numbers C and the numbers $\alpha = \{A, A'\}$ for which $A < A'$, which we shall indicate by $\alpha \cong -C$. In case $A = A'$, we shall write $\alpha \cong 0$. This is obviously the identity element for addition. We verify at once that

$$
\begin{aligned}
&\alpha \cong C \,.\, \beta \cong D \cdot\supset\cdot \alpha\beta \cong CD,\\
&\alpha \cong C \,.\, \beta \cong -D \cdot\supset\cdot \alpha\beta \cong -CD,\\
&\alpha \cong -C \,.\, \beta \cong D \cdot\supset\cdot \alpha\beta \cong -CD,\\
&\alpha \cong -C \,.\, \beta \cong -D \cdot\supset\cdot \alpha\beta \cong CD,\\
&\alpha \cong 0 \vee \beta \cong 0 \cdot\supset\cdot \alpha\beta \cong 0.
\end{aligned}
\tag{8:1}
$$

These statements show that the operation of multiplication in $\mathfrak{R}$ is well-defined. They also show that we could have made the extension of the system $(\mathfrak{Q}, +, \times)$ simply by introducing the artificial element 0 and the "tagged" elements $-C$. The formulas (8:1) would then become the definition of multiplication in the extended system. In the following proofs it is convenient to make use of both points of view.

For convenience a set of properties characterizing the real number system is collected in Sec. 9. It is easy to verify that the system we have been constructing has these properties. The property R2 follows at once from the general theory of Sec. 4. The first part of R3 has already been verified, and the associative, commutative, and distributive laws follow immediately from the original definitions of $+$ and $\times$. To verify R4 we recall that for arbitrary numbers A and C there is always a number B such that $AB = C$. Then for arbitrary numbers α and γ, with $\alpha \neq 0$, we have the following solutions of the equation $\alpha\beta = \gamma$ in the six cases:

1. $\alpha \cong A,\ \gamma \cong 0,\ \beta \cong 0.$
2. $\alpha \cong A,\ \gamma \cong C,\ \beta \cong B.$

3. $\alpha \cong A, \gamma \cong -C, \beta \cong -B.$
4. $\alpha \cong -A, \gamma \cong 0, \beta \cong 0.$
5. $\alpha \cong -A, \gamma \cong C, \beta \cong -B.$
6. $\alpha \cong -A, \gamma \cong -C, \beta \cong B.$

The properties R5 and R6 are readily verified using the original definitions of $+$ and $<$. We note also that $\alpha > 0$ if and only if there is a number C in $\mathfrak{Q}$ such that $\alpha \cong C$, and that $\alpha < 0$ if and only if there is a C such that $\alpha \cong -C$. Moreover, if $\alpha \cong C$, $\beta \cong D$, then $\alpha < \beta \cdot\sim\cdot C < D$, and if $\alpha \cong -C$, $\beta \cong -D$, then $\alpha < \beta \cdot\sim\cdot D < C$. The property R7 is now obvious, and we verify R8 as follows. If K is a subset of $\mathfrak{R}$, and $0 \leqq K$, but $0 \neq$ g.l.b. K, then $\exists\gamma > 0 \ni\cdot \gamma \leqq K$. Hence g.l.b. K exists by the Dedekind property of $\mathfrak{Q}$. On the other hand, if $\gamma \leqq K$, and $\exists\alpha < 0$ in K, let K_1 consist of all elements $C \cong -\alpha$ where $\alpha < 0$ and α is in K. Then $C_0 \geqq K_1$, where $C_0 \cong -\gamma$, and $\exists C_1 =$ l.u.b. K_1 by the Dedekind property of $\mathfrak{Q}$. Hence $-C_1 \cong$ g.l.b. K.

9. Properties Characterizing the Real Number System.—The real number system $(\mathfrak{R}, +, \times, <)$ is characterized by the following properties:

R1. The class $\mathfrak{R}$ contains at least two elements.
R2. $(\mathfrak{R}, +)$ is a commutative group.
R3. $\times$ is on $\mathfrak{R}\mathfrak{R}$ to $\mathfrak{R}$, and is associative and commutative, and distributive with respect to $+$.
R4. The class $\mathfrak{R}$ with the unit 0 for addition omitted, and $\times$, forms a group.
R5. $(\mathfrak{R}, <)$ forms a linearly ordered set.
R6. $\alpha < \beta \,.\, \gamma \cdot\supset\cdot \alpha + \gamma < \beta + \gamma.$
R7. $\alpha > 0 \,.\, \beta > 0 \cdot\supset\cdot \alpha\beta > 0.$
R8. $(\mathfrak{R}, <)$ has the Dedekind property.

A system having the properties R1 to R4 is called a **field,** and a system having the properties R1 to R7 is called an **ordered field.** (See, for example, Albert, *Modern Higher Algebra,* pages 27, 110.) The only ordered field with the Dedekind property is the real number system, in the sense that two systems having the properties R1 to R8 are necessarily simply isomorphic.

The real number system has the following additional properties, which are logically deducible from R1 to R8 without reference to the method of constructing the real numbers. The usual notation 1 is used for the unit element for multiplication, and we omit the sign $\times$ according to custom. Furthermore, we set $|\alpha| = \alpha$ if $\alpha \geqq 0$, $|\alpha| = -\alpha$ if $\alpha < 0$.

R9. $\alpha . \beta \cdot \supset \cdot \alpha \times 0 = 0 . \alpha(-\beta) = -(\alpha\beta) = (-\alpha)\beta.$
$$(-\alpha)(-\beta) = \alpha\beta.$$

R10. $0 < 1$.

R11. $\alpha > 0 . \beta < \gamma \cdot \supset \cdot \alpha\beta < \alpha\gamma$.

R12. There is a subset $\mathfrak{R}_{\mathrm{M}}$ of $\mathfrak{R}$ such that the system ($\mathfrak{R}_{\mathrm{M}}$, $+$, $\times$, $<$) is simply isomorphic to the system ($\mathfrak{M}$, $+$, $\times$, $<$) of Sec. 2. Every element μ of $\mathfrak{R}_{\mathrm{M}}$ satisfies $\mu > 0$. and 1 is the first element of $\mathfrak{R}_{\mathrm{M}}$.

R13. $\alpha > 0 . \beta > 0 \cdot \supset \cdot \exists \mu$ in $\mathfrak{R}_{\mathrm{M}} \ni \cdot\, \mu\alpha > \beta$.

R14. $\alpha < \beta \cdot \supset \cdot \exists \mu$ in $\mathfrak{R}_{\mathrm{M}} . \exists \nu$ in $\mathfrak{R}_{\mathrm{M}} \ni \cdot\, \alpha < \mu/\nu < \beta \vee \alpha < -\mu/\nu < \beta$.

R15. $\alpha . \beta \cdot \supset \cdot |\alpha + \beta| \leqq |\alpha| + |\beta| . |\alpha\beta| = |\alpha||\beta|$.

To prove R9, we see that, by the distributive law, $\alpha = \alpha \times 1 = \alpha(1 + 0) = \alpha \times 1 + \alpha \times 0 = \alpha + \alpha \times 0$, so that $\alpha \times 0 = 0$. Next, $\alpha(-\beta) + \alpha\beta = \alpha(-\beta + \beta) = \alpha \times 0 = 0$, so that $\alpha(-\beta) = -(\alpha\beta)$. Finally, $(-\alpha)(-\beta) + (-\alpha\beta) = (-\alpha)(-\beta) + (-\alpha)\beta = (-\alpha)(-\beta + \beta) = (-\alpha) \times 0 = 0$, so that $(-\alpha)(-\beta) = \alpha\beta$.

To prove R10, we note that, if $1 = 0$, then $\alpha = \alpha \times 1 = \alpha \times 0 = 0$ for every α, and this contradicts R1. Hence $1 < 0 \vee 1 > 0$ by R5. If $1 < 0$, then $0 = 1 + (-1) < -1$ by R6, and thus $1 = (-1)(-1) > 0$ by R7. The property R11 follows readily from R6 and R7.

To prove R12, let us say that a subclass $\mathfrak{R}_0$ of $\mathfrak{R}$ has the property (H) in case $\mathfrak{R}_0$ contains 1, and contains $\alpha + 1$ whenever it contains α. The subset $\mathfrak{R}_{\mathrm{M}}$ is defined as the logical product of all subclasses $\mathfrak{R}_0$ having the property (H). Thus $\mathfrak{R}_{\mathrm{M}}$ is the minimum subclass of $\mathfrak{R}$ having the property (H). If we let $\mathfrak{R}_1 =$ [all α in $\mathfrak{R}_{\mathrm{M}} \ni \cdot\, \alpha > 0$], we see at once that $\mathfrak{R}_1$ has the property (H), by R10 and R6, so that $\mathfrak{R}_1 = \mathfrak{R}_{\mathrm{M}}$. Setting $s(\alpha) = \alpha + 1$, we see at once that the system ($\mathfrak{R}_{\mathrm{M}}$, s) has the properties P1 to P4 of Sec. 2, with $m_0 = 1$. The operations of addition and multiplication defined in that section in terms of the function s are seen to coincide with the addition and multiplication of the real number system by virtue of the associative and commutative laws for addition, and the distributive law.

To prove the Archimedean property R13, we use an indirect

proof. Suppose every μ in $\Re_M$ satisfies $\mu \leqq \beta/\alpha$. Then $\exists\gamma = \text{l.u.b. } \Re_M$, by R8, and $\exists\mu$ in $\Re_M \ni\cdot\ \mu > \gamma - 1$. Then $\gamma < \mu + 1$ by R6, and this contradicts the definition of γ.

The density property R14 can be proved by means of the Archimedean property. Suppose first $0 \leqq \alpha < \beta$. Then by R13, $\exists\nu$ in $\Re_M \ni\cdot\ \nu(\beta - \alpha) > 2$, and $\exists\mu$ in $\Re_M \ni\cdot\ (\mu - 1)/\nu \leqq \alpha < \mu/\nu$, since every nonnull subset of $\Re_M$ has a first element, by property M11 of Sec. 2. From this, $\mu/\nu \leqq \alpha + 1/\nu < \alpha + (\beta - \alpha)/2 < \beta$. Next suppose $\alpha < 0$. Then from R6, R10, and R13, $\exists\sigma$ in $\Re_M \ni\cdot\ 0 < \sigma + \alpha < \sigma + \beta$. By the first case, $\exists\mu\,.\,\exists\nu \ni\cdot\ \sigma + \alpha < \mu/\nu < \sigma + \beta$, so that $\alpha < (\mu - \sigma\nu)/\nu < \beta$ by R6. If it should happen that $\mu - \sigma\nu = 0$, then by the first case, $\exists\mu'.\,\exists\nu' \ni\cdot\ 0 < \mu'/\nu' < \beta$.

It is easy to show that an isomorphism between two systems $(\Re_1, +, \times, <)$ and $(\Re_2, +, \times, <)$ having the properties R1 to R8 can be set up in one and only one way. In the first place it is clear that the units for addition in the two systems must correspond, and likewise the units for multiplication. Consequently the correspondence of the subsets $\Re_{1M}$ and $\Re_{2M}$ described in R12 is determined. If we let $\Re_{1F}$ and $\Re_{2F}$ denote the sets of positive rational numbers in the two systems, we see that the correspondence between $\Re_{1F}$ and $\Re_{2F}$ is likewise determined. Let elements of $\Re_{1F}$ be denoted by a_1 and let elements of $\Re_{2F}$ be denoted by a_2. For a given $\alpha_1 > 0$ in $\Re_1$, let $K_1 = [\text{all } a_1 > \alpha_1]$. Note that K_1 is a subset of $\Re_{1F}$. Then by R14, $\alpha_1 = \text{g.l.b. } K_1$. Let K_2 be the subset of $\Re_{2F}$ consisting of all the elements a_2 corresponding to elements a_1 of K_1, and let $\alpha_2 = \text{g.l.b. } K_2$ correspond to α_1. It is not difficult to verify that this correspondence is preserved under addition and multiplication. Obviously no other way of setting up the correspondence would preserve the order relation. Finally, the correspondence is set up for the negative real numbers in the obvious way. This process of establishing the isomorphism between two systems satisfying the postulates R1 to R8 follows in outline the process we have selected for constructing the real number system.

10. Additional Properties of the Real Number System.—In this section we shall use a variety of letters to stand for numbers and disregard the connotations in use in the preceding sections. The numbers considered are supposed to lie in an ordered field, *i.e.*, in a system $(\Re, +, \times, <)$ having the properties R1 to R7.

A **sequence** (a_n) in $\mathfrak{R}$ is a function that makes correspond to each positive integer n a uniquely determined number a_n in $\mathfrak{R}$. The notion of **limit of a sequence** is defined as follows:

$$\lim a_n = l :\equiv: \epsilon > 0 :\supset: \exists n_\epsilon \ni: n > n_\epsilon \cdot\supset\cdot |a_n - l| < \epsilon.$$

The significance of this definition is indicated graphically in the figure, where n is plotted along the x-axis, and a_n along the y-axis.

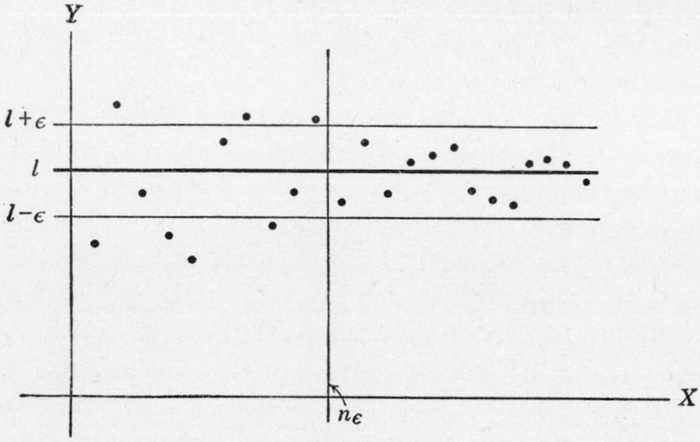

The graph of the function consists of isolated points. All the points of the graph to the right of the line $x = n_\epsilon$ are supposed to lie between the lines $y = l + \epsilon$ and $y = l - \epsilon$. A sequence (a_n) is a **Cauchy sequence,** or satisfies the **Cauchy condition,** in case

$$\epsilon > 0 :\supset: \exists n_\epsilon \ni: m > n_\epsilon \,.\, n > n_\epsilon \cdot\supset\cdot |a_m - a_n| < \epsilon.$$

THEOREM 5. *Every Cauchy sequence is bounded.*

THEOREM 6. *Every sequence having a limit in $\mathfrak{R}$ is a Cauchy sequence.*

THEOREM 7. *If the ordered field $\mathfrak{R}$ has the Dedekind property, every Cauchy sequence (a_n) in $\mathfrak{R}$ has a limit in $\mathfrak{R}$.*

Proof.—By Theorem 5, (a_n) is bounded, so that we may set $b_n =$ l.u.b. a_m for $m > n$, and $l =$ g.l.b. b_n. Then $\exists q \ni\cdot b_q \leqq l + \epsilon$. Let p be an integer greater than q and greater than the n_ϵ of the Cauchy condition. Then $n > p \cdot\supset\cdot a_n \leqq b_q \leqq l + \epsilon$. Also $\exists m > p \ni\cdot a_m > b_p - \epsilon \geqq l - \epsilon$. Then by the Cauchy condition $n > p \cdot\supset\cdot a_n \geqq a_m - \epsilon > l - 2\epsilon$, and finally we have $|a_n - l| < 2\epsilon$.

A Cauchy sequence is sometimes called a **regular** sequence, or a **convergent** sequence. The term **convergent sequence** is sometimes also used to mean one that has a limit. According to the last two theorems the two usages are equivalent in the real number system. However, when the numbers used are restricted to be rational, a Cauchy sequence need not have a limit.

A sequence (a_n) is said to be **nondecreasing** in case $n < m \cdot \supset \cdot a_n \leqq a_m$. It is said to be **nonincreasing** in case $n < m \cdot \supset \cdot a_n \geqq a_m$. A **monotonic** sequence is one which is either nondecreasing or nonincreasing.

THEOREM 8. *If the ordered field* $\mathfrak{R}$ *is Archimedean, every monotonic bounded sequence is a Cauchy sequence.*

This may be proved by an indirect proof.

THEOREM 9. *If the ordered field* $\mathfrak{R}$ *has the property that every nondecreasing bounded sequence has a limit, then* $\mathfrak{R}$ *has the Dedekind property.*

Proof.—We first show by an indirect proof that the field is Archimedean. Suppose there exist positive numbers a and b of the field such that $na \leqq b$ for every integer n. Then the sequence (na) is increasing and bounded, and so has a limit l. By definition of limit, $l - na < a$ for n sufficiently large, so that $l < (n + 1)a$. But it is easily seen that $l \geqq na$ for every n, so that we have arrived at a contradiction.

Now let K be a set of numbers which is bounded above. Let a be a number in K, let $b \geqq K$, and let $c_1 = (a + b)/2$. If $K \leqq c_1$, set $a_1 = a$, $b_1 = c_1$; otherwise set $a_1 = c_1$, $b_1 = b$. This indicates how to define recursively two sequences (a_n) and (b_n). If a_{n-1} and b_{n-1} have been defined, set $c_n = (a_{n-1} + b_{n-1})/2$. If $K \leqq c_n$, set $a_n = a_{n-1}$, $b_n = c_n$; otherwise set $a_n = c_n$, $b_n = b_{n-1}$. It is clear that the sequence (a_n) is nondecreasing and bounded, so that by hypothesis it has a limit l. Since $b_n - a_n = (b - a)/2^n$, it is easy to see by the Archimedean property that $\lim (b_n - a_n) = 0$, and hence $l = \lim b_n$. Also $K \leqq b_n$ for every n, and so $K \leqq l$. We note also that if $l \neq \text{l.u.b. } K$, $\exists \epsilon > 0 \ni\cdot K \leqq l - \epsilon$, and from this, $\exists n \ni\cdot K < a_n$, but this contradicts the definition of a_n, so that we must have $l = \text{l.u.b. } K$.

The last two theorems show that, if an ordered field is Archimedean and has the property that every Cauchy sequence has a limit in the field, then the field is complete, *i.e.*, has the Dedekind property. Thus there are three possible ways of formulating the concept of completeness for ordered fields, each of which has its advantages. It is worth remarking that the notions of limit and of Cauchy sequence may be used in situations where the relation of order and the operations of addition and multiplication are not defined.

Two sequences (a_n) and (b_n) are said to be **equivalent** in case $\lim (a_n - b_n) = 0$. This relation is easily seen to be reflexive, symmetric, and transitive, so that it may be used to divide the class of all sequences into mutually exclusive subclasses. By restricting attention to Cauchy sequences of rational numbers, we may introduce the construction of the real number system due to Cantor. According to Cantor, a real number is defined to be a maximal class of equivalent Cauchy sequences of rational numbers. It is easy to define addition, multiplication, and an order relation for such classes, and the system so set up may be shown to have the properties listed in Sec. 9. The correspondence between Cauchy sequences of rational numbers and the Dedekind cuts in the rational number system may be defined directly.

A sequence (a_n) is a **decimal sequence** in case a_1 is an integer (positive or negative), and $a_{n+1} = a_n + b_n/10^n$, where b_n is one of the numbers 0, 1, 2, . . . , 9. It is clear that every decimal sequence is bounded and nondecreasing and so has a limit in the real number system. A decimal sequence is **normal** in case $k \cdot \supset \cdot \exists n > k \ni \cdot b_n \neq 9$. By means of the Archimedean property it may be proved that every real number is the limit of exactly one normal decimal sequence. Thus we see that the real numbers might have been defined as the normal decimal sequences. Of course other bases than ten might have been used for a system of numeration. In particular the bases two and three are sometimes useful in discussing the properties of certain point sets.

A class is said to be **denumerable** in case it can be set into one-to-one correspondence with the class of natural numbers. A class K is said to be **finite** in case there exists a natural number m such that K can be set into one-to-one correspondence with the set of all natural numbers not greater than m, and K is then said to have m elements. It is important to note that the class of all rational numbers is denumerable, while the class of all real numbers is not. Since the class of even integers is denumerable, it suffices for the first statement to show that the class of positive rational numbers is denumerable. We can, for example, make each positive fraction p/q correspond to the integer $n = (p + q)(p + q - 1)/2 + p$. This makes infinitely many integers correspond to each positive fraction. By dropping out all but the first one in each case (obtained by representing the fraction in its lowest terms), we establish a one-to-one correspondence of the class of positive rational numbers with a subclass of the integers. It is easy to see then that the class of positive rational numbers is denumerable.

To show that the class of all real numbers is not denumerable, we suppose that (c_n) is a sequence containing all the real numbers and consider the normal decimal representation of each number c_n. We may readily define a normal decimal sequence whose digit in the nth decimal place differs from the corresponding digit of c_n, and thus determine a real number c which does not occur in the sequence (c_n).

The notions of the last two paragraphs are treated in a more general setting in Chap. XIII. See especially Secs. 5, 7, and 8.

REFERENCES

1. Stone, *The Theory of Real Functions*, 1940, Part I.
2. Hobson, *The Theory of Functions of a Real Variable*, 3d Ed., 1927, Vol. 1, Chap. 1.
3. Pierpont, *The Theory of Functions of Real Variables*, 1905, Vol. 1, Chap. 1.
4. Veblen and Lennes, *Infinitesimal Analysis*, 1907, Chap. 1.
5. Hölder, *Die Arithmetik in strenger Begründung*, 1929.
6. Landau, *Grundlagen der Analysis*, 1930.
7. Stolz und Gmeiner, *Theoretische Arithmetik*, 1900–1902.

Stone [1] contains a complete and careful development of the real number system, using the Cantor process. In this work, equivalence is called "equality." Veblen and Lennes [4] is easily readable but brief. It contains a list of postulates characterizing the real number system. Stolz und Gmeiner [7] contains a rather lengthy and exhaustive discussion of various topics connected with numbers.

CHAPTER III

POINT SETS

1. Space of k Dimensions.—A **point** in one-dimensional space is a real number or one of the ideal elements $+\infty$, $-\infty$. These two ideal elements $+\infty$ and $-\infty$ are introduced for convenience in connection with the theory of limits. We define an order relation between them and the real numbers by saying that for every real number b, $-\infty < b < +\infty$. There is not a great deal of use for a definition of the operations of algebra on these ideal elements, but they can easily be defined in a way that is consistent with the theory of limits except for those forms like $0\cdot\infty$ which are commonly called "indeterminate" forms.

By the **Cartesian product** of two classes P and Q is meant the class of all couples (p, q), of which the first element p is chosen from P and the second element q from Q. The Cartesian product of one-dimensional space by itself gives us a two-dimensional space, frequently called the **number plane.** By properly chosen definitions we obtain from the number plane an ordinary Euclidean plane plus four lines at infinity. The number plane corresponds to a coordinate system set up in the Euclidean plane. The four lines at infinity in the number plane are defined in terms of xy-coordinates by the equations $x = +\infty$, $x = -\infty$, $y = +\infty$, $y = -\infty$. By forming the Cartesian product of k classes each composed of the real numbers and the ideal elements $+\infty$ and $-\infty$, we obtain the k-dimensional number space of points $(x^{(1)}, \ldots, x^{(k)})$ each of whose coordinates $x^{(i)}$ is either a real number or $+\infty$ or $-\infty$. When it is not necessary to indicate the number of dimensions or to consider the individual coordinates, we shall use the abbreviated notation x for the point $(x^{(1)}, \ldots, x^{(k)})$. The definitions and theorems given in this chapter are equally valid for any finite number of dimensions. For explicitness and simplicity most of the examples are given in spaces of one and two dimensions.

The geometric language is used because of its convenience and suggestiveness. Much of this chapter is devoted to introducing the terminology of point-set theory and clarifying its meaning by means of examples. We recall that the terms "class," "family," and "aggregate" are used as synonyms for the term "set." In connection with point sets in a number space, the term "region" will be used as still another synonym.

2. Examples of Point Sets.—The first examples, A to F, are in one-dimensional space. The notation $E_x[\ \ ]$ or $E[\ \ ]$ will be used to denote the set of all points satisfying the condition written in the bracket. Occasionally the notation $S[\ \ ]$ is used to denote the *subset* of a given point set S which satisfies the condition written in the bracket.

A. An **open interval** (a, b) consists of all points x such that $a < x < b$, where a and b are fixed points, *i.e.*, $(a, b) = E_x[a < x < b]$.

B. A **closed interval** $[a, b] = E_x[a \leqq x \leqq b]$.

C. The set of points with positive integral coordinates.

D. The set of points whose coordinates are the reciprocals of the positive integers.

E. The set of all points with rational coordinates.

F. The **Cantor discontinuum.** This is formed from a closed interval $[a, b]$ by removing first the middle third, then the middle thirds of the remaining intervals, and so on indefinitely. It is understood that the intervals removed are *open* intervals. The set of points remaining after the infinite sequence of operations just described is called the "Cantor discontinuum." Its properties will be discussed in more detail in Sec. 4. Its construction may be varied by replacing the fraction $\frac{1}{3}$ by some other fraction.

The following examples G to K are in two-dimensional space:

G. An **open interval** $(a,c; b,d) = E_{xy}[a < x < b; c < y < d]$.

H. A **closed interval** $[a,c; b,d] = E_{xy}[a \leqq x \leqq b; c \leqq y \leqq d]$.

I. The set of all points on the circumferences of the circles with centers at $(1/2^n, 0)$ and radii respectively $1/2^{n+2}$, for $n = 1, 2, \ldots$.

J. The set of all points interior to the circles described in I.

K. The set of points $(-\infty, n)$, where $n = 1, 2, \ldots$.

L. The set $E_{xy}[-\infty < x < +\infty; x^2 \leqq y \leqq 2x^2]$.

M. The set composed of the points for which $0 < x \leqq 1$, $y = \sin(1/x)$, plus the interval $-1 \leqq y \leqq 1$ of the y-axis.

3. Operations on Aggregates.—Various operations on point sets will be discussed in this section. These operations are obviously applicable to aggregates of any nature whatever, as was indicated in Sec. 3 of Chap. I.

The **sum** of two sets A and B, denoted by the symbol $A + B$, consists of all points x that belong to at least one of the sets A and B. The **product** or **intersection,** denoted by AB, consists of all points x that belong to both sets A and B. These definitions are obviously extensible at once to collections of any number (finite or infinite) of sets A_α. For such sums and products we may use the ordinary abbreviated notations $\sum A_\alpha$ and $\prod A_\alpha$, respectively. Since there may not be any points belonging to both of two arbitrary classes A and B, it is convenient to speak of the **null class,** which has no elements whatever, and for which one of the notations Λ or 0 is frequently used. Thus, using the examples I and J, we may write

$$\text{IJ} = \Lambda \qquad \text{or} \qquad \text{IJ} = 0.$$

Two sets whose intersection is the null set are said to be **disjoint.**

The **difference** of two sets, written $A - B$, consists of all points x in A but not in B. Obviously the difference of two sets may also reduce to the null set. A special case of a difference is the complement of a set A, frequently written cA, which consists of all points x of space not in the set A. It is worth while to note that the complement of a product of sets is the sum of the complements of the respective sets and, vice versa, the complement of a sum is the product of the complements. Thus $AB = c(cA + cB)$. Also $A - B = AcB = c(cA + B)$. Thus the two operations of taking sums and complements may be taken as fundamental if this is desired. Referring to the examples C, D, and E, we note that $(\text{C} + \text{D}) - \text{E} \neq \text{C} + (\text{D} - \text{E})$.

Associated with each sequence of sets A_n are two limiting sets, frequently called the **limit inferior** (or the **restricted limit**) and the **limit superior** (or the **complete limit**) of the sequence, which may be defined by the respective formulas

$$\liminf A_n = \sum_m \prod_{n>m} A_n, \qquad \limsup A_n = \prod_m \sum_{n>m} A_n.$$

The limit inferior contains all those points which belong to all the sets A_n from a certain place on. The limit superior consists of all those points which belong to infinitely many of the sets A_n. In case the limit inferior and the limit superior turn out to be the same set, this set is called the **limit** of the sequence A_n. A sequence (A_n) is called **nondecreasing** in case $A_n \subset A_{n+1}$ for every n, and **nonincreasing** in case $A_n \supset A_{n+1}$ for every n. In either case it is called **monotonic.** A monotonic sequence of sets always has a limit. In the nondecreasing case, $\lim A_n = \sum A_n$, and in the nonincreasing case, $\lim A_n = \prod A_n$.[1]

The following examples in two-dimensional space illustrate the preceding definitions.

N. The set A_n consists of the interior of the circle with center at $(n, 0)$ which passes through the points $(0, 1)$ and $(0, -1)$. Then $\lim A_n$ consists of the points (x, y) in the finite part of the plane for which $x > 0$ and the points on the open segment from $(0, 1)$ to $(0, -1)$.

P. The set A_n consists of the interior of the circle with center at $((-1)^n n, 0)$ which passes through the points $(0, 1)$ and $(0, -1)$. Then $\liminf A_n$ consists of the points on the open segment from $(0, 1)$ to $(0, -1)$, while $\limsup A_n$ consists of the entire finite part of the plane except for those points on the y-axis for which $|y| \geqq 1$.

4. Some Fundamental Definitions and Theorems of Point-set Theory.—By the **ϵ-neighborhood** $N(b; \epsilon)$ of a point $b = (b^{(1)}, \ldots, b^{(k)})$ in k-dimensional space is meant the set of all points x, finite or infinite, such that $|x^{(i)} - b^{(i)}| < \epsilon$ if $b^{(i)}$ is finite; $x^{(i)} < -1/\epsilon$ if $b^{(i)} = -\infty$; $x^{(i)} > 1/\epsilon$ if $b^{(i)} = +\infty$, for $i = 1, \ldots, k$. It is supposed, of course, that $\epsilon > 0$. A useful consequence of this definition is that, if a point c is in the neighborhood $N(b; \epsilon)$ and d is in $N(c; \epsilon)$, then d is in $N(b; 2\epsilon)$ provided $2\epsilon^2 \leqq 1$ when b has one or more infinite coordinates. Furthermore, $b \neq c \cdot \supset \cdot \exists \epsilon > 0 \ni \cdot\ N(b; \epsilon)N(c; \epsilon) = 0$, that is, if b and c are

[1] It should be noted that occasionally an author will use the symbols $\liminf A_n$ and $\limsup A_n$ with a different meaning.

distinct points, there is a positive number ϵ, such that the neighborhoods $N(b; \epsilon)$ and $N(c; \epsilon)$ have no points in common.

If S is a set of points,

$$N(S; \epsilon) \equiv \sum_{b \text{ in } S} N(b; \epsilon).$$

that is, the **neighborhood** $N(S; \epsilon)$ consists of all points x that lie in the ϵ-neighborhood of some point b of S.

A point b is **interior** to a set S in case $\exists \epsilon > 0 \ni\cdot N(b; \epsilon) \subset S$, that is, in case there exists a neighborhood $N(b; \epsilon)$ containing only points of S. A point b is **exterior to** S in case $\exists \epsilon > 0 \ni\cdot SN(b; \epsilon) = 0$, that is, in case there is a neighborhood $N(b; \epsilon)$ containing no points of S. A point b is a **boundary point** or a **frontier point** of S in case $\epsilon > 0 \cdot \supset \cdot N(b; \epsilon)S \neq 0. N(b; \epsilon)cS \neq 0$, that is, in case every neighborhood $N(b; \epsilon)$ contains at least one point in S and at least one point not in S. The set of all the boundary points of a set S is called the **boundary** or **frontier** of S. It is easy to see that a point is a boundary point of a set if and only if it is neither an interior point nor an exterior point of the set. Thus with respect to a given set S all points of space are classified into three mutually exclusive classes: interior points, exterior points, and boundary points. A boundary point of a set may belong to the set or not.

A set of points having b as an interior point will also be called a **neighborhood** of b, and denoted by $N(b)$, when it is not important to specify the character of the neighborhood. Every neighborhood $N(b)$ contains an ϵ-neighborhood $N(b; \epsilon)$. Thus the interior of a circle in the plane constitutes a neighborhood of each of its points. A **deleted neighborhood** of b is obtained by striking out the point b from a neighborhood of b. As in Chap. I, we shall use the notation $\{b\}$ for the set consisting of the single element b.

A point b is an **accumulation point** or a **limit point** of a set S in case $\epsilon > 0 \cdot \supset \cdot N(b; \epsilon)S - \{b\} \neq 0$, that is, in case every deleted neighborhood of b contains points of S. A point b is an **isolated point** of a set S in case $\exists \epsilon > 0 \ni\cdot N(b; \epsilon)S = \{b\}$, that is, in case b belongs to S and there is a neighborhood of b containing no other point of S.

THEOREM 1. *In every neighborhood of an accumulation point of S there are infinitely many points of S.*

Proof.—If x_i is a point of S distinct from b, then $\exists \epsilon_i > 0 \ni : x_i$ not in $N(b; \epsilon_i)$. If only a finite number $x_1, x_2, \ldots, x_n$ of points of S distinct from b lie in a neighborhood $N(b; \epsilon_0)$, the smallest of the numbers $\epsilon_1, \ldots, \epsilon_n$ is a positive number ϵ, and $N(b; \epsilon)$ would contain no points of S distinct from b.

The following theorems are left to the reader as exercises.

THEOREM 2. *Every interior point of S is an accumulation point of S*

THEOREM 3. *An accumulation point of S is either an interior point of S or a boundary point of S.*

THEOREM 4. *A boundary point of S is either an accumulation point of S or an isolated point of S.*

The **derived set** or **derivative** of a set S, denoted by S', is the set consisting of all the accumulation points of S. The set $S + S'$ is frequently called the **closure** of S and denoted by $\bar{S}$. A set S is called **closed** in case it contains all its points of accumulation, *i.e.*, in case $S' \subset S$. A set S is called **open** in case it is composed entirely of interior points. It is readily seen that every ϵ-neighborhood $N(b; \epsilon)$ is an open set.

THEOREM 5. *If $S \subset T$, then $S' \subset T'$*, and $\bar{S} \subset \bar{T}$.

THEOREM 6. *The complement of a closed set is open; vice versa, the complement of an open set is closed.*

Proof.—If S is closed and b is in the complement of S, then b is in the complement of S', and so there is a neighborhood of b containing no points of S. If S is open and b is in $(cS)'$, then every neighborhood of b contains points of cS, so that b is not in S.

THEOREM 7. *Let (E_α) be a family of sets, $S = \sum E_\alpha, P = \prod E_\alpha$. If each E_α is closed, the product P is also closed. In case there are only a finite number of sets E_α, the sum S is also closed. If each E_α is open, the sum S is also open. In case there are only a finite number of sets E_α, the product P is also open.*

Proof.—If each E_α is closed, we have $P' \subset \prod E'_\alpha \subset \prod E_\alpha = P$. If in addition there are only a finite number of sets E_α, and b is not in $\sum E'_\alpha$, then

$$\alpha : \supset : \exists \epsilon_\alpha > 0 \ni : E_\alpha N(b; \epsilon_\alpha) - \{b\} = 0.$$

Let ϵ be the smallest ϵ_α. Then $SN(b; \epsilon) - \{b\} = 0$, so that b is not in S'. Hence $S' \subset \sum E'_\alpha \subset \sum E_\alpha = S$. The last part of the theorem follows from the first part by use of Theorem 6.

THEOREM 8. *The derived set S' of an arbitrary set S is closed. The boundary of S and the closure $\bar{S}$ of S are also closed sets.*

The proof of the last theorem is left to the reader. From it we see that the closure $\bar{S}$ of S is the minimum closed set containing S.

Note that the property of being closed or open or neither depends on the space in which the point set in question is regarded as embedded. Thus, the set C of the examples in Sec. 2 is not closed. But, if we had not introduced the points at infinity into the space, the set C would be closed, since it would have no point of accumulation whatever in the space. An open interval (a, b) of one-dimensional space is an open set A, but if the same set A is regarded as a subset of two-dimensional space then A is no longer open. It is sometimes convenient to introduce the notion of **relative closure.** A set S is said to be **closed relative to** a set T in case $S'T \subset S \subset T$. A set S is **open relative to** a set T in case $S \subset T$ and $T - S$ is closed relative to T. The form of the last definition is justified by Theorem 6.

It should be noted that a closed interval may be represented as a product of open intervals, and an open interval may be represented as a sum of closed intervals. Also every set is both closed and open relative to itself. Example D is closed relative to the open interval (0, 2), and D + (−1, 0) is open relative to D + [−2, 0].

A set T is said to be **dense in** a set S in case $S \subset T'$. As a special case, a set S is **dense-in-itself** in case $S \subset S'$. A set S is **nowhere dense** or **nondense** in case it is dense in no interval. A set S is **perfect** in case it is closed and dense-in-itself, *i.e.*, in case $S = S'$.

The following theorem is frequently useful:

THEOREM 9. *Every infinite set S in the number space contains a denumerable subset T such that $S \subset T + T'$. If S is dense-in-itself, then T is dense in S.*

Proof.—If space is one-dimensional, we fit a **net** G_n of intervals on it, with end points $i/2^n$, where i ranges over the integers from -2^{2n} to 2^{2n}. Thus each net G_n consists of a finite number of intervals of which the first and the last are the infinite intervals

$(-\infty, -2^n)$ and $(2^n, +\infty)$, respectively. If space is k-dimensional, the net G_n is to consist of the k-dimensional intervals each of which is the Cartesian product of k intervals chosen from the one-dimensional net just described. In particular, in two dimensions, the net G_n is composed of intervals with corners $(i/2^n, j/2^n)$, where i and j range independently from -2^{2n} to 2^{2n} and take also the values $-\infty$ and $+\infty$. Such a sequence of nets is frequently useful.

To obtain the set T we select from each interval of each net G_n a point of S, if there is one. Then for each point x in S and each n, there is an interval i_n of the net G_n containing x, and therefore containing a point of T. Hence x is in $T + T'$. From $S \subset T + T'$ we find $S' \subset T' + T'' = T'$, and from this the last statement of the theorem follows.

From the property R14 of Chap. II, Sec. 9, it is easy to see that the denumerable set Q composed of all points with rational coordinates is dense on the number space. An alternative proof for Theorem 9 is obtained by selecting a denumeration (z_n) of Q, and then selecting from each set $SN(z_n; 1/n)$ which is not null a point y_n, to obtain the desired subset T.

A set S is said to be **disconnected** in case it is the sum of two disjoint nonnull sets A and B such that neither part contains a point of accumulation of the other, that is,

$$AB + A'B + AB' = 0.$$

A set S is **connected** in case it is not disconnected. A **continuum** is a closed connected set. A set S is **convex** in case it contains the line segment joining each pair of its points.

An ϵ-neighborhood of a point b is an example of a convex set. A convex set is obviously connected. A connected set consisting of more than one point is dense-in-itself. A continuum is clearly always a perfect set, except in the degenerate case when it reduces to a single point. To avoid exceptions, we may agree to call the null set open, closed, perfect, and connected.

Use is occasionally made in analysis of other definitions of connectedness than the one given above. A set S is said to be **polygonally connected** in case every pair of its points can be joined by a polygon all of whose points are in S. A set S is said **to be arcwise connected** in case every pair of its points can be joined by a continuous arc all of whose points are in S. A **con-**

tinuous arc may be defined as the set of points

$$x^{(i)} = \phi^{(i)}(t) \qquad i = 1, \cdots, k,$$

given by k continuous functions $\phi^{(i)}(t)$ of a single real variable t on an interval $t_0 \leqq t \leqq t_1$. The properties of continuous functions are discussed in Chap. IV, Sec. 3. The notion of a continuous path curve is discussed in Chap. X, Sec. 7. The set L of the examples is arcwise connected but not polygonally connected, and the set M is connected but not arcwise connected. The set L becomes disconnected if the origin is deleted, but the set M remains connected when any finite set of points on the y-axis is deleted.

Let us consider the set F of the examples of Sec. 2, namely, the Cantor discontinuum. This set is closed, since its complementary set is a sum of open intervals. It is nondense since a piece of every subinterval of $[a, b]$ belongs to an interval of the complementary set, but it is dense-in-itself (and hence perfect) since in every neighborhood of a point of F there are intervals of the complementary set and hence end points of these intervals. It is disconnected, and all its points are boundary points. Let the interval $[a, b]$ be the interval $[0, 1]$, and let the points of this interval be represented in the ternary system (sometimes called the "decimal system with base three"). All points that can be represented exclusively in terms of the digits 0 and 2 belong to the set F. (We here waive the requirement that the representation shall be normal, in the sense of Sec. 10 of Chap. II.) This representation could also be used to verify the properties of the set F listed above. In the binary system every point of the interval $[0, 1]$ has a representation using only the digits 0 and 1. Thus there is established a correspondence between the points of the set F and the points of the inverval $[0, 1]$, which is one-to-one except that the two end points of a complementary interval of F correspond to the same point of $[0, 1]$. This shows that the set F has the same cardinal number as the interval.[1]

Exercises

1. For each set A to E and G to M of the examples, specify the set of interior points, of exterior points, and of boundary

[1] For the equivalence theorem needed here, see Chap. XIII, Sec. 5, Theorem 1.

points. Specify also the derived set and the set of isolated points.

2. For each set of the examples, tell whether the set is closed, open, dense-in-itself, perfect, or connected.

3. Determine the boundary points of the one-dimensional sets determined respectively by the inequalities: (*a*) $x^2 + x < 1$; (*b*) $-5 < x + \frac{1}{x} < 0$.

4. Prove that an open connected set S having no points at infinity is polygonally connected. HINT: For a given point a in S consider the subset A of S consisting of all points c that can be joined to a by a polygon in S.

5. Prove that if S and T are connected sets and $ST + ST' + S'T \neq 0$, then $S + T$ is connected.

6. Prove that a connected set having an isolated point contains no other point.

5. Sequences of Points, and the Weierstrass-Bolzano Theorem.—An infinite sequence (x_n) of points is said to have the point b as a **limit** in case $\epsilon > 0 :\supset: \exists m \ni: n > m \cdot\supset\cdot x_n$ in $N(b; \epsilon)$. When this condition holds, we use the notation $\lim x_n = b$. A point b is said to be a **point of accumulation** of a sequence (x_n) in case for every $\epsilon > 0$ there are infinitely many values of n for which x_n is in $N(b; \epsilon)$.

THEOREM 10. *A sequence (x_n) can have at most one point b as a limit. If $\lim x_n = b$, the point b is the only point of accumulation of the sequence.*

THEOREM 11. *If b is a point of accumulation of a set S, there exists a sequence (x_n) of distinct points of S such that $\lim_{n=\infty} x_n = b$. If b is a point of accumulation of a sequence (x_n), there is a subsequence (x_{n_k}) such that $\lim_{k=\infty} x_{n_k} = b$.*

A set S is said to be **bounded** in case there exists an ϵ-neighborhood of the origin containing S.

THEOREM 12. **The Weierstrass-Bolzano theorem.** *Every infinite set S has at least one point of accumulation, finite or infinite. If S is bounded, its points of accumulation are finite.*

Proof.—We fit a sequence of nets G_n on the space, as in the proof of Theorem 9. Since the set S is infinite, at least one interval of the net G_1 contains infinitely many points of S. Let

$[a_1, b_1]$ be such an interval. Likewise at least one interval $[a_2, b_2]$ of the net G_2 which is a subinterval of $[a_1, b_1]$ contains infinitely many points of S. Proceeding thus, we define by induction a nonincreasing sequence of intervals $[a_n, b_n]$ from the respective nets G_n, each of which contains infinitely many points of S. The coordinates $a_n^{(h)}$ form a nondecreasing sequence and the coordinates $b_n^{(h)}$ form a nonincreasing sequence, for each $h = 1, \cdots, k$. If $b_n^{(h)} = +\infty$ for every n, then $\lim_n a_n^{(h)} = +\infty$. If $a_n^{(h)} = -\infty$ for every n, then $\lim_n b_n^{(h)} = -\infty$. In every other case the sequence $(a_n^{(h)})$ is bounded above, the sequence $(b_n^{(h)})$ is bounded below, and hence both converge to the same limit. Let $c^{(h)} = \lim_n a_n^{(h)} = \lim_n b_n^{(h)}$, where $c^{(h)}$ may be $+\infty$ or $-\infty$. Thus a point c is determined which is contained in every interval $[a_n, b_n]$ of the sequence selected above. Moreover every neighborhood of c contains all the intervals $[a_n, b_n]$ from a certain one on, so that c must be a point of accumulation of S.

The theorem we have just proved is frequently stated under the additional hypothesis that the set S is bounded. This additional hypothesis would be necessary if we had not adjoined to space the points at infinity. The proof we have given covers both cases. The same remarks apply to the following four corollaries:

COROLLARY 1. *Every infinite sequence* (x_n) *has at least one point of accumulation, finite or infinite.*

Proof.—In case the same point c occurs infinitely many times in the sequence, it is by definition a point of accumulation. In case no point occurs infinitely many times, the set of points contained in the sequence is itself infinite, and the theorem applies to it.

COROLLARY 2. *If an infinite sequence* (x_n) *has just one point of accumulation* c, *then* $\lim x_n = c$.

Proof.—If the conclusion were not so, there would exist a neighborhood $N(c; \epsilon)$ such that x_n is not in $N(c; \epsilon)$ for infinitely many values of n. Then this subsequence of (x_n) would by the theorem have a point of accumulation distinct from c.

COROLLARY 3. *If* (E_n) *is a nonincreasing sequence of closed sets, the sets* E_n *have at least one point, finite or infinite, in common.*

Proof.—Select a point x_n in each E_n. The sequence (x_n) has a point of accumulation c, by Corollary 1. If $x_n = c$ for infinitely many values of n, then c is in all the sets E_n, since the sequence (E_n) is nonincreasing. In the remaining case there are infinitely many distinct points in the sequence (x_n), and x_n is in E_m for $n > m$. Thus c is a point of accumulation of each set E_m and so belongs to each E_m since each E_m is closed.

It is interesting to note that a special case of this corollary was proved and used in the proof of the theorem itself. As an example, we may consider the sequence of one-dimensional sets E_n where $E_n = E_x[n \leqq x]$. Then $\prod E_n$ reduces to the point $+\infty$. This illustrates the fact that, if we had not introduced the points at infinity, we should need the additional hypothesis that the sets E_n are bounded.

COROLLARY 4. *If S and T are closed point sets having no common point, there is a number $\epsilon > 0$ such that the neighborhoods $N(S; \epsilon)$ and $N(T; \epsilon)$ have no common point.*

Proof.—If not, there exists a sequence (ϵ_n) of positive numbers approaching zero, a sequence (a_n) of points of S, and a sequence (b_n) of points of T, such that each pair of neighborhoods $N(a_n; \epsilon_n)$ and $N(b_n; \epsilon_n)$ has a point d_n in common. The sequence (a_n) has a point of accumulation c, by Corollary 1, and by Theorem 11, there is a subsequence (a_{n_k}) such that $\lim_{k=\infty} a_{n_k} = c$. Suppose for simplicity of notation that $\lim_{k=\infty} b_{n_k} = c_1$. Then by hypothesis c is a point of S and c_1 is a point of T, and so $c \neq c_1$. But $\lim_{k=\infty} d_{n_k} = c$, and $\lim_{k=\infty} d_{n_k} = c_1$, which is in contradiction with Theorem 10.

As an example, let S be the Cantor discontinuum F and let T consist of the mid-points of the complementary intervals. Then every pair of neighborhoods $N(S; \epsilon)$ and $N(T; \epsilon)$ will have a point in common. But if we omit from T all but a finite number of its points, the conclusion of the corollary will hold. Another example in which the conclusion of the corollary fails is obtained by letting S consist of the points on a hyperbola and T of the points on the asymptotes.

6. The Heine-Borel Theorem.—A family $\mathfrak{F}$ of regions Q is said to **cover** a point set S in case each point of S is interior to at least one region Q of the family $\mathfrak{F}$.

THEOREM 13. *Let S be a closed point set covered by a family $\mathfrak{F}$ of regions Q. Then there is a finite subfamily, $(Q_1, \ldots, Q_m)$, of the family $\mathfrak{F}$ which also covers S.*

Proof.—Suppose the theorem is not true. Consider the sequence of successively finer nets G_n used in the proof of Theorem 9. Then there is an interval $[a_1,b_1]$ of the net G_1 such that the conclusion of the theorem does not hold for the portion of S contained in $[a_1, b_1]$. Similarly there is an interval $[a_2, b_2]$ of the net G_2 which is a subinterval of $[a_1, b_1]$ and such that the conclusion of the theorem is false for the portion of S contained in $[a_2, b_2]$. By an inductive procedure as in the proof of Theorem 12 there is defined a nonincreasing sequence of intervals $[a_n, b_n]$ which determines a point c belonging to all the intervals $[a_n, b_n]$, and also to the set S, since S is closed. By hypothesis the point c is interior to a region Q of the class $\mathfrak{F}$, and hence all the intervals $[a_n, b_n]$ from a certain point on are contained in this Q. This contradicts the property by means of which the intervals $[a_n, b_n]$ were determined.

Again it is to be noted that the hypothesis of boundedness is usually included in the theorem and may be omitted here only because we have included the points at infinity in the space.

Let us now consider some examples in connection with the Borel theorem. In example J, the circular regions constituting the set also constitute a covering family. But there is obviously no finite subfamily that covers J. Next, let S be the open interval (0, 1). To each point b of S we may make correspond the interval $(b/2, 3b/2)$. The family $\mathfrak{F}$ of such intervals covers S, but no finite subfamily does so. But if we adjoin to the family $\mathfrak{F}$ a neighborhood of the origin, however small, the interval (0, 1) will be covered by a finite subfamily of the enlarged family $\mathfrak{F}$.

REFERENCES

1. Hobson, *The Theory of Functions of a Real Variable*, Vol. 1, Chap. 2.
2. Pierpont, *The Theory of Functions of Real Variables*, Vol. 1, Chap. 5; Vol. 2, Chap. 10.
3. Littlewood, *The Elements of the Theory of Real Functions*.
4. Hausdorff, *Mengenlehre*, 3d Ed., 1935, Chaps. 1, 6.
5. Newman, *Elements of the Topology of Plane Sets of Points*, 1939, Chaps. 1 to 4.
6. Veblen and Lennes, *Infinitesimal Analysis*, Chap. 2.
7. Caratheodory, *Vorlesungen über reelle Funktionen*, Chap. 1.

8. Sierpinski, *Topology*, 1934.
9. Alexandroff and Hopf, *Topologie*, 1935, Vol. 1, Chaps. 1, 2.

The works of Hausdorff, Sierpinski, and Alexandroff and Hopf treat point-set theory from an abstract and general point of view, so as to include function spaces such as the space of continuous functions discussed in Chap. VII, Sec. 4. In an abstract treatment, one may take as the undefined notion distance, or neighborhood, or open set, or derived set, etc. When suitable postulates are taken as a basis, the other notions of point-set theory may then be defined and their properties derived. Several notions in addition to those described in this chapter are needed in a general theory, to care for the new phenomena that present themselves.

CHAPTER IV

FUNCTIONS AND THEIR LIMITS
PROPERTIES OF CONTINUOUS FUNCTIONS

1. Introduction.—In Sec. 4 of Chap. I, a function was defined as being the same thing as a relation. A function may also be described as a **correspondence** between two classes of objects. This correspondence need not be one-to-one, and we do not insist that each element of one class actually have a corresponding element in the other class. If the two classes of objects are $P = [p]$ and $Q = [q]$, we may use the following notation for the function. For each p in P let $g(p)$ denote the set of all elements of Q which correspond to p. Thus $g(p)$ is a subset of Q, which may be null. If S is a subset of P, let gS denote the logical sum of the sets $g(p)$ for p in S,

$$gS \equiv \sum_{p \text{ in } S} g(p).$$

The subset P_0 composed of all those elements p for which $g(p)$ is not empty is called the **domain** of the function g. The set $Q_0 = gP = gP_0$ is called the **range** of the function g. The domain P_0 is also called the **range of the independent variable** p; and the range Q_0 is also called the **range of the dependent variable** q. The latter name is sometimes applied to the whole class Q even when some of its elements are not included in the correspondence. The function g is said to be single-valued when each set $g(p)$ has not more than one element. In practice a function $g(p)$ is frequently specified by describing an operation or writing down an expression that makes correspond to each value of the independent variable p one or more values of the dependent variable q.

The same correspondence may be regarded from the reverse point of view. We use the notation g^{-1} for this **inverse function,** which has Q_0 for its domain and P_0 for its range. Thus $g^{-1}(q)$ consists of all those elements p such that q is in the set $g(p)$. Also $g^{-1}T$ consists of all elements p such that the intersection

$Tg(p)$ is not null. The notation cS is used for the complement of the set S. With these notations it is easy to verify the following relations which hold for every subset T of Q:

$$(1:1) \qquad gg^{-1}T \supset T \cdot gP.$$
$$(1:2) \qquad g^{-1}cT \supset cg^{-1}T \cdot g^{-1}Q.$$

In each case the class inclusion may be replaced by equality whenever the function g is single-valued. Corresponding statements with the roles of g and g^{-1} interchanged are obviously also valid. As a simple example, let us consider the following: $P = \{1, 2, 3\}$, $Q = \{a, b, c, d\}$, $g(1) = \{a, b\}$, $g(2) = \{b, c\}$, $g(3) = \Lambda$. Then $g^{-1}(a) = 1$, $g^{-1}(b) = \{1, 2\}$, $g^{-1}(c) = 2$, $g^{-1}(d) = \Lambda$, $g^{-1}g(1) = \{1, 2\}$, $gg^{-1}g(1) = \{a, b, c\}$. The reader will note that for our present purposes it is unnecessary to distinguish between an element a and the class $\{a\}$ whose only element is a.

A **function** g **on** P **to** Q is a single-valued function with domain P and range contained in Q. The theory of limits is applicable also to multiple-valued functions, and there are some cases in which it is convenient to include such functions. One of the phrases " . . . on . . . to . . . " or "single-valued" will be used whenever it is necessary to indicate the restriction to single-valued functions. In such cases it is not implied that the inverse function is single-valued. We shall be dealing in the sequel principally with functions whose domain is a set S in k-dimensional space and whose range is likewise in a space of one or more dimensions. A **real-valued** function is one whose range is contained in one-dimensional space. When multiple-valued real-finite-valued functions f and g are to be added, the values of $f(p)$ and of $g(p)$ are added in all possible combinations to obtain the set of values of $f + g$ at p. The same understanding applies to multiplication and to other operations. When algebraic operations are not involved, we frequently permit the values $+\infty$, and $-\infty$, as in Sec. 2 of this chapter and in Chaps. X to XII.

A function g whose domain and range are both one-dimensional is said to be **nondecreasing** in case $g(x_1) \geqq g(x_2)$ whenever $x_1 > x_2$. When the function g is multiple-valued, the inequality $g(x_1) \geqq g(x_2)$ is supposed to hold for every pair of functional values corresponding to x_1 and x_2. The term **nonincreasing** has a corresponding definition. A **monotonic** function is one that is either nonincreasing or nondecreasing.

2. Upper and Lower Bounds and Limits of Functions.—In this section we shall be discussing a function f whose domain S and range T are subsets of number spaces, and c will denote a point in the closure $\bar{S}$ of S. The following definition of **limit** generalizes the one discussed for sequences in Chaps. II and III:

$$\lim_{x=c} f(x) = b :\equiv: \epsilon > 0 :\supset: \exists N(c) \ni: x \text{ in } N(c)S \cdot\supset\cdot f(x) \subset N(b;\epsilon)$$

The class inclusion sign is used in this definition because for multiple-valued functions $f(x)$ may stand for a set of points rather than for a single point. The logical form of the definition is entirely unchanged from that given in Chap. II, Sec. 10; only the form of the restrictions on the variables is generalized. The limit b, when it exists, is always a point of the number space containing the range T of f. The following fundamental theorem is easily verified:

THEOREM 1. *If a function $f(x)$ has a limit at $x = c$, it has only one.*

We shall sometimes wish to consider only the values of the function f corresponding to a subset S_0 of its domain S. We may then use the phrase "**f as on S_0**" for such a **section** of the function f. When S_0 is a proper subset of S, the section f as on S_0 is regarded as a different function from the original function f. Thus f as on S_0 may have a limit b at a point c in $\bar{S}_0$ when no limit exists at c for the original function f, since the above definition may be satisfied when S is replaced by S_0 though not for S. However, if b is the limit at c of f, then b is the limit at c of f as on S_0, provided c is in $\bar{S}_0$. For example, let S be one-dimensional space, $f(x) = x^2$ for x rational, $f(x) = 1$ for x irrational. If S_0 consists of the rational points, $\lim_{x=0} f(x) = 0$ over S_0, that is, $f(x)$ as on S_0 has the limit 0 at $x = 0$. For another example let $f(x) = 1/(1 + e^{1/x})$, and let S_0 be the positive end of the x-axis. Then the limit of f as on S_0 at $x = 0$ has the value 0. This is also called the **right-hand limit** of $f(x)$ at $x = 0$. The **left-hand limit** of the same function at $x = 0$ has the value 1. For a right-hand limit at a point c we may also use the notations $\lim_{x=c+} f(x)$ and $f(c + 0)$, for a left-hand limit the notations $\lim_{x=c-} f(x)$ and $f(c - 0)$. We understand that the subset S_0 over which the limit is taken consists in the first case of the points x in S such that $x > c$, and in the second case of the points x in S such that $x < c$. The right-hand limit $f(c + 0)$ can have a meaning only when c is a right-hand accumulation point of S, that is, when c is an accumulation point of the subset of S lying to the right of c. A corresponding statement holds for the left-hand limit.

In defining limits many authors use only deleted neighborhoods $N(c)$. This usage may be included under the definition given above, by excluding the point c from S, *i.e.*, by considering f as on $S - \{c\}$. Thus the definition we have adopted is more flexible. We note that when c is in S, and $\lim_{x=c} f(x)$ exists, it must equal $f(c)$, and so f must be single-valued at c. When one-sided limits are being considered, it is convenient to exclude the point c, as was indicated above. Thus the value $f(c)$ has nothing to do with the existence or value of the limits $f(c + 0)$ and $f(c - 0)$.

For the following paragraphs until we come to Theorem 12 we shall be considering only real-valued functions.

The **least upper bound** of a function $f(x)$ on a set S is defined to be the least upper bound of the set fS composed of all the functional values. We shall use the abbreviations "l.u.b. $f(x)$ on S" and "$\overline{\text{B}}f(x)$." The **greatest lower bound** of $f(x)$ on S, abbreviated "g.l.b. $f(x)$ on S" or "$\underline{\text{B}}f(x)$," is defined in corresponding fashion.

THEOREM 2. *If the set S is in one-dimensional space, a monotonic single-valued function f defined on S has a right-hand limit at each right-hand accumulation point of S, and a left-hand limit at each left-hand accumulation point.*

Proof.—Let us assume for definiteness that f is nondecreasing. Let c be a right-hand accumulation point of S, and let $r =$ g.l.b. $f(x)$ for $x > c$. Then when r is finite

$$\epsilon > 0 : \supset : \exists x_\epsilon > c \ni : r \leqq f(x_\epsilon) < r + \epsilon,$$

and hence $c < x < x_\epsilon \cdot \supset \cdot f(x) \subset N(r; \epsilon)$. The proof for the other cases is similar.

In case the point c is in the closure $\bar{S}$ of the set S where f is defined, l.u.b. $f(x)$ on $SN(c; \delta)$ is a function $g(\delta)$ which is single-valued and nondecreasing for $\delta > 0$, and hence has a limit at $\delta = 0$, by Theorem 2. This limit is called the **upper limit** of $f(x)$ at c, and is denoted by $\limsup_{x=c} f(x)$ or $\overline{\lim}_{x=c} f(x)$, that is,

$$\limsup_{x=c} f(x) = \text{g.l.b. [l.u.b. } f(x) \text{ for } x \text{ in } SN(c;\delta)]$$
$$= \lim_{\delta=0} [\text{l.u.b. } f(x) \text{ for } x \text{ in } SN(c;\delta)].$$

A similar definition holds for the **lower limit,** denoted by $\liminf_{x=c} f(x)$ or $\underline{\lim}_{x=c} f(x)$. Note that the upper and lower limits always exist, finite or infinite, at every point of the closure of the domain of the function. As in the case of limits, we may also define right-hand and left-hand upper and lower limits for functions whose domains lie in one-dimensional space, by replacing S by $S[x > c]$, etc. For the right-hand upper limit, for example, we may use the notations $\limsup_{x=c+} f(x)$ and $\overline{f(c+0)}$. The proofs of Theorems 3 to 9 are left to the reader. In case the function $f(x)$ is multiple-valued, each inequality is supposed to hold for all the functional values. This is the reason for the use of the sign $\nless$ in Theorems 4 and 5, meaning that there is at least one functional value for which the relation $<$ does not hold.

THEOREM 3. *For every function* $f(x)$,

$$\liminf_{x=c} f(x) \leqq \limsup_{x=c} f(x).$$

THEOREM 4. $\limsup_{x=c} f(x)$ *is a finite number* U *if and only if:*

1. $\epsilon > 0 :\supset: \exists N(c) \ni: x \text{ in } N(c) \cdot\supset\cdot f(x) < U + \epsilon;$
2. $\epsilon > 0 \cdot\supset\cdot \exists x \text{ in } N(c;\epsilon) \ni\cdot f(x) \nless U - \epsilon.$

THEOREM 5. $\limsup_{x=c} f(x) = +\infty :\sim: \epsilon > 0 \cdot\supset\cdot \exists x \text{ in } N(c;\epsilon) \ni\cdot f(x) \nless 1/\epsilon.$

THEOREM 6. $\limsup_{x=c} f(x) = -\infty \vdots\sim\vdots\ \epsilon > 0 :\supset: \exists N(c) \ni: x \text{ in } N(c) \cdot\supset\cdot f(x) < -1/\epsilon.$ *In this case* $\exists \lim_{x=c} f(x) = -\infty$.

THEOREM 7. $\limsup_{x=c} f(x) = \liminf_{x=c} f(x) \cdot\sim\cdot \exists \lim_{x=c} f(x) \cdot\supset\cdot \limsup_{x=c} f(x) = \lim_{x=c} f(x).$

THEOREM 8. $\limsup_{x=c} f(x) < B :\supset: \exists N(c) \ni: x \text{ in } N(c) \cdot\supset\cdot f(x) < B.$

THEOREM 9. $\exists N(c) \ni: x \text{ in } N(c) \cdot\supset\cdot f(x) \leqq B :\supset: \limsup_{x=c} f(x) \leqq B.$

It is worth while to write out the statements of some of the above theorems for the special case when the function $f(x)$ is replaced by a sequence (a_n). For example, Theorem 4 in this case reads:

$\limsup_{n=\infty} a_n$ *is a finite number U if and only if*

1. $\epsilon > 0 : \supset : \exists n_\epsilon \ni : n > n_\epsilon \cdot \supset \cdot a_n < U + \epsilon;$
2. $\epsilon > 0 \cdot m \cdot \supset \cdot \exists n > m \ni \cdot a_n > U - \epsilon.$

Fig. 1 illustrates Theorem 4 with $c = 0$, and Fig. 2 illustrates the special case of a sequence. In Fig. 2, n is plotted along the

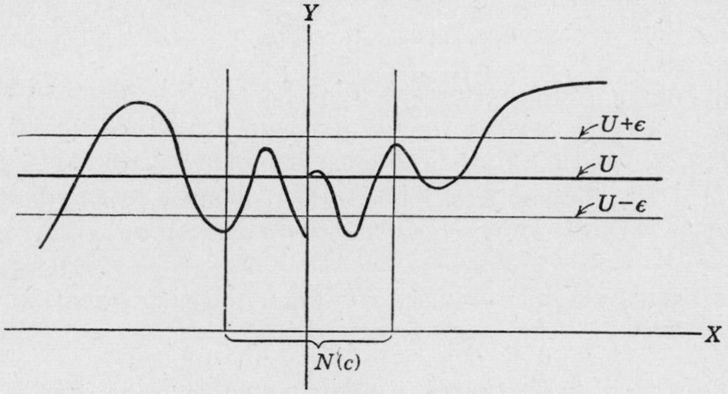

FIG. 1.

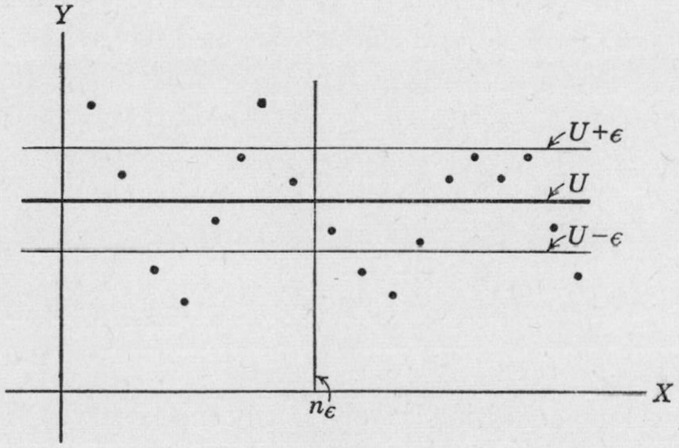

FIG. 2.

x-axis, and a_n along the y-axis, and all the points of the graph to the right of the line $x = n_\epsilon$ are supposed to lie below the line $y = U + \epsilon$; to the right of every vertical line there lie some points of the graph above the line $y = U - \epsilon$.

EXERCISES

1. Write out the theorems corresponding to Theorems 4 to 6, 8, 9 for lim inf $f(x)$.

2. As an application of Theorem 2, show the existence of $\lim_{n=\infty} (1 + 1/n)^n$, where n ranges over the natural numbers. Show also the finiteness of the limit.

3. Determine the upper and lower limits, and the right-hand and left-hand upper and lower limits, at $x = 0$ for the following functions:

(*a*) $\sin (1/x)$; (*b*) $1/x$;

(*c*) $\dfrac{\sin (1/x)}{1 + e^{1/x}}$; (*d*) $(1/x) \sin (1/x)$.

4. Let the *characteristic function* of a set S be denoted by ϕ_S, that is, $\phi_S(x) = 1$ when the point x is in S, and $\phi_S(x) = 0$ when x is in cS. Let (A_n) be a sequence of point sets, and let $L = \lim\inf A_n$, $U = \lim\sup A_n$. (These operations on sets were defined in Chap. III, Sec. 3.) Show that for each point x,

$$\liminf_{n=\infty} \phi_{A_n}(x) = \phi_L(x), \qquad \limsup_{n=\infty} \phi_{A_n}(x) = \phi_U(x).$$

The following theorem is Cauchy's condition for the existence of a finite limit of a function. It generalizes the condition stated in Sec. 10 of Chap. II and may be proved in various ways. We recall that we are permitting $f(x)$ to be multiple-valued.

THEOREM 10. *Let $f(x)$ be a finite-real-valued function defined on S, and let c be a point of $\bar{S}$. Then a necessary and sufficient condition for $\lim_{x=c} f(x)$ to exist and be finite is that*

$$(2:1) \quad \epsilon > 0 :\supset: \exists N(c) \ni: x \text{ and } x' \text{ in } SN(c) \cdot\supset\cdot |f(x) - f(x')| < \epsilon.$$

Proof.—The condition is obviously necessary. To show its sufficiency, let $b = \limsup_{x=c} f(x)$, and let $N_1(c)$ correspond to $\epsilon = 1$ in (2:1). Then for a fixed point x'' of $N_1(c)$ and one of the values $f(x'')$ we have $f(x'') - 1 < f(x) < f(x'') + 1$ for all x in $N_1(c)$ and all values of $f(x)$ (in case f is multiple-valued), and hence $f(x'') - 1 \leqq b \leqq f(x'') + 1$, so that b is finite. By Theorem 4, there exists a point x' in $N(c)$ and a value $f(x')$ such that

$$b - \epsilon < f(x') < b + \epsilon,$$

and thus

$$b - 2\epsilon < f(x) < b + 2\epsilon$$

for every x in $N(c)$ and every value of $f(x)$.

THEOREM 11. *Suppose the functions $f(x)$ and $g(x)$ are both defined on the same set S, and suppose $\lim_{x=c} f(x) = A$, $\lim_{x=c} g(x) = B$, with A and B both finite. Then*

$$\lim_{x=c} [f(x) \pm g(x)] = A \pm B; \tag{2:2}$$

$$\lim_{x=c} f(x)g(x) = AB; \tag{2:3}$$

$$\lim_{x=c} f(x)/g(x) = A/B \quad \text{if} \quad B \neq 0. \tag{2:4}$$

COROLLARY. *If $P(y, z)$, $Q(y, z)$ are polynomials in y and z with $Q(A, B) \neq 0$, then*

$$\lim_{x=c} \frac{P[f(x), g(x)]}{Q[f(x), g(x)]} = \frac{P(A, B)}{Q(A, B)}.$$

We shall give the proof of (2:3). The proof of the remainder of the theorem is left to the reader. Let $\epsilon > 0$, and let $\epsilon_1 < \epsilon/(1 + |A| + |B|)$ and $0 < \epsilon_1 < 1$. Then $\exists N(c) \ni: x$ in $N(c)S \cdot\supset\cdot |f(x) - A| < \epsilon_1$, $|g(x) - B| < \epsilon_1$, and hence $|g(x)| < |B| + 1$, $|f(x)g(x) - AB| \leqq |f(x)g(x) - Ag(x)| + |Ag(x) - AB| < \epsilon_1(|B| + 1) + |A|\epsilon_1 < \epsilon$. It is clear that the corollary may be generalized to the case of rational functions of any number of functions and that it includes the special case of rational functions of $f(x)$ alone.

Let $f(x)$ be a function with domain S, and $g(y)$ a function with domain T and range contained in the same space as the set S. Then the composite function $h(y) \equiv fg(y)$ has for its domain the set $g^{-1}S$. When the function $g(y)$ is multiple-valued, the notation $fg(y)$ means the transform by the function f of the set $g(y)$. For such functions, the following theorem is valid:

THEOREM 12. *Let $\lim_{x=a} f(x) = c$, $\lim_{y=b} g(y) = a$. Then $\lim_{y=b} h(y) = c$, provided the point b is in the closure of the domain $g^{-1}S$.*

Proof.—$\epsilon > 0 :\supset: \exists \delta > 0 \ni: x$ in $SN(a; \delta) \cdot\supset\cdot f(x) \subset N(c; \epsilon)$. $\exists N(b) \ni: y$ in $TN(b) \cdot\supset\cdot g(y) \subset N(a; \delta)$. Thus y in $(g^{-1}S)N(b) \cdot\supset\cdot h(y) \subset N(c; \epsilon)$.

Although the theorem is valid in such a case as $f(x) =$ principal value of $\csc^{-1} x$, $g(y) = \sin y$, its result may be trivial. In this example $g^{-1}S$ consists of the odd multiples of $\pi/2$.

THEOREM 13. *A necessary and sufficient condition for the existence of* $\lim\limits_{x=a} f(x)$ *is that for each sequence* (x_n) *in* S *with* $\lim\limits_{n=\infty} x_n = a$ *the corresponding sequence* $(f(x_n))$ *has a limit.*

Proof.—The necessity of this condition is a special case of Theorem 12. To show the sufficiency of the condition, we note first that $\lim\limits_{n=\infty} f(x_n)$ has the same value for all sequences (x_n) whose limit is a. For if two such sequences (x_n) and (y_n) made $\lim\limits_{n=\infty} f(x_n) \neq \lim\limits_{n=\infty} f(y_n)$, and if we set $z_{2n-1} = x_n$, $z_{2n} = y_n$, then the sequence $(f(z_n))$ would not have a limit. Let c denote this common limit, and suppose the condition is not sufficient. Then $\exists\ \epsilon > 0 \ni: n \cdot\supset\cdot \exists x_n$ in $SN(a; 1/n) \ni\cdot f(x_n) \not\subset N(c; \epsilon)$. But $\lim\limits_{n=\infty} x_n = a$, and hence $\lim\limits_{n=\infty} f(x_n) = c$, which is a contradiction.

The following inequalities involving the upper and lower bounds and upper and lower limits of sums and differences of functions are sometimes useful.

THEOREM 14. *Let* f *and* g *be real-valued functions defined on the same set* S. *Then the following inequalities hold, provided those involving indeterminate forms are omitted:*

$$(2{:}5)\quad \underline{B}f + \underline{B}g \leqq \underline{B}(f+g) \leqq \left\{\begin{matrix}\underline{B}f + \overline{B}g \\ \overline{B}f + \underline{B}g\end{matrix}\right\} \leqq \overline{B}(f+g) \leqq \overline{B}f + \overline{B}g,$$

$$(2{:}6)\quad \underline{B}f - \overline{B}g \leqq \underline{B}(f-g) \leqq \left\{\begin{matrix}\underline{B}f - \underline{B}g \\ \overline{B}f - \overline{B}g\end{matrix}\right\} \leqq \overline{B}(f-g) \leqq \overline{B}f - \underline{B}g,$$

$$(2{:}7)\quad \underline{\lim}\, f + \underline{\lim}\, g \leqq \underline{\lim}\,(f+g) \leqq \left\{\begin{matrix}\underline{\lim}\, f + \overline{\lim}\, g \\ \overline{\lim}\, f + \underline{\lim}\, g\end{matrix}\right\} \leqq \overline{\lim}\,(f+g) \leqq \overline{\lim}\, f + \overline{\lim}\, g,$$

$$(2{:}8)\quad \underline{\lim}\, f - \overline{\lim}\, g \leqq \underline{\lim}\,(f-g) \leqq \left\{\begin{matrix}\underline{\lim}\, f - \underline{\lim}\, g \\ \overline{\lim}\, f - \overline{\lim}\, g\end{matrix}\right\} \leqq \overline{\lim}\,(f-g) \leqq \overline{\lim}\, f - \underline{\lim}\, g.$$

In (2:7) *and* (2:8) *all the upper and lower limits are supposed to be taken at the same point* a *of* $\overline{S}$.

Proof.—The inequalities (2:5) are readily verified. Those in (2:6) follow from (2:5) by means of the fact that $\overline{\mathrm{B}}(-g) = -\underline{\mathrm{B}}g$. Those in (2:7) and (2:8) follow from (2:5) and (2:6), respectively, by means of Theorem 11, when the limits involved are finite.

3. Continuous and Semicontinuous Functions.—In this section it becomes less useful to admit points at infinity into the range of the functions considered. Therefore for definiteness we shall assume throughout this section that the functions considered have no infinite values. They may be multiple-valued and are supposed to be defined on a set S unless otherwise specified.

A function $f(x)$ is **continuous** at a point b in case b is in S and $\lim_{x=b} f(x)$ exists. As a consequence of this definition,

$$\lim_{x=b} f(x) = f(b),$$

and f is single-valued at b. It is also evident that when $f(x)$ is continuous at b, $f(x)$ is a continuous function of each variable $x^{(i)}$ at $b^{(i)}$. The converse is not true (see Chap. VII). A real-valued function $f(x)$ is **lower semicontinuous** at b in case b is in S, f is single-valued at b, and $\liminf_{x=b} f(x) = f(b)$, and **upper semi-continuous** at b in case b is in S, f is single-valued at b, and $\limsup_{x=b} f(x) = f(b)$. It is clear that $f(x)$ is lower semicontinuous if and only if $-f(x)$ is upper semicontinuous and with the help of Theorem 7 of the preceding section that a real-valued function is continuous at b if and only if it is both upper and lower semi-continuous at b. In case the domain S of f lies in one-dimensional space, we say that $f(x)$ is **continuous on the right** at a point b in case f as on S_1 is continuous at b, where $S_1 = S[x \geqq b]$. An analogous definition holds for **continuity on the left.** A function f is **continuous** (lower or upper semicontinuous, or continuous on the left or right) **on a set** $S_0 \subset S$ in case the corresponding property holds at every point of S_0.

THEOREM 15. *Let $f(x)$ be upper semicontinuous at b, and $f(b) < u$, where u is finite. Then there is a neighborhood $N(b)$ on which $f(x) < u$. Thus f is bounded above on $N(b)$.*

THEOREM 16. *Let $f(x)$ and $g(x)$ be real-valued functions continuous at b. Then the functions $f(x) \pm g(x)$ and $f(x)g(x)$ are continuous at b. So also is $f(x)/g(x)$, provided $g(b) \neq 0$. Moreover, if $P(y, z)$, $Q(y, z)$ are polynomials with $Q[f(b), g(b)] \neq 0$,* *then*

$$\frac{P[f(x), g(x)]}{Q[f(x), g(x)]}$$

is continuous at b.

THEOREM 17. *Let $f(x)$ be continuous at $x = a$, let $g(y)$ be continuous at $y = b$, and let $g(b) = a$. Then the composite function $fg(y)$ is continuous at $y = b$.*

THEOREM 18. *Let f and g be two functions continuous on S and let $f(x) = g(x)$ on a subset T of S. Then $f(x) = g(x)$ on $S\bar{T}$.*

As an example to which this theorem applies we note the important case when f and g are continuous on an interval (a, b) and are equal at the points of (a, b) with rational coordinates. They must then be equal at all points of (a, b).

THEOREM 19. *Let $f(x)$ and $g(x)$ be upper semicontinuous at b. Then $f(x) + g(x)$ is also upper semicontinuous at b.*

Theorems 15 to 19 follow from Theorems 8, 11, 12, 1, and 14 of Sec. 2.

THEOREM 20. *A necessary and sufficient condition that a single-real-valued function f with domain S be upper semicontinuous on S is that the set $S_u = S[f(x) \geqq u]$ be closed relative to S for every real number u, or for every rational number u.*

Proof.—The necessity of the condition follows by indirect proof from Theorem 15. Suppose that the condition is not sufficient. Then there is a point b of S and a rational number u such that

$$f(b) < u < \limsup_{x=b} f(x), \tag{3:1}$$

and by Theorem 9 every neighborhood $N(b; \epsilon)$ contains a point x of S such that $f(x) > u$. Since S_u is closed relative to S by hypothesis, $f(b) \geqq u$, but this contradicts (3:1).

THEOREM 21. *Let a and b be two points of a connected set S on which $f(x)$ is real-valued and continuous, and let $f(a) < u < f(b)$. Then there is in S a point x_0 such that $f(x_0) = u$.*

Proof.—Let $S_0 \equiv S[f(x) \geqq u]$, $T \equiv S - S_0$. Since S_0 is closed relative to S by Theorem 20 and S is connected, S_0 must contain a point x_0 of T'. Since $f(x) \leqq u$ on T' by the analogue of Theorem 15 for lower semicontinuous functions, we must have $f(x_0) = u$.

That a function f may be everywhere discontinuous and yet have the property stated in the last theorem is shown by the following example.[1] Let the number x in the interval [0, 1] be expressed as a decimal $.a_1a_2a_3 \ldots a_n \ldots$. If the decimal $.a_1a_3a_5a_7 \cdots$ is not periodic, set $f(x) = 0$; if it is periodic and the first period commences with a_{2n-1}, set $f(x) = .a_{2n}a_{2n+2}a_{2n+4} \cdots$. In every subinterval, however small, of [0, 1], this function takes every value between 0 and 1, and consequently it must be everywhere discontinuous while still satisfying the conclusion of the last theorem.

A real-valued function f is said to have a **minimum** on the set S in case the greatest lower bound of f on S is a value actually assumed by f on S, and f has a **maximum** in case the least upper bound is a value assumed. The following theorem is a basic one for many proofs in mathematics.

THEOREM 22. *If S is closed and f is lower semicontinuous on S, then f has a minimum on S.*

Proof.—Let $m = \text{g.l.b. } f(x)$ on S. Then there is a sequence (x_n) of points of S, called a "minimizing sequence," such that $\lim f(x_n) = m$. By the first corollary of Theorem 12 of Chap. III, the sequence (x_n) has at least one point b of accumulation, and b must be in S since S is closed. By the assumed lower semicontinuity of f, $f(b) \leqq \lim f(x_n) = m$, and hence $m \neq -\infty$. But $m \leqq f(b)$ by definition of m, and hence $f(b) = m$.

For Theorem 22 the assumption is frequently made that the set S is bounded, but this is unnecessary when the points at infinity are included in the space.

In place of the absolute minimum considered in Theorem 22, it is sometimes desirable to consider a relative minimum. A function f is said to have a **relative minimum** at a point b of S in case $\exists N(b) \ni: x \text{ in } SN(b) \cdot \supset \cdot f(x) \geqq f(b)$.

Theorem 22 has the following corollaries:

COROLLARY 1. *If S is closed and f is continuous on S, then f is bounded on S.*

COROLLARY 2. *Suppose S is a closed set contained in the one-dimensional interval $[a, b]$, and that a and b are, respectively, right-hand and left-hand accumulation points of S. Suppose that f is lower semicontinuous on S and has relative maxima at a and b. Then f has an absolute minimum at a point between a and b.*

COROLLARY 3. *Let S be a closed set in one-dimensional space, and suppose that f is continuous on S and has no relative maxima*

[1] See Lebesgue, *Leçons sur l'integration*, 2d Ed., p. 97.

or minima between the points a and b of S. Then f is properly monotonic between the points a and b.

A function f is said to be **uniformly continuous** on the set S in case

$$\epsilon > 0 : \supset : \exists \delta > 0 \ni : x \text{ in } S \cdot x' \text{ in } SN(x;\delta) \cdot \supset \cdot f(x') \text{ in } N(f(x);\epsilon).$$

A slight generalization of this definition is the following: f is **uniformly continuous** on the subset S_0 of its domain S in case

$$\epsilon > 0 : \supset : \exists \delta > 0 \ni : x \text{ in } S_0 \cdot x' \text{ in } SN(x;\delta) \cdot \supset \cdot f(x') \text{ in } N(f(x);\epsilon).$$

It is evident that, when a function is uniformly continuous on S_0, it is single-valued and continuous on S_0. The proof of the following converse theorem is based on the Heine-Borel theorem. In the proof given by Heine[1] of this theorem on uniform continuity occur the essential ideas of a proof of the Heine-Borel theorem, which was stated by Borel[2] in a more restricted form than that given in Chap. III.

THEOREM 23. *Let S_0 be a closed subset of the domain S of f, and let f be continuous on S_0. Then f is uniformly continuous on S_0.*

Proof.—Let ϵ be an arbitrary positive number. Then by hypothesis,

$$x \text{ in } S_0 : \supset : \exists \delta_x > 0 \ni : x' \text{ in } SN(x; 2\delta_x) \cdot \supset \cdot f(x') \text{ in } N(f(x);\epsilon).$$

In case S_0 contains any points at infinity, we also require that $\delta_x < \sqrt{2}/2$. If to each x in S_0 we make correspond the neighborhood $N(x;\delta_x)$, this family of neighborhoods plainly covers the set S_0. Hence by the Heine-Borel theorem there is a *finite* subset T of S_0 such that x in $S_0 \cdot \supset \cdot \exists a$ in $T \ni \cdot x$ in $N(a;\delta_a)$. Let β be the smallest of the numbers δ_a for a in T. If x is in S_0 and x' is in $SN(x;\beta)$ then x' is in $N(a;2\delta_a)$, and hence $f(x)$ and $f(x')$ are both in $N(f(a);\epsilon)$ and $f(x')$ is in $N(f(x);2\epsilon)$. We note that here it is essential that $f(x)$ be restricted to have finite values.

EXERCISE

Determine which of the following functions are uniformly continuous, (*a*) on the interval $0 < x < 1$; (*b*) on the interval $0 < x < \infty$.

[1] *Journal für die reine und angewandte Mathematik*, Vol. 74 (1872), p.188.

[2] *Annales scientifiques de l'école normale supérieure*, Series 3, Vol. 12 (1895), p. 51.

1. $1/(x-1)$. 2. x^2. 3. $1/(x-2)$.
4. $\sqrt{x}$. 5. $\sin x$. 6. $\sin(1/x)$.

* Theorem 20 suggests that continuous functions might be characterized by the closure of the inverse transforms of closed sets. It is sometimes convenient to characterize them by means of the closure of their graphs. We now state some theorems of these types.

* We note that every set W of points $w = (x, y)$ in the Cartesian product of x-space and y-space may be regarded as the graph of a (possibly multiple-valued) function $y = f(x)$, whose domain S is the x-projection of W and whose range T is the y-projection of W. With these notations we state the following theorems:

* THEOREM 24. *If W is closed, then its x-projection S and its y-projection T are closed. If W is open, then S and T are open.*

Proof.—If x is in S', and $\lim_{n=\infty} x_n = x$, where the sequence (x_n) is chosen from S, then a corresponding sequence (x_n, y_n) chosen from W has a point of accumulation (x, y) in W, and hence x is in S. To prove the last statement of the theorem we note that, if $N(x, y; \epsilon) \subset W$, then $N(x; \epsilon) \subset S$.

* THEOREM 25. *When the function f is single-valued, a necessary and sufficient condition that f be continuous is that whenever T_0 is closed relative to T, $f^{-1}(T_0)$ is also closed relative to S. A second necessary and sufficient condition is that whenever T_0 is open relative to T, $f^{-1}(T_0)$ is also open relative to S. When f is single-valued and its domain S is bounded and closed, a third necessary and sufficient condition that f be continuous is that its graph W be bounded and closed. In this last case, for every closed subset S_0 of S, $f(S_0)$ is also closed, and whenever $T_0 \subset T$ and $f^{-1}(T_0)$ is open relative to S, T_0 is open relative to T.*

Proof.—To prove the necessity of the first condition, let $\lim_{n=\infty} x_n = x$, where x_n is in $f^{-1}(T_0)$ and x is in S. Then $\lim_{n=\infty} f(x_n) = f(x)$, $f(x)$ is in T_0, and so x is in $f^{-1}(T_0)$. Since f is single-valued, $f^{-1}(T - T_0) = S - f^{-1}(T_0)$, and so the first condition implies the second. The second condition is sufficient for f to be continuous, since, for each $\epsilon > 0$ and each x_0 in S, $T_0 = TN(y_0; \epsilon)$ is open relative to T, where $y_0 = f(x_0)$, and so $f^{-1}(T_0)$ is open relative to S. Thus there is a number $\delta > 0$ such that $SN(x_0; \delta)$

$\subset f^{-1}(T_0)$. To prove the necessity of the third condition, we note that $f(x)$ must be bounded, and that every convergent sequence of points $(x_n, f(x_n))$ in the graph W must have its limit in W. To prove the sufficiency of the third condition, suppose that f is not continuous at x_0. Then there is a point $y_0 \neq f(x_0)$ and a sequence (x_n) in S such that $(x_n, f(x_n))$ converges to (x_0, y_0). Then (x_0, y_0) is in W, and so $y_0 = f(x_0)$, which is a contradiction. To prove the final statement in the theorem, consider a sequence of points $y_n = f(x_n)$ in $f(S_0)$, converging to a point y_0. The sequence (x_n) has a subsequence (x_{n_k}) converging to a point x_0 in S_0. Then since f is continuous, $y_0 = f(x_0)$, and so y_0 is in $f(S_0)$. The proof for the case when $f^{-1}(T_0)$ is open relative to S is obtained by considering the set $S_0 = f^{-1}(T - T_0)$.

We note that the transform $f(S_0)$ of an open set S_0 may fail to be open, as in the example $f(x) = x^3 - 3x$, $S_0 = (-1.5, 1.5)$, where $f(S_0)$ is the closed interval $[-2, 2]$.

REFERENCES

1. Hobson, *The Theory of Functions of a Real Variable*, Vol. 1, Chap. 5.
2. Pierpont, *The Theory of Functions of Real Variables*, Vol. 1, Chaps. 6, 7.
3. Veblen and Lennes, *Infinitesimal Analysis*, Chaps. 3 to 5.
4. Caratheodory, *Vorlesungen über reelle Funktionen*, Chaps. 2 to 4.

CHAPTER V

FUNDAMENTAL THEOREMS ON DIFFERENTIATION

1. Functions of One Variable.—In this section we shall consider only single-real-finite-valued functions whose domain is a point set in one-dimensional space with the points at infinity omitted. Let the function f have domain S, and let c be a point of S which is also an accumulation point of S. Then f is said to have a **derivative** or a **differential coefficient** at c (over S) in case

$$\lim_{x=c} \frac{f(x) - f(c)}{x - c}$$

exists, where the limit is of course taken over the set S with the point c excluded. The derivative $f'(c)$, when it exists, may be finite or have either of the values $+\infty$, $-\infty$. In case c is a right-hand accumulation point of S and the limit exists when taken over the subset of S to the right of c, it is called the **right-hand derivative,** or the **derivative on the right,** and may be denoted by $f'^{+}(c)$ when occasion arises for a distinguishing notation. The left-hand derivative may be denoted by $f'^{-}(c)$. If $g(x) = -f(-x)$, then $g'^{-}(-c) = f'^{+}(c)$, $g'^{+}(-c) = f'^{-}(c)$.

THEOREM 1. *Let f have a finite derivative at c. Then* $\exists M < \infty \cdot \exists \epsilon > 0 \ni: x$ *in* $SN(c;\ \epsilon) \cdot \supset \cdot |f(x) - f(c)| \leqq M|x - c|$. *Hence f is continuous at c.*

The usual calculus proofs show that if two functions f and g have finite derivatives at c, then their sum, difference, product, and quotient have derivatives at c, given by the usual formulas, provided, in the case of the quotient, that the denominator is not zero. In the case of the sum, one or both of the derivatives may be allowed to be infinite, except that they may not have infinite values of opposite sign. In the case of the product, we may allow the derivative of one factor, say g, to be infinite, provided g is continuous at c, and we agree to replace fg' by 0 in case f vanishes at c. Under the same restriction, we may in the case of the quotient f/g allow either f or g to have an infinite derivative.

The reader may see the need for the precautions mentioned by experimenting with combinations involving fractional powers of x.

THEOREM 2. *Let f have a right-hand derivative $f'^{+}(c) > 0$ at c. Then* $\exists b > c \ni : c < x < b \cdot \supset \cdot f(x) > f(c)$.

By considering left-hand derivatives and by suitably changing the sense of the inequalities in hypothesis and conclusion, we obtain three other theorems from Theorem 2. These four theorems have the following corollary:

COROLLARY. *If f has a maximum or a minimum at a point c which is both a right-hand and a left-hand accumulation point of S, and if f has a derivative at c, then $f'(c) = 0$.*

THEOREM 3. **Rolle's theorem.** *Suppose f is continuous on the finite closed interval $[a, b]$ and has a derivative (finite or infinite) at each point of the open interval (a, b). Let $f(a) = f(b)$. Then there is a point c in the open interval (a, b) such that $f'(c) = 0$.*

Proof.—By Theorem 22 of Chap. IV, the function f has a maximum and a minimum on the interval $[a, b]$. When f is constant, the point c may be chosen arbitrarily in the interval. In the remaining case either the maximum value or the minimum value is different from $f(a)$, and hence this maximum or minimum is attained at a point c interior to the interval. Then $f'(c) = 0$ by the Corollary of Theorem 2.

Calculus textbooks frequently base the proof of Rolle's theorem on the false assumption that, if f is not constant, then there must be some point at which f stops increasing and starts decreasing or else stops decreasing and starts increasing. The falsity of this assumption is shown by an example given in Hobson [1], Vol. 1, pages 412–421, of a function satisfying the hypotheses of Rolle's theorem which has maxima and minima on every subinterval but is not a constant. It is clear that such a function cannot have a *continuous* derivative. A simpler example of a function having a continuous derivative and having a minimum at a point at which it does not stop decreasing and start increasing is obtained by setting $f(x) = x^4[2 - \sin(1/x)]$ for $x \neq 0$, $f(0) = 0$. The simple proof given above for Rolle's theorem is based on the theorem that a function continuous on a finite closed interval has a maximum and a minimum on that interval. In a beginning course in calculus this property may well be taken as intuitively evident.

THEOREM 4. **Theorem of the Mean.** *Suppose f is continuous on the finite closed interval* $[a, b]$ *and has a derivative (finite or infinite) at each point of the open interval* (a, b). *Then there is a point c in the open interval* (a, b) *such that*

$$f(b) = f(a) + f'(c)(b - a).$$

COROLLARY 1. *If* $f'(x) > 0$ *on the open interval* (a, b), *then* $f(b) > f(a)$.

COROLLARY 2. *If* $f'(x) = 0$ *on the open interval* (a, b), *then* $f(x)$ *is constant on the closed interval.*

For an example of a family of functions having the same derivative, but no pair of which differ by a constant, see Ruziewicz, "Sur les fonctions, qui ont même dérivée, et dont la différence n'est pas constante," *Fundamenta Mathematicae*, Vol. 1 (1920), pages 148–151. From Corollary 2, it is apparent that the difference of two functions of such a family cannot have a derivative everywhere, so that the derivatives of the original functions must be infinite at some points.

COROLLARY 3. *If* $|f'(x)| \leqq M$ *on the open interval* (a, b), *then*

$$|f(x) - f(\bar{x})| \leqq M|x - \bar{x}| \tag{1:1}$$

for every x and $\bar{x}$ in the closed interval $[a, b]$.

A function satisfying the condition (1:1) is said to satisfy a **Lipschitz condition** with constant M. This condition will enter the hypotheses of several theorems occurring in later chapters.

COROLLARY 4. *If* $\lim_{x=a} f'(x) = A$, *then f has a right-hand derivative* $f'^{+}(a) = A$.

THEOREM 5. *If $f(x)$ is continuous and has a derivative $f'(x)$ at each point of the closed interval* $[a, b]$ *and if* $f'(a) < C < f'(b)$, *then there is a point x_0 in the open interval (a, b) such that* $f'(x_0) = C$.

Proof.—Let $g(x) = f(x) - Cx$. Then $g'(x) = f'(x) - C$, and $g'(a) < 0$, $g'(b) > 0$. Hence the minimum value of $g(x)$ occurs at a point x_0 between a and b, so that $g'(x_0) = 0$, and $f'(x_0) = C$.

Note that, although continuous functions and derivative functions have in common the property stated in Theorem 5, a derivative function need not be continuous. For example, let $f(x) = x^2 \sin(1/x)$ for $x \neq 0$, $f(0) = 0$. This function has a derivative everywhere which is discontinuous at the origin. By means of this function, other functions whose derivatives have infinitely many discontinuities may readily be constructed.

For the mth **derivative** $f^{(m)}(x)$ we adopt the usual inductive definition, that is, we say that $f(x)$ has an mth derivative $f^{(m)}(c)$ at a point c in case $f(x)$ has an $(m - 1)$st derivative $f^{(m-1)}(x)$ at each point of a neighborhood $N(c)$, and $f^{(m-1)}(x)$ has a derivative $f^{(m)}(c)$ at c. The usual modification is made in case c is an end point of the interval of definition of $f(x)$.

THEOREM 6. **Extended theorem of the mean, or Taylor's formula with remainder.** *Suppose that $f(x)$ and its first $m - 1$ derivatives are defined and continuous on the closed interval $[a, b]$, and that the* m*th derivative $f^{(m)}(x)$ exists, finite or infinite, at each point of the open interval (a, b). Then there is a point x_0 of the open interval (a, b) such that*

$$f(b) = f(a) + (b - a)f'(a) + \cdots + \frac{(b-a)^{m-1}}{(m-1)!} f^{(m-1)}(a) + \frac{(b-a)^m}{m!} f^{(m)}(x_0).$$

Proof.—Let

$$g(x) = f(b) - f(x) - (b - x)f'(x) - \cdots - \frac{(b-x)^{m-1}}{(m-1)!} f^{(m-1)}(x) - \frac{(b-x)^m}{m!} P,$$

where P is a number such that $g(a) = 0$. Then also $g(b) = 0$ and g has a derivative $g'(x) = [P - f^{(m)}(x)](b - x)^{m-1}/(m - 1)!$. Hence the conclusion follows at once from Rolle's theorem.

THEOREM 7. **Differentiation of a function of a function.** *Suppose that the function $f(u)$ has a finite derivative $f'(a)$ at a point a of its domain S, and that $g(x)$ has a finite derivative $g'(b)$ at a point b of its domain T. Suppose also that $g(b) = a$, and that b is an accumulation point of the domain T_0 of the composite function $h(x) = f(g(x))$. Then the function h has a derivative at b, and $h'(b) = f'(a)g'(b)$.*

Proof.—In case there is a neighborhood $N(b)$ such that $g(x) \neq g(b)$ whenever x is in the deleted neighborhood $N(b)$ and in T, the usual proof applies. In the contrary case, every deleted neighborhood $N(b)$ contains a point x in T such that $g(x) = g(b)$. Thus we must have $g'(b) = 0$. Let T_1 denote the subset of T for which $g(x) = g(b)$, and let $T_2 = T_0 - T_1$. For x in T_1,

$$\frac{h(x) - h(b)}{x - b} = 0,$$

and hence the derivative of h at b over T_1 is zero. If b is an accumulation point of T_2, the derivative of h at b over T_2 is also zero, since the usual proof applies on T_2 and $g'(b) = 0$.

An example in which the usual calculus proof is not valid is obtained by taking $g(x) = x^2 \sin(1/x)$ for $x \neq 0$, $g(0) = 0$.

*When a function $f(x)$ does not have a derivative, it is sometimes useful to consider the one-sided upper and lower limits of the difference quotient, which always exist when we admit the values $\pm\infty$. Let the domain S of f be the closed interval $[a, b]$, and let the difference quotient or incrementary ratio

$$\frac{f(x_1) - f(x_2)}{x_1 - x_2}$$

be denoted by $I(x_1, x_2)$. It is clear that I is a symmetric function of its arguments. Let the variable t be restricted to small positive values. Then

$$\limsup_{t=0} I(x+t, x)$$

is called the **upper right-hand derivate** of f and denoted by $D^+(x)$. The lower limit of $I(x + t, x)$ is called the **lower right-hand derivate** of f and denoted by $D_+(x)$. The **left-hand derivates,** denoted by $D^-(x)$ and $D_-(x)$, are defined in a similar way. The notations $D^+f(x)$, $D_+f(x)$, $D^-f(x)$, $D_-f(x)$ will be used when it is desirable to indicate the dependence of these functions on the function f, as in Chap. X, Sec. 5. The right-hand derivates are of course not defined at b, and the left-hand derivates are not defined at a. When all four derivates are equal at a point, the function has a derivative at the point. As an example, the function $f(x) = x \sin(1/x)$, with $f(0) = 0$, has upper derivates at $x = 0$ equal to $+1$, and lower derivates equal to -1. The function

$$f(x) = \frac{x^{1/3} \sin(1/x)}{1 + e^{1/x}}, \qquad f(0) = 0,$$

has at $x = 0$ a right-hand derivative equal to zero, an upper left-hand derivate equal to $+\infty$, and a lower left-hand derivate equal to $-\infty$. With the help of these concepts we can obtain the following generalization of Theorems 4 and 5. Again the proof is based on Theorem 22 of Chap. IV.

*THEOREM 8. *Let $f(x)$ be continuous on $[a, b]$. Then there is a point c in the open interval (a, b) such that either*

$$D^-(c) \leqq I(a, b) \leqq D_+(c), \tag{1:2}$$

or else

$$D_-(c) \geqq I(a, b) \geqq D^+(c). \tag{1:3}$$

Moreover, if $D_+(a) < C < D^-(b)$, there is a point x_0 in (a, b) such that

$$D^-(x_0) \leqq C \leqq D_+(x_0). \tag{1:4}$$

*COROLLARY 1. *All of the functions $I(x_1, x_2)$, $D^+(x)$, $D_+(x)$, $D^-(x)$, $D_-(x)$ have the same least upper bound U and the same greatest lower bound L on the open interval (a, b), and the values of the bounds are the same for the closed interval $[a, b]$. Moreover, for an arbitrary $\epsilon > 0$, each of the following inequalities is satisfied at infinitely many points of (a, b):*

$$\begin{aligned} &D_+(x) > U - \epsilon, && (D_+(x) > 1/\epsilon \text{ if } U = +\infty), \\ &D_-(x) > U - \epsilon, && \\ &D^+(x) < L + \epsilon, && (D^+(x) < -1/\epsilon \text{ if } L = -\infty), \\ &D^-(x) < L + \epsilon. && \end{aligned}$$

Proof.—Suppose l.u.b. $D^-(x) = U > U' =$ l.u.b. $D_+(x)$ on (a, b), and let $\epsilon > 0$ and β in (a, b) be such that $D^-(\beta) > U - \epsilon > U'$. Then there exists a point $\alpha < \beta$ such that $D_+(\alpha) < U - \epsilon$, so by (1:4) we are led to a contradiction. Hence l.u.b. $D^-(x) \leqq$ l.u.b. $D_+(x)$. By applying this case to the function g defined by $g(y) = -f(x)$ where $y = -x$, we see that l.u.b. $D^+(x) \leqq$ l.u.b. $D_-(x)$. So all four derivates have the same least upper bound. The equality of the lower bounds is obtained by considering the function h defined by $h(x) = -f(x)$. From the definition of derivates and (1:2) and (1:3) it follows that the difference quotient $I(x_1, x_2)$ has the same bounds. Since f is continuous, $I(x_1, x_2)$ has the same bounds on the closed interval $[a, b]$, and hence this property carries over to the derivates. To obtain the last statement of the corollary, suppose that for some $\epsilon > 0$, $D_+(x) \leqq U - \epsilon$ except at a finite set of points. Then by what has already been proved, $D_+(x) \leqq U - \epsilon$ on $[a, b]$, contradicting the definition of U. A similar argument proves the remaining inequalities. We recall that $D^+(x) \geqq D_+(x)$, etc.

*COROLLARY 2. *$f(b) - f(a) = \mu(b - a)$, where μ is a number between the upper and lower bounds of an arbitrary one of the derivates of f.*

The second corollary is a generalized form of the theorem of the mean.

*COROLLARY 3. *If one of the four derivates of f is continuous at a point c, so are the other three, and all four have the same value at c, so that the derivative $f'(c)$ exists.*

Proof.—If $D^+(x)$ is continuous at c, the upper and lower bounds of $D^+(x)$ (and hence also of the other three derivates) on a sufficiently small interval containing c will be arbitrarily near $D^+(c)$. From this the result stated readily follows.

2. Differentiation of Functions of Several Variables.—In this section we consider single-real-finite-valued functions whose domain is a point set in the k-dimensional number space. It is more convenient in this section as in the preceding not to include the points at infinity in the domain of the functions concerned. For such functions of several variables, the notion of **total differential** assumes considerable importance. Without it we could not obtain theorems generalizing those of Sec. 1. Note that most of the definitions and theorems generalize at once to the case when the values of the functions considered lie in a space of any finite number of dimensions with the points at infinity excluded.

For present purposes it is convenient to define a **linear function** $f(x)$ to be one whose domain is the whole finite space and which satisfies the equation

$$f(a_1x_1 + a_2x_2) = a_1f(x_1) + a_2f(x_2)$$

for every pair of points x_1, x_2 and pair of real numbers a_1, a_2.[1] An equivalent definition states that a linear function $f(x)$ is one expressible in the form

$$f(x) = \phi_1x^{(1)} + \cdots + \phi_kx^{(k)}, \tag{2:1}$$

where the coefficients ϕ_i are real numbers.

[1] Here $a_1x_1 + a_2x_2$ denotes the point whose coordinates are $a_1x_1^{(1)} + a_2x_2^{(1)}$, . . . , $a_1x_1^{(k)} + a_2x_2^{(k)}$.

A **bilinear function** $g(x, y)$ is one which is linear in x for each y, and linear in y for each x. An equivalent definition states that a bilinear function is one expressible in the form

$$g(x, y) = \sum_{i,j=1}^{k} \gamma_{ij} x^{(i)} y^{(j)}.$$

The **norm** of a point x, denoted by $\|x\|$, is defined to be the greatest of the numbers $|x^{(i)}|$. The norm is a generalization of absolute value and has analogous properties. A norm could be defined in various other ways, for example, as the distance of x from the origin. For a finite point c it is plain that the neighborhood $N(c; \epsilon)$ consists of all points x such that $\|x - c\| < \epsilon$.

Theorem 9. *If* $f(x)$ *is linear then* $\exists M < \infty \ni : x \cdot \supset \cdot |f(x)| \leqq M\|x\|$.

It is plain that for a given f the set of all such numbers M is a closed set. Its greatest lower bound is denoted by $\|f\|$ and called the norm of f. With our definition for $\|x\|$, the expression (2:1) leads to the formula

$$\|f\| = \sum_{i=1}^{k} |\phi_i|.$$

Now let f be an arbitrary function with domain S, and let c be a point in S which is an accumulation point of S. Then f is said to have a **differential** $df(c; z)$ at c in case the function df is linear in its second argument z, and

$$\epsilon > 0 : \supset : \exists N(c) \ni : x \text{ in } SN(c) \cdot \supset \cdot |f(x) - f(c) - df(c; x - c)| \leqq \epsilon\|x - c\|.$$

It is often convenient and suggestive to use the symbol dx for the second argument of the differential df.

It is clear from the definition that a function of a single real variable has a differential at c if and only if it has a finite derivative at c. But for functions of more than one variable the situation is slightly different, as is indicated below.

Theorem 10. *Let f have a differential at the point c. Then*

$$\exists M < \infty . \exists \epsilon > 0 \ni : x \text{ in } SN(c; \epsilon) \cdot \supset \cdot |f(x) - f(c)| \leqq M\|x - c\|.$$

Hence f is continuous at c.

The preceding theorem is a generalization of Theorem 1.

THEOREM 11. *If f has a differential $df(c;\ dx) = \phi_1\, dx^{(1)} + \cdots + \phi_k\, dx^{(k)}$ at an interior point c of its domain S, then f has finite first partial derivatives at c, and the partial derivative with respect to $x^{(i)}$ equals ϕ_i. Hence in this case the differential is uniquely determined.*

It follows from Theorem 11 that when $f(x)$ has a differential at a point c interior to its domain S, this differential is the sum of the differentials of the k functions obtained from $f(x)$ by fixing all but one variable. A simple example in which the differential is not uniquely determined is obtained by taking for the domain S of f the set of points (x, y) in two-dimensional space for which $|x| \leqq y^2$, and taking $f(x, y) = x^2 + y^2$. Then a differential at the origin $df(0, 0;\ dx, dy) = \varphi_1\, dx + \varphi_2\, dy$ must have $\varphi_2 = 0$, but φ_1 is quite arbitrary. The converse of Theorem 11 is not true, as is shown by the following example. Let $f(x, y) = xy/(x^2 + y^2)$ for $(x, y) \neq (0, 0)$, $f(0, 0) = 0$. This function is discontinuous at the origin, although it has finite partial derivatives everywhere. Another example, in which the function is continuous but still does not have a differential at the origin, is obtained by setting $f(x, y) = xy/(x^2 + y^2)^{1/2}$ for $(x, y) \neq (0, 0)$, $f(0, 0) = 0$. However, Theorem 11 has the following partial converse:

THEOREM 12. *Let c be an interior point of the domain S such that f has finite first partial derivatives at each point of a neighborhood $N(c)$ which are continuous at c. Then f has a differential at c.*

The proof is made by means of the theorem of mean value. A slightly more general theorem is indicated by Pierpont [2], page 271.

THEOREM 13. *Suppose that each of the k functions $g^{(i)}(z)$, with common domain T, has a differential $dg^{(i)}(c;\ dz)$ at c, and that the function $f(x)$ has a differential $df(b;\ dx)$ at $b = g(c)$. Then if c is an accumulation point of the domain of the composite function $h(z) \equiv f[g(z)]$, h has a differential $dh(c;\ dz) = df[b; dg(c; dz)]$ at c.*

Proof.—It is plain that the function $dh(c;\ dz)$ is linear in its argument dz. Suppose $\epsilon > 0$. By hypothesis,

$$\exists \delta > 0 \ni: \|x - b\| < \delta \cdot\supset\cdot |f(x) - f(b) - df(b;\ x - b)| \leqq \epsilon\|x - b\|.$$

By hypothesis and by Theorem 10,

$$\exists M \cdot \exists \beta > 0 \ni: \|z - c\| < \beta \cdot \supset \cdot \|g(z) - b\| \leqq M\|z - c\| < \delta.$$
$$\|g(z) - g(c) - dg(c; z - c)\| \leqq \epsilon\|z - c\|.$$

Note that M is independent of ϵ. Hence for $\|z - c\| < \beta$ we have

$$\begin{aligned}|h(z) - h(c) - df[b; dg(c; z - c)]| &\leqq |f[g(z)] - f(b) \\ &\quad - df[b; g(z) - b]| + |df[b; g(z) - b - dg(c; z - c)]| \\ &\leqq \epsilon M\|z - c\| + \|df\|\epsilon\|z - c\|.\end{aligned}$$

It is interesting to note that the above proof is also a valid proof of Theorem 7.

If in the third example following Theorem 11 we set $x = y = z$, the resulting function $h(z) = |z|/\sqrt{2}$ fails to have a derivative at $z = 0$, although the function f is continuous and has partial derivatives everywhere. This with Theorem 13 shows that this function f cannot have a differential at the origin.

By combining the results in Theorems 11 to 13 we obtain the usual calculus rules for computing differentials. Thus, if $f(x)$ is linear, $df(x; dx) = f(dx)$, and hence $d(ax) = a\,dx$, $d(x + y) = dx + dy$. By fixing first y and then x in the product xy, we get linear functions, and hence $d(xy) = y\,dx + x\,dy$. From Theorem 13 and these results we have $d(f + g) = df + dg$, $d(fg) = f\,dg + g\,df$, etc.

Consider a function $f(x)$ for which $df(x; dx_1)$ exists for x on a neighborhood $N(c)$. If for each dx_1 the function df considered as a function of x has a differential $d^2f(c; dx_1, dx_2)$ at c the function d^2f is called the **second differential** of f at c. It is easy to show that d^2f is linear in dx_1 as well as in dx_2. In a similar manner, differentials of all orders may be defined when they exist for the function $f(x)$.

Either of the notations $f_{x^{(i)}}$ and $\partial f/\partial x^{(i)}$ may be used to indicate the first partial derivatives of a function f, with obvious extensions for the partial derivatives of higher order.

A function f is said to be of **class** C' on an open set S in case it has a differential $df(x; dx)$ at every point x of S, and $df(x; dx)$ is continuous as a function of x for every value of dx. In general, f is said to be of **class** $C^{(m)}$ on S in case it is of class C', and $df(x; dx)$ is of class $C^{(m-1)}$ on S for every dx. By use of Theorems 11 and 12 and induction it can be shown that an equivalent definition is that the function f has all its partial derivatives up to and including those of order m existing and continuous on the set S. This latter form of the definition is more convenient for the type of functions we are considering.

THEOREM 14. *Let the functions $f_i(x)$ be of class $C^{(m)}$ on S, for $i = 1, \cdots, n$, and let $P(y)$ and $Q(y)$ be polynomials in $y^{(1)}, \ldots, y^{(n)}$. Then $P[f(x)]$ is of class $C^{(m)}$ on S, and its derivatives are expressible as polynomials in $f_1, \ldots, f_n$ and their derivatives. If $Q[f(x)] \neq 0$ on S, then the quotient $P[f(x)]/Q[f(x)]$ is of class $C^{(m)}$ on S, and its derivatives are expressible as polynomials in $f_1, \ldots, f_n$ and their derivatives divided by appropriate powers of $Q[f(x)]$.*

Proof.—The usual formal proof may be made for the first derivatives of sums, differences, products, and quotients. Hence by induction the statement of the theorem holds for $m = 1$. The proof is completed by induction on m.

THEOREM 15. *Suppose the function $f(x)$ is of class $C^{(m)}$ on the open set S of k-dimensional space, and the k functions $g^{(i)}(z)$ are of class $C^{(m)}$ on the open set T of l-dimensional space, and suppose that the subset T_0 of T for which the point $g(z)$ is in S is not null. Then the set T_0 is open, and the function $h(z) \equiv f[g(z)]$ is of class $C^{(m)}$ on T_0.*

Proof.—The set T_0 is open since the functions $g^{(i)}(z)$ are continuous by Theorem 10. The theorem is true for $m = 1$, by Theorem 13, and Theorem 16 of Chap. IV, Sec. 3, and

$$\partial h/\partial z^{(j)} = \sum_i \partial f/\partial x^{(i)} \, \partial g^{(i)}/\partial z^{(j)}.$$

If the theorem is true for $m = p - 1$, then the functions $f_{x^{(i)}}[g(z)]$ and $\partial g^{(i)}/\partial z^{(j)}$ are of class $C^{(p-1)}$, and hence $h_{z^{(j)}} = \partial h/\partial z^{(j)}$ is of class $C^{(p-1)}$ by Theorem 14.

The expression for the second differential, for example, of the function $h(z)$ is as follows:

$$d^2h(z; dz_1, dz_2) = d^2f[g(z); dg(z; dz_1), dg(z; dz_2)] + df[g(z); d^2g(z; dz_1, dz_2)].$$

It should be noted that when derivatives and differentials of order higher than the first are concerned, use of the notation for dependent variables easily leads to confusion. Strict adherence to the functional notation is then both safer and simpler.

Compare the remarks in Goursat [4], pages 22–26, and Pierpont [2], pages 274–279.

The second differential $d^2f(x; dx_1, dx_2)$ of a function f of class C'' is always symmetric in its differential arguments dx_1 and dx_2. This is implied by the following theorem on interchange of order of differentiation for functions of two real variables. For other related theorems see Pierpont [2], page 265.

THEOREM 16. *Let $f(x, y)$ be a function of two real variables defined in a neighborhood $N(a, b)$, and suppose the partial derivatives f_x, f_y, and f_{xy} exist and are finite in $N(a, b)$ and f_{xy} is continuous at (a, b). Then the partial derivative f_{yx} exists at (a, b) and equals $f_{xy}(a, b)$.*

Proof.—Let $g(x, y) \equiv f(x, y) - f(x, b)$, and $h(x, y) \equiv [g(x, y) - g(a, y)]/(x - a)(y - b)$. Then by applying the theorem of mean value twice, we find that there exists a point x_1 between a and x and a point y_1 between b and y such that

$$h(x, y) = \frac{g_x(x_1, y)}{y - b} = f_{xy}(x_1, y_1).$$

Hence, by the assumed continuity of f_{xy} at (a, b),

$$\lim_{\substack{x=a\\y=b}} h(x, y) = f_{xy}(a, b).$$

Also from the definition of $f_y(x, b)$ we obtain

$$\lim_{y=b} h(x, y) = \frac{f_y(x, b) - f_y(a, b)}{x - a}.$$

From this it easily follows that

$$\lim_{x=a} \frac{f_y(x, b) - f_y(a, b)}{x - a} = f_{xy}(a, b).$$

But the expression on the left is by definition the partial derivative $f_{yx}(a, b)$.

THEOREM 17. **Taylor's theorem with remainder.** *Let the function $f(x)$ be of class $C^{(m)}$ on the convex open set S. Then for every pair of points a and b in S there is a number t_0 such that $0 < t_0 < 1$ and*

$$\begin{aligned} f(b) = f(a) &+ df(a; b - a) + d^2f(a; b - a, b - a)/2! \\ &+ \cdots + d^{(m-1)}f(a; b - a, \cdots, b - a)/(m - 1)! \\ &+ d^{(m)}f(a + t_0(b - a); b - a, \cdots, b - a)/m! \end{aligned}$$

Proof.—The function $f[a + t(b - a)]$ has a continuous mth derivative with respect to t on the closed interval $[0, 1]$, by Theorem 15. Hence the theorem follows at once from Theorem 6.

***3. Indeterminate Forms.**—In this section we shall develop some theorems that justify the methods employed in elementary calculus for the evaluation of indeterminate forms. We are concerned only with single-real-valued functions of a single real variable. The first theorem is an extension of the Theorem of the Mean.

THEOREM 18. *Suppose $f(x)$ and $g(x)$ are continuous on the closed interval $[a, b]$ and have derivatives f' and g' which are neither simultaneously zero nor simultaneously infinite on the open interval (a, b). Suppose also that $g(b) \neq g(a)$. Then there is a point c between a and b such that $g'(c) \neq 0$ and*

$$\frac{f(b) - f(a)}{g(b) - g(a)} = \frac{f'(c)}{g'(c)}.$$

Proof.—Apply Rolle's theorem to the function

$$h(x) \equiv f(x) - f(a) - \frac{f(b) - f(a)}{g(b) - g(a)} [g(x) - g(a)].$$

THEOREM 19. *Suppose $f(x)$ and $g(x)$ and their first $m - 1$ derivatives are continuous on the closed interval $[a, b]$, and vanish at $x = a$. Suppose also that the mth derivatives $f^{(m)}(x)$ and $g^{(m)}(x)$ exist and are not simultaneously infinite and $g^{(m)}(x) \neq 0$ on the open interval (a, b). Then there is a point c between a and b such that*

$$\frac{f(b)}{g(b)} = \frac{f^{(m)}(c)}{g^{(m)}(c)}.$$

Proof.—By the Theorem of the Mean (Theorem 4) it is seen that none of the derivatives $g^{(m-1)}(x), \ldots, g'(x)$, can vanish on the interval (a, b). Then the desired result follows from Theorem 18 by induction. The reader should note that it is not an essential generalization of the theorem to assume only that the functions $f, f', \ldots, f^{(m-1)}, g, g', \ldots, g^{(m-1)}$ have limits equal to zero at the point a, without actually being defined there. For in that case we may set $f(a) = g(a) = 0$, and then the hypotheses of the theorem as stated are all fulfilled, by Corollary 4 of Theorem 4.

THEOREM 20. *In addition to the hypotheses of Theorem 18, suppose that* $f(a) = g(a) = 0$. *Let S be the subset of the open interval* (a, b) *on which* $g(x) \neq 0$, *and let T be the subset on which* $g'(x) \neq 0$ *and* $f'(x)$ *is finite. Then every limiting value of the quotient* $f(x)/g(x)$ *over a sequence* (x_n) *chosen from S and converging to a is also a limiting value of the quotient* $f'(x)/g'(x)$ *over a sequence* $(\bar{x}_n)$ *chosen from T and converging to a. In particular, if* $\lim_{x=a} f'(x)/g'(x) = B$ *over T, then* $\lim_{x=a} f(x)/g(x) = B$ *over S.*

This follows at once from Theorem 18. A similar theorem on indeterminate forms follows from Theorem 19. However, most of the elementary problems involving the indeterminate form 0/0 are solvable by repeated applications of Theorem 20. Another theorem which is sometimes useful is the following:

THEOREM 21. *Let the function f and its first* $m - 2$ *derivatives* $f', \ldots, f^{(m-2)}$ *be continuous on the closed interval* $[a, b]$. *Suppose also that the* $(m - 1)$*st derivative* $f^{(m-1)}$ *exists and is finite on* $[a, b]$, *and that* $f^{(m)}(a)$ *exists, while* $f(a) = f'(a) = \cdots = f^{(m-1)}(a) = 0$. *Then*

$$\lim_{h=0} \frac{f(a+h)}{h^m} = \frac{f^{(m)}(a)}{m!}.$$

If similar conditions hold for a function g, except that the integer m is replaced by n, and if $f^{(m)}(a)$ *and* $g^{(n)}(a)$ *are finite and not zero, then*

$$\begin{aligned} \lim_{x=a} \frac{f(x)}{g(x)} &= 0 && \text{if } n < m, \\ &= \pm\infty && \text{if } n > m, \\ &= f^{(m)}(a)/g^{(m)}(a) && \text{if } n = m. \end{aligned}$$

When $n \leqq m$, *the requirement that* $f^{(m)}(a) \neq 0$ *may be omitted.*

Proof.—By the definition of derivative,

$$\lim_{h=0} \frac{f^{(m-1)}(a+h)}{h} = f^{(m)}(a).$$

Then from Theorem 19, with m replaced by $m - 1$, it follows that

$$\lim_{h=0} \frac{f(a+h)}{h^m} = \lim_{h=0} \frac{f^{(m-1)}(a+h)}{m!h} = \frac{f^{(m)}(a)}{m!}.$$

The final part of the theorem readily follows from the first part. Since $g^{(n)}(a) \neq 0$, it follows that $g(x) \neq 0$ in a deleted neighborhood of a.

The reader should note that the limits considered in Theorems 20 and 21 are one-sided limits, so that they are more generally applicable than they would be if our consideration had been restricted to two-sided limits. However, the limiting value a of the variable x is supposed to be finite. The case when this limiting value is infinite is taken care of by the simple artifice indicated in the proof of the following theorem:

THEOREM 22. *Suppose that $f(x)$ and $g(x)$ are continuous and have derivatives $f'(x)$ and $g'(x)$ which are neither simultaneously zero nor simultaneously infinite on the open interval $b < x < +\infty$. Suppose also that $\lim_{x=+\infty} f(x) = \lim_{x=+\infty} g(x) = 0$. Let the sets S and T be defined as in Theorem 20. Then every limiting value of the quotient $f(x)/g(x)$ over a sequence (x_n) chosen from the set S and approaching $+\infty$ is also a limiting value of the quotient $f'(x)/g'(x)$ over a sequence $(\bar{x}_n)$ chosen from the set T and approaching $+\infty$. In particular, if $\lim_{x=+\infty} f'(x)/g'(x) = B$ over T, then $\lim_{x=+\infty} f(x)/g(x) = B$ over S.*

Proof.—We may suppose that $b > 0$, so that the transformation $x = 1/y$ carries the interval $b < x < +\infty$ into the interval $0 < y < 1/b$. Let $h(y) = f(1/y)$, $h(0) = 0$, $k(y) = g(1/y)$, $k(0) = 0$. Then the hypotheses of Theorem 20 are satisfied by the functions h and k on an interval $0 \leqq y \leqq c$.

In the next theorem the limiting value a of x may be either finite or infinite.

THEOREM 23. *Suppose that $f(x)$ and $g(x)$ are continuous and have derivatives f' and g' which are neither simultaneously zero nor simultaneously infinite on the open interval (a, b). Suppose also that $\lim_{x=a} |g(x)| = +\infty$. Then every limiting value of the quotient $f(x)/g(x)$ over a sequence (x_n) converging to a is also a limiting value of the quotient $f'(x)/g'(x)$ over a sequence $(\bar{x}_n)$ converging to a and such that $f'(\bar{x}_n)$ is finite and $g'(\bar{x}_n) \neq 0$. In particular, if $\lim_{x=a} f'(x)/g'(x) = B$, then $\lim_{x=a} f(x)/g(x) = B$.*

Proof.—Let $\lim_n x_n = a$, $\lim_n f(x_n)/g(x_n) = L$, $\lim_k c_k = a$, where x_n and c_k are in the open interval (a, b). Then for each k there is an integer n_k such that $a < x_{n_k} < c_k$, and

$$\left|\frac{f(c_k)}{g(x_{n_k})}\right| < \frac{1}{k}, \qquad \left|\frac{g(x_{n_k})}{g(x_{n_k}) - g(c_k)} - 1\right| < \frac{1}{k}.$$

By Theorem 18, there is a point $\bar{x}_k$ between x_{n_k} and c_k such that

$$\frac{f'(\bar{x}_k)}{g'(\bar{x}_k)} = \frac{f(x_{n_k}) - f(c_k)}{g(x_{n_k}) - g(c_k)}$$
$$= \left[\frac{f(x_{n_k})}{g(x_{n_k})} - \frac{f(c_k)}{g(x_{n_k})}\right]\left[\frac{g(x_{n_k})}{g(x_{n_k}) - g(c_k)}\right].$$

Hence $\lim_k f'(\bar{x}_k)/g'(\bar{x}_k) = L$, and obviously $\lim_k \bar{x}_k = a$.

EXERCISES

In each of the following examples, determine whether Theorem 20 or 21, or neither, is applicable in evaluating $\lim_{x=0} f(x)/g(x)$.

1. $f(x) = x^2 \sin 1/x$, $g(x) = e^x - 1$.
2. $f(x) = e^{x^3} - 1$, $g(x) = x^3 \sin 1/x + x^2$.
3. $f(x) = x^4 \sin 1/x - x^2$, $g(x) = 1 - \cos^2 x$.
4. $f(x) = x^3 \sin 1/x$, $g(x) = \sin^2 x$.
5. $f(x) = e^y - y - 1 - x^2$, $y = x^3 \sin 1/x$, $g(x) = e^{x^2} - 1$.

REFERENCES

1. Hobson, *The Theory of Functions of a Real Variable*, Vol. 1, Chap. 5; Vol. 2, Chap. 6.
2. Pierpont, *The Theory of Functions of Real Variables*, Vol. 1, Chaps. 8, 10, 11.
3. Veblen and Lennes, *Infinitesimal Analysis*, Chaps. 6, 7.
4. Goursat, *Mathematical Analysis*, Vol. 1, Chaps. 1, 3.
5. Jordan, *Cours d'analyse*, Vol. 1, Chaps. 1, 3.
6. W. H. Young, *The Fundamental Theorems of the Differential Calculus*, Cambridge Tracts, 1910.

Jordan [5] collects several formulas for the remainder in Taylor's theorem (Theorem 17 above) at the beginning of Chap. 3.

CHAPTER VI

THE RIEMANN INTEGRAL

1. Conditions for the Existence of the Integral.—The definition of a definite integral as the limit of a sum, as presented in elementary calculus, was formulated by Riemann in the last century. This definition will be reviewed here, and necessary and sufficient conditions for the existence of the integral will be developed. Throughout this chapter we shall restrict attention to real-valued bounded functions $f(x)$ whose domain is a finite closed interval $[a, b]$ in one-dimensional space. The functions considered need not be single-valued.

Consider a **partition** P of the interval $[a, b]$ into closed subintervals I_j. It is understood that the intervals I_j are nonoverlapping, that is, any pair of them have at most end points in common. Let Δ_j denote the length of I_j, and x_j a point of I_j, and let $N(P)$ = greatest Δ_j. Let

$$S(P) = \sum_j f(x_j)\Delta_j.$$

The sum S is in general a multiple-valued function, whether regarded as a function of P or of $N(P)$. The bounded function $f(x)$ is said to be **Riemann-integrable** or **R-integrable** in case

$$\lim_{N(P)=0} S(P)$$

exists. When it exists, this limit is denoted by the familiar symbol

$$\int_a^b f(x)\,dx.$$

It is easy to see that the limit cannot exist and be finite when $f(x)$ is unbounded.

Let U_j = l.u.b. $f(x)$ on I_j, L_j = g.l.b. $f(x)$ on I_j,

$$S^*(P) = \sum_j U_j\,\Delta_j, \qquad S_*(P) = \sum_j L_j\,\Delta_j.$$

The greatest lower bound of the sums $S^*(P)$ for all partitions P is called the **upper integral** of f, and denoted by the symbol

$$\overline{\int_a^b} f(x)\,dx.$$

Likewise the least upper bound of the sums $S_*(P)$ is called the **lower integral** of f, and denoted by the symbol

$$\underline{\int_a^b} f(x)\,dx.$$

It is plain that $S^*(P)$ is the least upper bound of all the values of $S(P)$. Likewise $S_*(P) = \text{g.l.b. } S(P)$.

THEOREM 1. *For every bounded function* f, $\underline{\int_a^b} f(x)\,dx \leqq \overline{\int_a^b} f(x)\,dx$.

Proof.—Let $S^*(P_1)$ and $S_*(P_2)$ correspond to two partitions P_1 and P_2, and let P_3 be a partition formed by using all the partition points of both P_1 and P_2, which is therefore "finer" than both P_1 and P_2. It is clear that

$$S_*(P_2) \leqq S_*(P_3) \leqq S^*(P_3) \leqq S^*(P_1),$$

and from this the theorem follows.

THEOREM 2. *For every bounded function* f,

$$\underline{\int_a^b} f(x)\,dx = \lim_{N(P)=0} S_*(P), \qquad \overline{\int_a^b} f(x)\,dx = \lim_{N(P)=0} S^*(P).$$

Proof.—Since $f(x)$ is bounded, there is a number A such that $f(x) + A > 0$. Hence we may assume $f(x) \geqq 0$. Corresponding to an arbitrary positive number ϵ, there exists a partition P_0 such that

$$S^*(P_0) < \overline{\int_a^b} f(x)\,dx + \epsilon.$$

Let q be the number of partition points in P_0, $U = \text{l.u.b. } f(x)$, $\delta = \epsilon/Uq$. Then for an arbitrary partition P with $N(P) < \delta$,

$$\overline{\int_a^b} f(x)\,dx \leqq S^*(P) < \overline{\int_a^b} f(x)\,dx + 2\epsilon.$$

For, $S^*(P) = S_1^* + S_2^*$, where S_1^* is the sum of the terms corresponding to intervals contained in intervals of the partition P_0, and S_2^* is the sum of the terms corresponding to intervals containing in their interiors partition points of P_0. Thus $S_1^* \leqq S^*(P_0)$, since $f(x) \geqq 0$, and $S_2^* \leqq UqN(P) < \epsilon$. This proves the formula for the upper integral of f. The formula for the lower integral of f follows from that for the upper integral of the function $-f$.

In Theorems 3, 4, 6, and 7 we shall consider a series of conditions each of which is necessary and sufficient for a bounded function $f(x)$ to be R-integrable. The condition given in Theorem 4 suggests a possible alternative definition for the Riemann integral. The condition stated in Theorem 7 is usually the most useful one.

THEOREM 3. *A necessary and sufficient condition for $f(x)$ to be R-integrable on $[a, b]$ is that*

$$\lim_{N(P_1)=0, N(P_2)=0} [S(P_1) - S(P_2)] = 0.$$

This follows from Theorem 10 of Chap. IV, if we regard $S(P)$ as a function of $N(P)$.

THEOREM 4. *A necessary and sufficient condition for $f(x)$ to be R-integrable on $[a, b]$ is that the upper and lower integrals of f be equal.*

Proof.—The condition is sufficient, by Theorem 2, since $S_*(P) \leqq S(P) \leqq S^*(P)$ for every partition P. Let us suppose that the condition is not necessary. Then there is a function f such that

$$C \equiv \overline{\int_a^b} f(x)\, dx - \underline{\int_a^b} f(x)\, dx > 0.$$

For every $\epsilon > 0$, there is a partition P_1 with $N(P_1) < \epsilon$ such that

$$0 \leqq S^*(P_1) - \overline{\int_a^b} f(x)\, dx < C/3.$$

Associated with the partition P_1, there is a value of the sum $S(P_1)$ such that

$$0 \leqq S^*(P_1) - S(P_1) < C/3,$$

and therefore

$$\left| \overline{\int_a^b} f(x)\, dx - S(P_1) \right| < C/3.$$

It may be shown in a similar way that there is a partition P_2 with $N(P_2) < \epsilon$, and a value of the sum $S(P_2)$ such that

$$\left|\int_a^b f(x)\,dx - S(P_2)\right| < C/3.$$

Then $|S(P_1) - S(P_2)| > C/3$, and hence f is not integrable, by Theorem 3.

The **oscillation** of a function f **on a closed subinterval** $[c, d]$ of $[a, b]$, denoted by the symbol $o[c, d]$, is defined to be the difference between the least upper bound and the greatest lower bound of $f(x)$ on the interval. The **oscillation** of f **at a point** x of $[a, b]$, denoted by the symbol $\omega(x)$, is defined to be the difference between the upper limit and the lower limit of f at the point x. It is easily seen that

$$\omega(x) = \lim_{\delta=0} o[x - \delta, x + \delta],$$

and that $o[c, d] \geqq \omega(x)$ whenever the point x is interior to the interval $[c, d]$. Also f is continuous at a point if and only if ω vanishes at that point. The next theorem is a generalization of the theorem on uniform continuity (Theorem 23 of Chap. IV).

THEOREM 5. *If $\omega(x) < \epsilon$ on the interval $[a, b]$, there exists a number $\delta > 0$ such that $o[c, d] < \epsilon$ on every subinterval $[c, d]$ of length less than δ.*

Proof.—For every x in $[a, b]$ there exists a $\delta_x > 0$ such that $o[x - 2\delta_x, x + 2\delta_x] < \epsilon$. By the Heine-Borel theorem, a finite subset of the family of intervals $(x - \delta_x, x + \delta_x)$ covers the interval $[a, b]$. The number δ equal to the least of the numbers δ_x corresponding to this finite subset satisfies the conditions of the theorem.

The **exterior Jordan content** of a point set E is the greatest lower bound of the sum of the lengths of a finite set of intervals covering E (in the sense of Sec. 6 of Chap. III), for all such coverings. The value obtained for the exterior content of a set E would be the same if the points of E were not required to be interior to the intervals. However, this requirement is a convenient one for the proofs of the next two theorems. In case the exterior content of E is zero, we say simply that E has **Jordan content zero.**

The **exterior Lebesgue measure** of a set E is defined in a similar way, the only difference being that the covering set of intervals is permitted to be denumerably infinite. This difference makes the concept of Lebesgue measure much more useful than that of Jordan content. The theory of Lebesgue measure will be developed in detail in Chap. X. When the exterior measure of E is zero, we say simply that E has **Lebesgue measure zero.** This is the only case we shall need to consider in the present chapter.

The content and the measure of an interval are both equal to its length. It is easy to see that every subset of a set of measure (content) zero has measure (content) zero, and that the sum of a finite number of sets of measure (content) zero has measure (content) zero. The statement about sums extends to denumerably infinite sums for measure, but not for content. Thus a denumerable set has measure zero, although its exterior content may have any value whatever. For example, the set of rational points in the interval $[a, b]$ has exterior content $(b - a)$. However, the Cantor discontinuum (example F in Sec. 2, Chap. III) has content zero, although it is nondenumerable.

THEOREM 6. *Let* $E_\delta \equiv E[\omega(x) \geqq \delta]$. *Then* $f(x)$ *is R-integrable on* $[a, b]$ *if and only if for every* $\delta > 0$ *the set* E_δ *has Jordan content zero.*

Proof.—Suppose there is a number $\delta > 0$ such that the exterior content of E_δ is a number $\eta > 0$. Then for every partition P the sum of the lengths of the intervals of P containing points of E_δ in their interiors is not less than η. Hence $S^*(P) - S_*(P) \geqq \delta\eta > 0$, and by Theorems 2 and 4, $f(x)$ cannot be integrable. To prove the converse, let δ and η be arbitrarily small positive numbers, and let T be a set of intervals covering the set E_δ, with length sum less than η. By Theorem 5 the parts of the interval $[a, b]$ not contained in the intervals of T may be subdivided into intervals I_k on each of which the oscillation of f is less than δ. The partition P obtained by using the end points of the intervals I_k and the end points of the intervals of T as partition points is such that $S^*(P) - S_*(P) \leqq (U - L)\eta + (b - a)\delta$, where $L \leqq f(x) \leqq U$ on $[a, b]$. Hence the upper and lower integrals of $f(x)$ are equal, and $f(x)$ is integrable, by Theorem 4.

THEOREM 7. *A bounded function* $f(x)$ *is R-integrable on* $[a, b]$ *if and only if the set* D *of points where* $f(x)$ *is discontinuous has Lebesgue measure zero.*

Proof.—To show that the condition is necessary, consider a sequence (δ_n) of positive numbers with $\lim_n \delta_n = 0$. Then the set D is the sum of the sets E_{δ_n} as defined in Theorem 6. By Theorem 6, each E_{δ_n} is covered by a finite family of intervals with length sum $< \eta/2^n$, where η is an arbitrary positive number. Hence D is covered by a denumerable family with length sum $< \eta$, and therefore has Lebesgue measure zero. To show that the condition is sufficient, let T be a denumerable family of intervals covering D and having length sum $< \eta$, where η is again arbitrary. Every set E_δ is closed and contained in D. Hence by the Heine-Borel theorem a finite number of the intervals of the family T cover E_δ, so that E_δ has Jordan content zero. Thus $f(x)$ is integrable by Theorem 6.

2. The Fundamental Theorem of Integral Calculus.—We make the usual agreement that

$$\int_b^a f(x)\,dx = -\int_a^b f(x)\,dx.$$

In case the function f is R-integrable on $[a, b]$ and c is a point of $[a, b]$, the function

$$g(x) = \int_c^x f(x)\,dx$$

is called an **indefinite integral** of $f(x)$. If $f(x)$ and $h(x)$ are *single-valued* functions defined on $[a, b]$ and if $h(x)$ has a derivative and $h'(x) = f(x)$ on $[a, b]$, then $h(x)$ is called a **primitive** or **antiderivative** of $f(x)$. A function f may be R-integrable without having an antiderivative, or vice versa. For example, let $f(x) = 0$ for x irrational, and $f(p/q) = 1/q$ when p/q is a fraction in its lowest terms. Then f is continuous except for rational values of x, and so is R-integrable on every interval, and its integral has the value zero. For an example of a function which has an antiderivative but is not R-integrable the reader may consult Hobson [1], page 490.

Before stating the fundamental theorem, we shall list in Theorems 8 and 9 some elementary properties of the Riemann integral, which follow readily from its definition and from Theorem 7.

THEOREM 8. *Suppose $f(x)$ and $g(x)$ are R-integrable on $[a, b]$. Then*

1. *$f(x)$ is R-integrable on every subinterval of $[a, b]$;*

2. *For every triple of points c, d, and e in* $[a, b]$,

$$\int_c^d f(x)\,dx + \int_d^e f(x)\,dx = \int_c^e f(x)\,dx;$$

3. *If* $f(x)$ *is also R-integrable on the interval* $[b, c]$, *it is so on the extended interval* $[a, c]$;

4. $f(x) + g(x)$ *is R-integrable, and*

$$\int_a^b [f(x) + g(x)]\,dx = \int_a^b f(x)\,dx + \int_a^b g(x)\,dx;$$

5. $f(x)g(x)$ *is R-integrable, and in particular* $cf(x)$ *is R-integrable for every real number c, and*

$$\int_a^b cf(x)\,dx = c\int_a^b f(x)\,dx;$$

6. *If* $f(x) \leqq g(x)$ *on* $[a, b]$,

$$\int_a^b f(x)\,dx \leqq \int_a^b g(x)\,dx;$$

7. $|f(x)|$ *is R-integrable, and*

$$\left|\int_a^b f(x)\,dx\right| \leqq \int_a^b |f(x)|\,dx.$$

THEOREM 9. *Suppose* $f(x)$ *is R-integrable on* $[a, b]$, *and let* $g(x)$ *be an indefinite integral of* $f(x)$. *Then*

1. $|g(x_1) - g(x_2)| \leqq M|x_1 - x_2|$ *for every* x_1 *and* x_2 *in* $[a, b]$, *where* $M = \text{l.u.b. } |f(x)|$ *on* $[a, b]$;

2. $g(x)$ *is continuous on* $[a, b]$;

3. *If* $f(x)$ *is continuous at a point c of* $[a, b]$, *then* $g(x)$ *has a derivative at c, and* $g'(c) = f(c)$.

The proof is based on the relations 2, 6, and 7 of Theorem 8.

COROLLARY. *Every function continuous on an interval has an antiderivative on that interval.*

THEOREM 10. **Fundamental theorem of the integral calculus.** *Suppose* $f(x)$ *is R-integrable on* $[a, b]$ *and also has an antiderivative* $h(x)$ *on* $[a, b]$. *Then*

$$h(b) - h(a) = \int_a^b f(x)\,dx.$$

Proof.—Let P be an arbitrary partition of $[a, b]$, with partition points α_i, where $a = \alpha_0 < \alpha_1 < \cdots < \alpha_{n-1} < \alpha_n = b$. Then

$$h(b) - h(a) = \sum_{i=1}^{n} [h(\alpha_i) - h(\alpha_{i-1})] = \sum_{i=1}^{n} f(x_i)(\alpha_i - \alpha_{i-1}),$$

where $\alpha_{i-1} < x_i < \alpha_i$, by the theorem of the mean for derivatives. But the last sum is one of the values of $S(P)$, and since

$$\lim_{N(P)=0} S(P)$$

exists, it has the value $h(b) - h(a)$ as stated in the theorem.

A simple example of a discontinuous function satisfying the conditions of the fundamental theorem is obtained by setting $f(x) = 2x \sin (1/x) - \cos (1/x)$ for $x \neq 0$, $f(0) = 0$. The function $h(x) = x^2 \sin (1/x)$ with $h(0) = 0$ is an antiderivative of $f(x)$. A bounded function $f(x)$ having only a finite number of discontinuities at which its right-hand and left-hand limits exist is always R-integrable but cannot have an antiderivative and so does not satisfy the conditions of the fundamental theorem. It does however have an antiderivative in a generalized sense, satisfying the conclusion of the theorem, and this suggests a generalization of the fundamental theorem. A further generalization will be taken up in connection with the Lebesgue integral in a later chapter. We first state an immediate generalization of Theorem 9.

*THEOREM 11. *Let $f(x)$ be bounded on $[a, b]$, and let*

$$g_u(x) = \overline{\int_a^x} f(x)\, dx, \qquad g_l(x) = \underline{\int_a^x} f(x)\, dx.$$

Then both the functions $g_u(x)$ and $g_l(x)$ have all the properties stated in Theorem 9.

Since relations 2, 6, and 7 of Theorem 8 are applicable to the upper and lower integrals, the method of proving Theorem 9 is also applicable here.

*THEOREM 12. *Let $f(x)$ be bounded on $[a, b]$, and let $h(x)$ be a continuous function such that for each x*

$$\phi(x) \leqq f(x) \leqq \psi(x),$$

where $\phi(x)$ and $\psi(x)$ are two of the derivates of h. Then the upper R-integrals of $f(x)$ and of the four derivates of h are all equal, and the same holds true for the lower R-integrals. Moreover, the difference $h(b) - h(a)$ lies between the upper and lower

R-integrals of $f(x)$ on $[a, b]$. Hence in case f (or an arbitrary one of the derivates of h) is R-integrable, so are the remaining derivates, and

$$h(b) - h(a) = \int_a^b f(x)\,dx.$$

Proof.—The upper R-integral of $f(x)$ is defined to be g.l.b, $S^*(P)$, where P is a partition of $[a, b]$ into intervals $[\alpha_{j-1}, \alpha_j]$ $S^*(P) = \sum U_j \Delta_j$, $\Delta_j = \alpha_j - \alpha_{j-1}$, and $U_j =$ l.u.b. $f(x)$ on the closed interval $[\alpha_{j-1}, \alpha_j]$. If $V_j =$ l.u.b. $f(x)$ on the open interval (α_{j-1}, α_j), then

$$T^*(P) \equiv \sum V_j \Delta_j \leqq S^*(P).$$

It is easy to see, however, that g.l.b. $T^*(P) =$ g.l.b. $S^*(P)$, so that it is immaterial whether we use open intervals or closed intervals in defining the upper and lower R-integrals. To prove this we may temporarily assume (as in the proof of Theorem 2) that $f(x) \geqq 0$. Corresponding to an arbitrary $\epsilon > 0$, choose the partition P so that

$$T^*(P) \leqq \text{g.l.b. } T^*(P) + \epsilon. \tag{2:1}$$

Insert additional partition points to form a partition P_1, and let the sums over the intervals of P_1 which have a point of P as an end point be denoted by $S_0^*(P_1)$, $T_0^*(P_1)$, while the sums over the remaining intervals are denoted by $S_1^*(P_1)$, $T_1^*(P_1)$. Since f is bounded, the partition P_1 may be so chosen that $S_0^*(P_1) < \epsilon$, and since f is nonnegative, we shall always have $S_1^*(P_1) \leqq T^*(P)$. By combining these inequalities with (2:1) we find that $S^*(P_1) <$ g.l.b. $T^*(P) + 2\epsilon$ and, since ϵ is arbitrary, g.l.b. $S^*(P) =$ g.l.b. $T^*(P)$.

To complete the proof of the theorem we note that by Corollary 1 of Theorem 8 in Chap. V the bounds of the four derivates of h on the open interval (α_{j-1}, α_j) are the same, and hence the same as the bounds of f on that interval. By Corollary 2 of the same theorem, $h(\alpha_j) - h(\alpha_{j-1}) \leqq V_j \Delta_j$, so that $h(b) - h(a) \leqq T^*(P)$, and thus

$$h(b) - h(a) \leqq \overline{\int_a^b} f(x)\,dx.$$

The corresponding inequality for the lower integral follows from the above in the usual way by considering the negatives of h and f.

EXERCISE

What is the solution of the following paradox? If

$$h(x) = \frac{1}{1 + e^{1/x}}$$

and

$$f(x) = \frac{e^{1/x}}{x^2(1 + e^{1/x})^2}$$

then $f(x) \geqq 0$, $h'(x) = f(x)$, and so

$$0 \leqq \int_{-1}^{1} f(x)\,dx = h(1) - h(-1) = \frac{1 - e}{1 + e} < 0.$$

3. Further Properties of the Integral.—More general theorems than some of the following can be proved even for the Riemann integral but, since corresponding theorems will be proved for the Lebesgue integral in a later chapter, we shall content ourselves in this section with theorems whose proofs are comparatively simple. The first two theorems are easily proved by means of Theorems 8 and 10.

THEOREM 13. **Integration by parts.** *Suppose $f(x)$ and $g(x)$ have derivatives $f'(x)$ and $g'(x)$ which are R-integrable on $[a, b]$. Then*

$$f(b)g(b) - f(a)g(a) = \int_a^b f(x)g'(x)\,dx + \int_a^b f'(x)g(x)\,dx.$$

THEOREM 14. **Integration by substitution.** *Suppose $f(x)$ is continuous on $[a, b]$, and $g(t)$ has a derivative $g'(t)$ which is R-integrable on $[c, d]$. Suppose $a \leqq g(t) \leqq b$ for t on $[c, d]$, and let $g(c) = a_1$, $g(d) = b_1$. Then*

$$\int_{a_1}^{b_1} f(x)\,dx = \int_c^d f[g(t)]g'(t)\,dt.$$

*When the function $g(t)$ is monotonic, the other requirements for the validity of the formula for change of variable may be lightened, as is indicated by the following theorem:

*THEOREM 15. *Let $f(x)$ be bounded on $[a, b]$, and suppose that $g(t)$ is nondecreasing on $[c, d]$ and that $\phi(t)$, one of the derivates of $g(t)$, is R-integrable on $[c, d]$. Let $a = g(c)$, $b = g(d)$. Then*

$$\overline{\int_a^b} f(x)\,dx = \overline{\int_c^d} f[g(t)]\phi(t)\,dt,$$
$$\underline{\int_a^b} f(x)\,dx = \underline{\int_c^d} f[g(t)]\phi(t)\,dt.$$

Hence if either of the Riemann integrals

$$\int_a^b f(x)\,dx, \int_c^d f[g(t)]\phi(t)\,dt$$

exists, so does the other, and they have the same value.

Proof.—Let $M \equiv$ l.u.b. $|f(x)|$ on $[a, b]$, $K \equiv$ l.u.b. $\phi(t)$ on $[c, d]$. Let $\bar{P}$ be a partition of $[c, d]$ into intervals $\bar{I}_j$ of length $\bar{\Delta}_j$, and let P be the corresponding partition of $[a, b]$ determined by the function $g(t)$, with intervals I_j of length Δ_j. Some of the partition points of P may be coincident, and so some of the lengths Δ_j may be zero, but this will not affect the validity of the argument. Let $U_j \equiv$ l.u.b. $f(x)$ on I_j, $\bar{U}_j \equiv$ l.u.b. $f[g(t)]\phi(t)$ on $\bar{I}_j$, $u_j \equiv$ l.u.b. $\phi(t)$ on $\bar{I}_j$, $l_j \equiv$ g.l.b. $\phi(t)$ on $\bar{I}_j$, $S^*(P) = \sum U_j \Delta_j$, $S^*(\bar{P}) = \sum \bar{U}_j \bar{\Delta}_j$. Then since ϕ is nowhere negative, $\bar{U}_j = U_j\sigma_j$ where $l_j \leqq \sigma_j \leqq u_j$, and by Corollary 2 of Theorem 8 in Chap. V, $\Delta_j = \bar{\Delta}_j\theta_j$, where $l_j \leqq \theta_j \leqq u_j$. Hence

$$|S^*(\bar{P}) - S^*(P)| = \left|\sum [\bar{U}_j \bar{\Delta}_j - U_j \Delta_j]\right| = \left|\sum U_j \bar{\Delta}_j(\sigma_j - \theta_j)\right|$$
$$\leqq M \sum \bar{\Delta}_j|\sigma_j - \theta_j| \leqq M \sum \bar{\Delta}_j(u_j - l_j),$$

and the last sum approaches zero with $N(\bar{P})$ since ϕ is R-integrable. Also $N(P) \leqq KN(\bar{P})$, so that

$$\lim_{N(\bar{P})=0} S^*(P) = \overline{\int_a^b} f(x)\,dx,$$

and hence the statement of the theorem about the upper integrals follows at once. The statement involving the lower integrals follows from that for the upper integrals with f replaced by $-f$.

THEOREM 16. **Taylor's theorem with new form of remainder.** *Suppose $f(x)$ has derivatives up to and including the one of order m on the closed interval $[a, b]$, and suppose the mth derivative $f^{(m)}(x)$ is R-integrable on $[a, b]$. Then*

$$f(b) = f(a) + (b - a)f'(a) + \cdots + \frac{(b-a)^{m-1}}{(m-1)!} f^{(m-1)}(a) + \frac{(b-a)^m}{(m-1)!} \int_0^1 (1-t)^{m-1} f^{(m)}[a + t(b-a)]\, dt.$$

Proof.—For $m = 1$, the theorem follows from Theorems 15 and 10. The proof is completed by induction and use of integration by parts. For other forms of the remainder, see Jordan [5], Vol. I, pages 245*ff*.

THEOREM 17. *If S is a convex open set in k-dimensional space, and $f(x)$ is of class $C^{(m)}$ on S, then for every pair of points a and b in S,*

$$f(b) = f(a) + df(a; b-a) + \cdots + \frac{d^{(m-1)}f(a; b-a, \cdots, b-a)}{(m-1)!} + \int_0^1 \frac{(1-t)^{m-1}}{(m-1)!} d^{(m)}f[a + t(b-a); b-a, \cdots, b-a]\, dt.$$

THEOREM 18. **First Theorem of the Mean for integrals.** *Suppose that the functions $g(x)$ and $f(x)g(x)$ are both R-integrable on $[a, b]$, and that $g(x)$ does not assume both positive and negative values on $[a, b]$. Let $L =$ g.l.b. $f(x)$ on $[a, b]$, $U =$ l.u.b. $f(x)$ on $[a, b]$. Then*

$$\int_a^b f(x)g(x)\, dx = \mu \int_a^b g(x)\, dx \tag{3:1}$$

where $L \leqq \mu \leqq U$. If $f(x)$ has a continuous antiderivative, then we may take $\mu = f(x_0)$, where $a < x_0 < b$.

Proof.—It is plainly sufficient to consider the case when $g(x) \geqq 0$. Then $Lg(x) \leqq f(x)g(x) \leqq Ug(x)$, and hence

$$L \int_a^b g(x)\, dx \leqq \int_a^b f(x)g(x)\, dx \leqq U \int_a^b g(x)\, dx.$$

From this statement (3:1) follows immediately. In case $g(x) = 0$ at all its points of continuity, we have

$$\int_a^b g(x)\, dx = 0,$$

and the number μ may be chosen arbitrarily. In the contrary case there is a number $\delta > 0$ and a subinterval $[\alpha, \beta]$ such that

$g(x) > \delta$ on $[\alpha, \beta]$. The function $f(x)$ must also be R-integrable on $[\alpha, \beta]$, and hence either $f(x) = L$ at all its points of continuity in $[\alpha, \beta]$, or else there is a number $\epsilon > 0$ and a subinterval $[\alpha_1, \beta_1]$ of $[\alpha, \beta]$ such that $f(x) > L + \epsilon$ on $[\alpha_1, \beta_1]$. In the latter case

$$\int_a^b f(x)g(x)\,dx \geqq L \int_a^b g(x)\,dx + \epsilon\delta(\beta_1 - \alpha_1),$$

and thus $\mu > L$. Thus if $\mu = L$, we must have $f(x) = \mu$ at all its points of continuity at least in the interval $[\alpha, \beta]$. A similar statement is true if $\mu = U$. Finally, in case $L < \mu < U$, the desired conclusion follows from Theorem 5 of Chap. V.

Note that in the special case where $g(x)$ is constant, the final statement of the theorem may be derived directly from the Theorem of the Mean for derivatives with the help of the fundamental theorem of integral calculus.

The Second Theorem of the Mean for integrals is proved in Chap. XI, Sec. 7.

References

1. Hobson, *The Theory of Functions of a Real Variable*, Vol. 1, Chap. 6.
2. Pierpont, *The Theory of Functions of Real Variables*, Vol. 1, Chaps. 12 to 16; Vol. 2, Chaps. 1, 2.
3. Veblen and Lennes, *Infinitesimal Analysis*, Chaps. 8, 9.
4. Goursat, *Mathematical Analysis*, Vol. 1, Chaps. 4, 6, 7.
5. Jordan, *Cours d'analyse*, Vol. 1, Chap. 1, Nos. 41 to 58; Vol. 2, Chap. 2.

CHAPTER VII

UNIFORM CONVERGENCE

1. The Cauchy Condition for Uniform Convergence.—Let $f(x, y)$ be a real-finite-valued function whose domain is the Cartesian product ST. This is understood to mean that the variable x ranges over the set S in a space of one or more dimensions, and the variable y ranges over the set T. In the following we shall suppose that a is a point of the closure $\bar{S}$, and b is a point of the closure $\bar{T}$. In case $\lim_{y=b} f(x, y)$ exists for every x in S, it defines a function of x, which is necessarily single-valued, even though $f(x, y)$ is a multiple-valued function. When this limit does not exist, we may consider $\limsup_{y=b} f(x, y)$ and $\liminf_{y=b} f(x, y)$. For the following definitions we shall suppose that the functions $g(x)$ and $u(x)$ also have only finite values.

We say that $\lim_{y=b} f(x, y) = g(x)$ **uniformly on** S in case

$$\epsilon > 0 :\supset: \exists N(b) \ni: x \text{ in } S \,.\, y \text{ in } N(b) \cdot\supset\cdot |f(x, y) - g(x)| < \epsilon.$$

In order to phrase a definition of uniformity applicable to upper limits, let us recall that, if

$$\phi(x, \delta) \equiv \text{l.u.b. } f(x, y) \text{ for } y \text{ in } N(b; \delta),$$

then

$$\limsup_{y=b} f(x, y) = \lim_{\delta=0} \phi(x, \delta).$$

We say that $\limsup_{y=b} f(x, y) = u(x)$ **uniformly on** S in case $\lim_{\delta=0} \phi(x, \delta) = u(x)$ uniformly on S.

The definition applicable to the lower limit is an analogous one.

In the figure there appear the graphs of $z = u(x)$ and of $z = f(x, y)$ for a value of y in $N(b; \delta)$, where δ is such that $\phi(x, \delta) < u(x) + \epsilon$.

Although it seems more convenient to require in the preceding definitions that $g(x)$ and $u(x)$ take only finite values on S, the definitions could have been phrased without this requirement. We could also consider functions $f(x, y)$ whose domain is an arbitrary set R in xy-space. If S is a set of points x such that (x, b) is in the closure of the set of points (x, y) in R, then the above definitions extend at once.

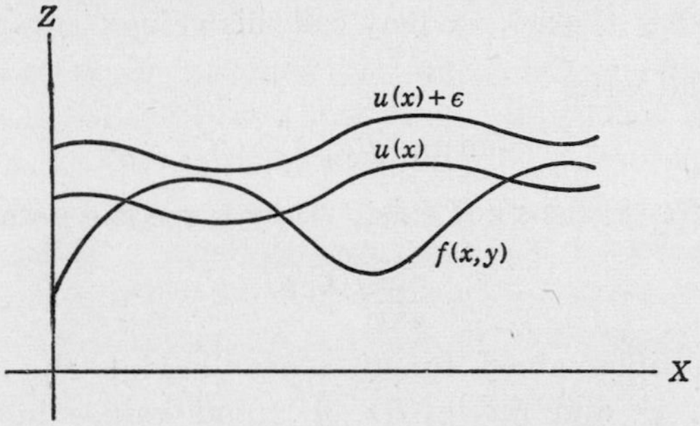

The somewhat less restrictive notion of **uniform convergence at a point** is occasionally useful. If $\lim_{y=b} f(x, y) = g(x)$ on S, and $\lim_{\substack{x=a\\y=b}} [f(x, y) - g(x)] = 0$, we say that $\lim_{y=b} f(x, y) = g(x)$ **uniformly at** a.[1]

THEOREM 1. *A necessary and sufficient condition that a finite-valued function $g(x)$ exist such that $\lim_{y=b} f(x, y) = g(x)$ uniformly on S is that $\lim_{\substack{y=b\\y'=b}} [f(x, y) - f(x, y')] = 0$ uniformly on S, i.e., that*

$$\epsilon > 0 :\supset: \exists N(b) \ni: x \text{ in } S \,.\, y \text{ in } N(b) \,.\, y' \text{ in } N(b) \cdot\supset\cdot |f(x, y) - f(x, y')| < \epsilon.$$

Proof.—The necessity of the condition follows in an obvious way from the definition. To prove the sufficiency, we note that everything but the uniformity of the convergence follows from Theorem 10 of Chap. IV. Thus, if y and y' are in $N(b)$,

$$|f(x, y) - g(x)| \leqq |f(x, y) - f(x, y')| + |f(x, y') - g(x)| < \epsilon + |f(x, y') - g(x)|.$$

Since the left side of this inequality is independent of y' and

[1] See Hobson [1], Vol. 2, p. 110. Pierpont uses a more restrictive definition for this term. See [2], Vol. 2, p. 157.

since $\lim_{y'=b} |f(x, y') - g(x)| = 0$, it follows that $|f(x, y) - g(x)| \leqq \epsilon$ for all x in S and y in $N(b)$.

2. Interchange of Order in Repeated Limits.—When

$$\lim_{y=b} f(x, y) = g(x)$$

and $\lim_{x=a} g(x) = C$ exist, we may call this value C a **repeated limit** of $f(x, y)$ and write

$$\lim_{x=a} \lim_{y=b} f(x, y) = C.$$

When $\lim_{y=b} f(x, y)$ does not exist, we may use the notation

$$\overline{\underline{\lim}}_{y=b} f(x, y)$$

for the multiple-valued function $g(x)$ having the two values $\limsup_{y=b} f(x, y)$ and $\liminf_{y=b} f(x, y)$, (and values in between if desired). Then when $\lim_{x=a} g(x) = C$ exists, we may write

$$\lim_{x=a} \overline{\underline{\lim}}_{y=b} f(x, y) = C$$

and call this a **generalized repeated limit.**

The following fundamental theorem on interchange of order of repeated limits is frequently called the "Moore theorem" (or the Moore-Osgood theorem).[1] Its proof is given following Theorem 3, with indications of possible weakening of the hypotheses.

THEOREM 2. **The Moore theorem.** *Suppose that the functions $f(x, y)$, $g(x)$, and $h(y)$ are all real-finite-valued and that*

(2:1) $\qquad \lim_{x=a} f(x, y) = h(y)$ *on* T,

(2:2) $\qquad \lim_{y=b} f(x, y) = g(x)$ *uniformly on* S.

Then the limits

$$\lim_{\substack{x=a \\ y=b}} f(x, y), \qquad \lim_{x=a} g(x), \qquad \lim_{y=b} h(y)$$

all exist and are equal and finite.

[1] See E. H. Moore, "Lectures on Advanced Integral Calculus" (Unpublished), University of Chicago, Autumn Quarter, 1900. Manuscript in University of Chicago library, worked out by Oswald Veblen. See also W. F. Osgood, *Funktionentheorie*, Vol. I, (1907), p. 519, for the special case of double sequences.

Theorem 3. *Suppose that*

$$\lim_{\substack{x=a\\y=b}} f(x, y) = C.$$

Then the generalized repeated limits

$$\lim_{x=a} \overline{\lim_{y=b}} f(x, y), \qquad \lim_{y=b} \overline{\lim_{x=a}} f(x, y)$$

also exist and are equal to C.

Theorem 3 follows immediately from the definitions.

For more general theorems, giving necessary and sufficient conditions for the existence and equality of the generalized repeated limits, see Hobson [1], Vol. I, pages 409–414.

Proof of Theorem 2.—We replace (2:2) by the weaker hypothesis

$$(2:3) \qquad \lim_{\substack{x=a\\y=b}} [f(x, y) - g(x)] = 0.$$

Since

$$(2:4) \qquad \underline{\lim}_{x=a} [f(x, y) - g(x)] = h(y) - \overline{\lim_{x=a}}\, g(x),$$

$$(2:5) \qquad \overline{\lim_{x=a}} [f(x, y) - g(x)] = h(y) - \underline{\lim}_{x=a}\, g(x),$$

we find by Theorem 3 that

$$\lim_{y=b} h(y) = \overline{\lim_{x=a}}\, g(x) = \underline{\lim}_{x=a}\, g(x),$$

and this with (2:3) gives the desired conclusion.

We could also replace (2:1) by the weaker hypothesis that

$$\lim_{y=b} [\overline{\lim_{x=a}} f(x, y) - \underline{\lim}_{x=a} f(x, y)] = 0,$$

where the upper and lower limits are finite-valued functions, and still obtain the existence of $\lim_{\substack{x=a\\y=b}} f(x, y)$. Then in the proof (2:4) and (2:5) would need to be replaced by inequalities obtained from Theorem 14 of Chap. IV.

We include the following extension of the Moore theorem, since it is sometimes useful to know that uniformity with respect to a parameter is preserved for the limits occurring in that theorem.

THEOREM 4. *Suppose that the functions $f(x, y, z)$, $g(x, z)$, and $h(y, z)$ are all real-finite-valued for x in S, y in T, and z in U, and that*

$$\lim_{x=a} f(x, y, z) = h(y, z) \text{ uniformly on } U \text{ for each } y \text{ in } T,$$
$$\lim_{y=b} f(x, y, z) = g(x, z) \text{ uniformly on } SU.$$

Then $\lim_{\substack{x=a\\y=b}} f(x, y, z) = \lim_{x=a} g(x, z) = \lim_{y=b} h(y, z)$ *uniformly on* U.

Proof.—Let $C(z)$ denote the common value of the three limits in the conclusion. If $|f(x, y, z) - g(x, z)| < \epsilon$ for all y in $N(b)$, x in S, and z in U, and $|f(x, y, z) - h(y, z)| < \epsilon$ for all y in $N(b)$, x in a neighborhood $N_y(a)$ depending on y, and z in U, then $|h(y, z) - g(x, z)| < 2\epsilon$ for all y in $N(b)$, x in $N_y(a)$, and z in U. Hence $|h(y, z) - C(z)| \leqq 2\epsilon$ for all y in $N(b)$ and z in U. If we fix y_1 in $N(b)$, we then find $|g(x, z) - C(z)| < 4\epsilon$ for all x in $N_1(a) = N_{y_1}(a)$ and for all z in U, and finally $|f(x, y, z) - C(z)| < 5\epsilon$ for all x in $N_1(a)$, y in $N(b)$, and z in U.

A function $f(x, y)$ is said to be **continuous in** y **at** $y = b$ **uniformly for** x in S in case b is a point of T, $f(x, b)$ is finite and $\lim_{y=b} f(x, y) = f(x, b)$ uniformly for x in S.

THEOREM 5. *Suppose $f(x, y)$ is continuous in y at $y = b$ uniformly for x in S, and continuous in x at $x = a$ for each y in T. Then $f(x, y)$ is continuous in (x, y) at (a, b).*

This follows immediately from Theorem 2. An example of a function that is continuous in x for each y and continuous in y for each x, but not continuous in (x, y) at $(0, 0)$, is obtained by setting $f(x, y) = xy^2/(x^2 + y^4)$ for $(x, y) \neq (0, 0)$, $f(0, 0) = 0$. In this example, f approaches zero along every ray through the origin.

The next theorem is closely related to Theorem 5 and is also an immediate corollary of Theorem 2. The reader should note the special case when $f(x, y)$ is replaced by $f_n(x)$, and $b = +\infty$.

THEOREM 6. *Suppose $f(x, y)$ is continuous in x at $x = a$ for each y in T, and $\lim_{y=b} f(x, y) = g(x)$ uniformly on S, where $g(x)$ has finite values. Then $g(x)$ is continuous at $x = a$.*

The next two theorems are concerned with interchange of order of limit and integral, and of limit and derivative, respectively. In them we shall suppose that the range S of the variable x is a closed interval $[\alpha, \beta]$ of one-dimensional space.

THEOREM 7. *Let $f(x, y)$ be R-integrable on $[\alpha, \beta]$ for each y in T, and suppose that $\lim_{y=b} f(x, y) = g(x)$ uniformly on $[\alpha, \beta]$. Then $g(x)$ is R-integrable on $[\alpha, \beta]$, and*

$$\int_\alpha^\beta g(x)\,dx = \lim_{y=b} \int_\alpha^\beta f(x, y)\,dx.$$

Proof.—Since $f(x, y)$ is bounded as a function of x for each y, it is easily seen that $g(x)$ is also bounded. Now let (y_n) be a sequence of values chosen from T such that $\lim_{n=\infty} y_n = b$. Let D_n be the set of discontinuities of the function $f(x, y_n)$, and D that of $g(x)$. Then D is contained in the sum of the sets D_n, by Theorem 6. Each D_n has measure zero, by Theorem 7 of Chap. VI, and so is enclosable in a set of intervals the sum of whose lengths is less than $\epsilon/2^n$. Thus D is enclosable in a set of intervals the sum of whose lengths is less than ϵ, and so D also has measure zero. Hence $g(x)$ is R-integrable, again by Theorem 7 of Chap. VI. By Theorem 8 of Chap. VI we have

$$\left|\int_\alpha^\beta [f(x, y) - g(x)]\,dx\right| \leqq (\beta - \alpha) \text{ l.u.b. } |f(x, y) - g(x)| \quad \text{for } \alpha \leqq x \leqq \beta,$$

and from this and the hypothesis of uniform convergence the desired conclusion follows immediately.

When the convergence is not uniform, the conclusion in Theorem 7 sometimes fails. For example, if the sequence (x_i) is a denumeration of the rational numbers in the interval $[\alpha, \beta]$, and $f_n(x_i) = 1$ for $i = 1, \cdots, n$, $f_n(x) = 0$ for all other values of x, then $\lim_{n=\infty} f_n(x)$ is not R-integrable. However, if $f_n(x) = 1$ for $\alpha < x < \alpha + 1/n$, $f_n(x) = 0$ for all other values of x, then $\lim_{n=\infty} f_n(x) = 0$, and $\lim_{n=\infty} \int_\alpha^\beta f_n(x)\,dx = 0$.

THEOREM 8. *Let $f(x, y)$ have a finite partial derivative $f_x(x, y)$ for each y in T and x on $[\alpha, \beta]$. Let x_0 be a point of $[\alpha, \beta]$ at which $\lim_{y=b} f(x_0, y)$ exists and is finite, and suppose that $\lim_{y=b} f_x(x, y) = h(x)$ uniformly on $[\alpha, \beta]$. Then there exists the finite limit $\lim_{y=b} f(x, y)$*

$\equiv g(x)$ *uniformly on* $[\alpha, \beta]$, *and* $g(x)$ *has a derivative* $g'(x) = h(x)$ *on* $[\alpha, \beta]$.

Proof.—From the Cauchy condition, we have

$$(2:6) \qquad \begin{aligned} &\lim_{\substack{y_1=b\\ y_2=b}} [f(x_0, y_1) - f(x_0, y_2)] = 0, \\ &\lim_{\substack{y_1=b\\ y_2=b}} [f_x(x, y_1) - f_x(x, y_2)] = 0 \text{ uniformly on } [\alpha, \beta]. \end{aligned}$$

Let c be an arbitrary point of $[\alpha, \beta]$, and set

$$F(x, y) = \frac{f(x, y) - f(c, y)}{x - c},$$

for $x \neq c$. By applying the Theorem of the Mean to the function $f(x, y_1) - f(x, y_2)$, first on the interval from x_0 to x, and then on the interval from c to x, we find

$$(2:7) \qquad \begin{aligned} f(x, y_1) - f(x, y_2) &= [f_x(\bar{x}, y_1) - f_x(\bar{x}, y_2)](x - x_0) \\ &\qquad + f(x_0, y_1) - f(x_0, y_2), \\ F(x, y_1) - F(x, y_2) &= f_x(x^*, y_1) - f_x(x^*, y_2), \end{aligned}$$

where $\bar{x}$ and x^* depend on x, y_1, and y_2. Thus from (2:6) and (2:7) and the Cauchy condition, we obtain the first part of the conclusion, and also

$$\lim_{y=b} F(x, y) = \frac{g(x) - g(c)}{x - c} \text{ uniformly.}$$

From this we obtain the desired result by use of Theorem 2.

The reader who is familiar with the theory of functions of a complex variable will recall that when x is a complex variable ranging over a region S of the complex plane, $f(x, y)$ has a derivative $f_x(x, y)$ for x in S and y in T, and $\lim_{y=b} f(x, y) = g(x)$ uniformly on S, then $g(x)$ must be analytic and $\lim_{y=b} f_x(x, y) = g'(x)$ uniformly on S_1, where S_1 is an arbitrary closed region interior to S. It is important to have clearly in mind the difference between this result and Theorem 8.

The next theorems are concerned with the continuity of functions defined by integrals depending on a parameter, and with formulas for the integrals and derivatives of such functions.

THEOREM 9. *Suppose that* $f(x, y)$ *is integrable on* $\alpha \leqq x \leqq \beta$ *for each* y *in a set* T, *and that* $f(x, y)$ *is continuous in* y *at* $y = b$

uniformly for x *on* $[\alpha, \beta]$. *Then the function*

$$g(y, z, w) \equiv \int_z^w f(x, y)\, dx$$

is continuous in (y, z, w) *at* $y = b$ *for* z *and* w *in* $[\alpha, \beta]$.

Proof.—Since

$$\int_z^w f\, dx = \int_\alpha^w f\, dx - \int_\alpha^z f\, dx,$$

it is clearly sufficient to consider the function

$$h(y, w) \equiv \int_\alpha^w f(x, y)\, dx.$$

If $|f(x, y) - f(x, b)| \leqq \epsilon$ for $\alpha \leqq x \leqq \beta$, then $|h(y, w) - h(b, w)| \leqq \epsilon|\beta - \alpha|$ by Theorem 8 of Chap. VI, so that $h(y, w)$ is continuous in y at $y = b$ uniformly for w on $[\alpha, \beta]$. By Theorem 9 of Chap. VI, $h(y, w)$ is continuous in w for each y. Hence h is continuous in the two variables together, by Theorem 5.

The next theorem, on interchange of order for iterated integrals, is a very special one. We restrict attention to this case here because we have not considered multiple Riemann integrals. A much more general theorem will be given in terms of Lebesgue integrals in Chap. XI.

THEOREM 10. *Suppose* $f(x, y)$ *is continuous in* (x, y) *on* $\alpha \leqq x \leqq \beta$, $\gamma \leqq y \leqq \delta$. *Then*

$$\int_\alpha^\beta \int_\gamma^\delta f(x, y)\, dy\, dx = \int_\gamma^\delta \int_\alpha^\beta f(x, y)\, dx\, dy.$$

Proof.—The function f is uniformly continuous, by Theorem 23 of Chap. IV, and the two iterated integrals always exist, by Theorem 9, and Theorem 7 of Chap. VI. Let η be a positive number such that $|f(x, y) - f(x', y')| < \epsilon$ for $|x - x'| < \eta$, $|y - y'| < \eta$. Then if P_x is a partition of $[\alpha, \beta]$ with intervals denoted by Δx_i, and P_y is a partition of $[\gamma, \delta]$ with intervals denoted by Δy_j, and if $N(P_x) < \eta$, $N(P_y) < \eta$, we have

$$\begin{aligned}\Big|\sum_j \sum_i f(x_i, y_j)\, \Delta x_i\, \Delta y_j - \sum_j \int_\alpha^\beta f(x, y_j)\, dx\, \Delta y_j\Big| \\ = \Big|\sum_j \sum_i \int_{\Delta x_i} [f(x_i, y_j) - f(x, y_j)]\, dx\, \Delta y_j\Big| \\ \leqq \epsilon(\beta - \alpha)(\delta - \gamma).\end{aligned}$$

By combining this result with a similar one in which the roles of x and y are interchanged, we find that

$$\left|\sum_j \int_\alpha^\beta f(x, y_j)\, dx\, \Delta y_j - \sum_i \int_\gamma^\delta f(x_i, y)\, dy\, \Delta x_i\right| \leqq 2\epsilon(\beta - \alpha)(\delta - \gamma).$$

From this the equality of the two integrals readily follows.

THEOREM 11. *Suppose that $f(x, y)$ and its partial derivative $f_y(x, y)$ are continuous in (x, y) on $\alpha \leqq x \leqq \beta$, $\gamma \leqq y \leqq \delta$. Let $g(y)$ and $h(y)$ be defined and have finite derivatives at b, and let $\gamma < b < \delta$, $\alpha < g(b) < \beta$, $\alpha < h(b) < \beta$. Then the function*

$$F(y) \equiv \int_{g(y)}^{h(y)} f(x, y)\, dx$$

has a derivative at b, and

$$F'(b) = \int_{g(b)}^{h(b)} f_y(x, b)\, dx + f[h(b), b]h'(b) - f[g(b), b]g'(b).$$

Proof.—Let us set

$$G(y, z, w) \equiv \int_z^w f(x, y)\, dx.$$

Then by the Theorem of the Mean,

$$\frac{G(y, z, w) - G(b, z, w)}{y - b} - \int_z^w f_y(x, b)\, dx = \int_z^w \{f_y[x, \bar{y}(x)] - f_y(x, b)\}\, dx,$$

where $\bar{y}(x)$ lies between y and b. By the uniform continuity of $f_y(x, y)$, this expression approaches zero with $(y - b)$. Hence G has a partial derivative

$$G_y(y, z, w) = \int_z^w f_y(x, y)\, dx,$$

since in the above argument, b may be any value between γ and δ, and G_y is continuous by Theorem 9. The partial derivative $G_w = f(w, y)$, and $G_z = -f(z, y)$, by Theorem 9 of Chap. VI, and these are continuous functions by hypothesis. Thus G has a total differential by Theorem 12 of Chap. V, and then $F'(b)$ exists and has the value stated, by Theorem 13 of Chap. V.

EXERCISES

1. Prove the following theorem: Let $f(x)$ have a derivative $f'(x)$ which is continuous on $[a, b]$. Then

$$\lim_{h=0} \frac{f(x+h) - f(x)}{h} = f'(x) \text{ uniformly on } [a, b].$$

2. Discuss the existence of the following limits and of the associated repeated limits:

$$(a) \lim_{\substack{x=0\\y=0}} \frac{xy}{x^2+y^2}; \quad (b) \lim_{\substack{x=+\infty\\y=+\infty}} \frac{x}{x+y}; \quad (c) \lim_{\substack{m=\infty\\n=\infty}} (-1)^{m+n}[2^{-m} + 2^{-n}].$$

3. Discuss the applicability of Theorems 7 and 8 to the case where $f_n(x) = n^\lambda x \exp(-n^\mu x^2)$, for various values of λ and μ, in particular:
(a) $\lambda = 0, \mu > 0$;
(b) $\lambda > 0, \mu > 2\lambda$;
(c) $0 < \mu < 2\lambda < 2\mu$.

3. Infinite Series.—If $\sum a_i$ is an infinite series of real numbers, let s_m denote the sum of the first m terms. The series $\sum a_i$ is said to be **convergent** in case the corresponding sequence (s_m) of partial sums has a finite limit. The series is said to be **divergent** in case $\lim s_m$ is infinite. In either case the **sum of the series** is by definition equal to $\lim s_m$. When $\lim s_m$ does not exist, the series is said to be **oscillatory.**

This section will be devoted to the theory of convergent series. However, divergent and oscillatory series have their uses and, to indicate the nature of those uses, some remarks will be included at the end of the section on methods of summation for oscillatory series, and on computation and the study of functions by the use of oscillatory or divergent series.

It is clear that a series is, like a sequence, a function whose domain is the class of natural numbers. The difference lies in the operations that are, if possible, to be performed. In view of the above definition, every theorem concerned with infinite sequences and their limits can be translated into a corresponding theorem on infinite series. The selection of a subsequence from the sequence (s_m) corresponds to a **grouping of the terms** of the series $\sum a_i$. When lim s_m exists, every subsequence has the same limit. Hence the grouping of terms in a convergent series cannot affect the value of the sum. But for each accumulation point c of the sequence (s_m) there is a method of grouping the terms of the series $\sum a_i$ to form a series $\sum b_i$ whose sum is c. For example, the terms of the oscillatory series $\sum a_i$, where $a_i = (-1)^i$, can be grouped to obtain the sum -1 or the sum 0.

A **rearrangement** of a series $\sum a_i$ is effected by a one-to-one transformation (i_j) of the class $\mathfrak{M}$ of natural numbers into itself. The rearranged series may be denoted by $\sum b_j$, where $b_j = a_{i_j}$. For example, a rearrangement of the series $1 - \frac{1}{2} + \frac{1}{3} - \frac{1}{4} + \ldots$ is obtained by taking first the first term with a negative sign, next the first 10 terms with positive sign, then the second term with negative sign, then the next 10^2 terms with positive sign, then the third term with negative sign, then the next 10^3 terms with positive sign, and so on, with no terms omitted or repeated. In this case the original series converges while the rearranged series diverges to $+\infty$.

A series $\sum a_i$ is said to **converge unconditionally** when every rearrangement of it converges and has the same sum. A series $\sum a_i$ is said to **converge absolutely** when $\sum |a_i|$ converges.

THEOREM 12. *A necessary and sufficient condition for a series $\sum a_i$ of nonnegative terms to converge is that the sequence of partial sums be bounded.*

An immediate corollary of this theorem is the comparison test for series of nonnegative terms.

THEOREM 13. *If a series of nonnegative terms converges, it converges unconditionally.*

Proof.—Let $\sum b_i$ be a rearrangement of $\sum a_i$, and let $\sum a_i = S$. Let t_m denote the sum of the first m terms of the series $\sum b_i$. Then $m \cdot \supset \cdot \exists p \ni \cdot\ t_m \leqq s_p \leqq S$. Thus the sequence (t_m) is monotonic and bounded and has a limit $T \leqq S$. In the same way it follows that $S \leqq T$.

THEOREM 14. *Let $\sum a_i$ be a series that converges but does not converge absolutely. Let C be an arbitrary point of the interval*

$[-\infty, +\infty]$. *Then there exists a rearrangement* $\sum b_i$ *of the series whose sum is* C.

Proof.—Let $c_i = (|a_i| + a_i)/2$, $d_i = (|a_i| - a_i)/2$. Then $c_i + d_i = |a_i|$, $c_i - d_i = a_i$. Since $\sum a_i$ converges but $\sum |a_i|$ diverges, it follows that $\sum c_i$ and $\sum d_i$ both diverge, although $\lim a_i = \lim c_i = \lim d_i = 0$. Let t_m denote the sum of the first m terms of the rearrangement $\sum b_i$ which is to be determined. Then we may select for the first k_1 terms of the series $\sum b_i$, the first k_1 nonnegative terms of the series $\sum a_i$, where k_1 is the minimum integer for which $t_{k_1} > C$ if C is finite, $t_{k_1} > 1$ if $C = +\infty$, and where $k_1 = 1$ if $C = -\infty$. For the next $(k_2 - k_1)$ terms of $\sum b_i$, select the first $(k_2 - k_1)$ negative terms of $\sum a_i$, where k_2 is the minimum integer greater than k_1 for which $t_{k_2} < C$ if C is finite, $t_{k_2} < -2$ if $C = -\infty$, and where $k_2 = k_1 + 1$ if $C = +\infty$. For the next $(k_3 - k_2)$ terms of $\sum b_i$, select the first $(k_3 - k_2)$ nonnegative terms of $\sum a_i$ not already used, where k_3 is the minimum integer greater than k_2 such that $t_{k_3} > C$ if C is finite, $t_{k_3} > 3$ if $C = +\infty$, and where $k_3 = k_2 + 1$ if $C = -\infty$. The rearrangement $\sum b_i$ is defined by the indefinite continuation of these alternate selections of positive and negative terms. When C is infinite, clearly $\sum b_i = C$. When C is finite and $k_j \leqq m < k_{j+1}$, $|t_m - C| \leqq |b_{k_j}|$ and $\lim b_{k_j} = 0$ since $\lim a_i = 0$.

THEOREM 15. *A series* $\sum a_i$ *converges unconditionally if and only if it converges absolutely.*

Proof.—Let $\sum c_i$ and $\sum d_i$ be the series introduced in the proof of Theorem 14. Then if $\sum |a_i|$ converges, $\sum c_i$ and $\sum d_i$ also converge, by the comparison test, and hence $\sum a_i$ converges. The convergence is unconditional, by Theorem 13. An unconditionally convergent series must converge absolutely, by Theorem 14.

It follows from the preceding theorems that, when every rearrangement of a given series converges, they must all have the same sum.

We next take up some fundamental notions concerning series of functions. Let the functions $u_i(x)$ be single-real-finite valued on the set S. The series $\sum u_i(x)$ is said to **converge absolutely-uniformly on** S in case $\sum |u_i(x)|$ converges uniformly on S. The series $\sum u_i(x)$ is said to **converge unconditionally-uniformly** on S in case every rearrangement of $\sum u_i(x)$ converges uniformly on S.

THEOREM 16. *If $\sum u_i(x)$ converges absolutely-uniformly on S, then $\sum u_i(x)$ converges unconditionally-uniformly on S, and conversely.*

Proof.—Let $\sum v_j(x)$ be a rearrangement of $\sum u_i(x)$. By the Cauchy condition for uniform convergence (Theorem 1),

$$\epsilon > 0 : \supset : \exists m \ni : p \geqq m \,.\, x \text{ in } s \cdot \supset \cdot \sum_{i=m}^{p} |u_i(x)| < \epsilon.$$

For each m there is an integer n such that the functions $u_1, \ldots, u_{m-1}$ are among the functions $v_1, \ldots, v_{n-1}$ in the rearrangement, and for each q there is an integer p such that the functions $v_1, \ldots, v_q$ are among the functions $u_1, \ldots, u_p$. Then

$$q \geqq n \,.\, x \text{ in } S \cdot \supset \cdot \left|\sum_{j=n}^{q} v_j(x)\right| \leqq \sum_{i=m}^{p} |u_i(x)| < \epsilon.$$

Thus we have verified the Cauchy condition for the uniform convergence of the rearrangement $\sum v_j(x)$.

To prove the converse, let us suppose that the series $\sum |u_i(x)|$ does not converge uniformly. Then by the Cauchy condition,

$$(3:1) \qquad \exists \epsilon > 0 \ni : m \cdot \supset \cdot \exists p \geqq m \cdot \exists x \ni \cdot \sum_{i=m}^{p} |u_i(x)| > \epsilon.$$

Let $m_1 = 1$, and let p_1 and x_1 be the corresponding values of p and x given by (3:1). When m_k, p_k, and x_k have been determined, let $m_{k+1} > p_k$, and let p_{k+1} and x_{k+1} be the corresponding values of p and x given by (3:1). We can now show how to obtain a rearrangement $\sum v_j(x)$ which does not converge uniformly, as follows. In the group of terms

$$\sum_{i=m_k}^{p_k} u_i(x)$$

let us rearrange the terms so that those which are positive at x_k come first, and those which are negative at x_k come last. Let the sum of the first group be denoted by A_k^+, and the sum of the second group by A_k^-. Then

$$\sum_{j=m_k}^{p_k} v_j(x_k) = A_k^+ + A_k^-, \qquad \sum_{i=m_k}^{p_k} |u_i(x_k)| = A_k^+ - A_k^- > \epsilon,$$

and hence either $A_k^+ > \epsilon/2$ or $A_k^- < -\epsilon/2$. Thus by the Cauchy condition, $\sum v_j(x)$ cannot converge uniformly.

The next theorem gives a useful sufficient condition for absolute-uniform convergence. It is frequently called the "Weierstrass M-test." It is an immediate corollary of the Cauchy condition.

THEOREM 17. *If the series $\sum M_i$ converges and if $|u_i(x)| \leqq M_i$ for every x in S and every i, then $\sum u_i(x)$ converges absolutely-uniformly on S.*

We shall now consider an example of a series that converges absolutely and uniformly but not absolutely-uniformly. Consequently, by Theorem 16, it may be rearranged to form a series that does not converge uniformly. Let

$$\begin{aligned} u_i(x) &= (-x)^i/i \qquad &&\text{for } 0 \leqq x < 1, \\ &= 0 &&\text{for } x = 1. \end{aligned}$$

The series obviously converges absolutely. To show that it converges uniformly, we may use Abel's identity, which may be expressed as follows. Let

$$A_{pq} = \sum_{i=p}^{q} a_i, \qquad B_{pq} = \sum_{i=p}^{q} a_i t_i,$$

where $p \leqq q$. Then

$$B_{pq} = t_p A_{pp} + \sum_{i=p+1}^{q} (A_{pi} - A_{p,i-1})t_i$$
$$= \sum_{i=p}^{q-1} A_{pi}(t_i - t_{i+1}) + A_{pq}t_q.$$

To treat our example, set $a_i = (-1)^i/i$, $t_i = x^i$. Then for $0 \leqq x < 1$ we have

$$\left|\sum_{i=p}^{q} u_i(x)\right| = |B_{pq}| = \left|\sum_{i=p}^{q-1} A_{pi}(x^i - x^{i+1}) + A_{pq}x^q\right|$$
$$\leqq \sum_{i=p}^{q-1} |A_{pi}|(x^i - x^{i+1}) + |A_{pq}|x^q$$
$$\leqq M_p x^p < M_p,$$

where $M_p =$ l.u.b. $|A_{pi}|$ for $i \geqq p$. Since $\sum a_i$ converges, $\lim M_p = 0$, and $\sum u_i(x)$ converges uniformly, by the Cauchy condition. To show that the series does not converge absolutely-uniformly, we note that, since $\sum |a_i|$ does not converge,

$$p \cdot \supset \cdot \exists q > p \ni \cdot \sum_{i=p}^{q} |a_i| > 1,$$

and hence

$$\exists x \ni \cdot \sum_{i=p}^{q} |u_i(x)| > 1.$$

For other examples see Hobson [1], Vol. 2, page 119, example (7); Pierpont [2], Vol. 2, page 165. The proof given for the uniform convergence of the series in the example above may be generalized to give a useful criterion for uniform convergence of a series, as on page 117 of Hobson.

The theorems on series may be extended to multiple series.(1) We shall restrict ourselves here to a brief consideration of double

1 See, for example, Hobson [1], Vol. 2, pp. 49–56; Pierpont [2], Vol. 2, Chap. 4; Reid [8], Chap. 4.

series. Let the double series be denoted by $\sum a_{ij}$, and let

$$s_{mn} = \sum_{i=1}^{m} \sum_{j=1}^{n} a_{ij}.$$

When the row series converge, we may let

$$s_{m\infty} = \sum_{i=1}^{m} \sum_{j=1}^{\infty} a_{ij}.$$

By definition, a double series $\sum a_{ij}$ is **convergent** in case $\lim_{m=\infty, n=\infty} s_{mn}$ exists and is finite. The series is **convergent by rows** in case the row series converge, and $\lim_{m=\infty} s_{m\infty}$ exists and is finite. The definition for **convergence by columns** is analogous.

Other definitions for convergence of double series have been used,[1] but the one given above is the commonly accepted one. We may also consider convergence by rows and convergence by columns in the generalized sense corresponding to that given for repeated limits in Sec. 2.

THEOREM 18. *A necessary and sufficient condition for a double series $\sum a_{ij}$ of nonnegative terms to converge is that the partial sums s_{mn} are bounded.*

Proof.—If $m < n$, we have $s_{mm} \leqq s_{mn} \leqq s_{nn}$. The sequence (s_{nn}), being monotonic, has a limit S, which by the preceding inequalities is also the limit of the double sequence (s_{mn}). It is clear that S is finite if and only if (s_{mn}) is bounded.

THEOREM 19. *If a double series $\sum a_{ij}$ is absolutely convergent, then the series*

1. *Converges,*
2. *Converges by rows,*
3. *Converges by columns,*
4. *Converges when arranged as a simple series in any order.*

Moreover, the sums so obtained are all equal.

Proof.—As indicated in the proof of Theorem 14, the given series may be represented as the difference of two series of nonnegative terms, and each of these will be convergent when the

[1] See, for example, Jordan [4], Vol. 1, Chap. 3, No. 316.

given series is absolutely convergent. Hence we may suppose $a_{ij} \geqq 0$, and let S denote the sum of the series, $\sum b_i$ an arrangement as a simple series, and

$$t_q = \sum_{i=1}^{q} b_i.$$

Then $s_{mn} \leqq S$, $t_q \leqq S$, and from these inequalities the conclusions (2), (3), and (4) follow, by Theorem 12. Moreover, $s_{mn} \leqq s_{m\infty}$ and $s_{mn} \leqq t_q$ if q is sufficiently large. Hence $\lim s_{m\infty} = S$, $\lim t_q = S$.

Another criterion for the existence and equality of the sum, the sum by rows, and the sum by columns, of a double series may be obtained from Theorem 2. Other types of theorems may be found in the references at the end of the chapter.

*There are several useful methods for assigning a value to an infinite series which apply to some oscillatory series $\sum a_j$ such as the one for which $a_j = (-1)^j$. Perhaps the simplest of these is the method of arithmetic means. If (s_m) is the sequence of partial sums of the series $\sum a_j$, and the associated sequence of arithmetic means

$$t_m = \frac{1}{m} \sum_{j=1}^{m} s_j$$

has a finite limit L, the series $\sum a_j$ is said to be **summable** $(C, 1)$ or $(H, 1)$ to the value L. When the sequence of arithmetic means of the sequence (t_m) has the limit L, the series $\sum a_j$ is said to be **summable** $(H, 2)$ to the value L. This use of successive applications of the process of taking arithmetic means was developed by Hölder. Cesàro suggested a different extension of the method of arithmetic means. It has since been proved that the methods of Cesàro and of Hölder give the same result. Several other methods of summation have been invented by other mathematicians. (See Hobson [1], Vol. II, Chap. 1; Knopp [7], Chap. 13; Fort [6], Chap. 17.) An essential requirement for the acceptability of a method of summation is that the value it associates with a convergent series shall be the ordinary sum of that series.

*The theory of summability has applications in connection with Fourier series. The Fourier series for a given function $f(x)$ may fail to converge for some values of x, but under certain conditions the value of the function may still be recovered from the series by a suitable method of summation. A similar statement holds for power series. The series

$$1 - x + x^2 - x^3 + \cdots$$

converges to $1/(1 + x)$ for $-1 < x < 1$, and it is summable $(C, 1)$ to the value of that function for $x = 1$. This suggests the Abel method of summation. If $\sum a_j$ is such that the corresponding power series $\sum a_j x^j$ converges for $|x| < 1$ to $f(x)$, and if the left-hand limit $f(1 - 0)$ exists and is finite, the series $\sum a_j$ is said to be **summable** (A) to the value $f(1 - 0)$.

*Although convergent series are of predominant importance in mathematical theory, oscillatory and divergent series are frequently of practical use in computation. If a certain number of terms of a series are to be used to compute a function, some assurance is needed that the error committed lies within the required limits, but the convergence of the series is quite irrelevant. A convergent series may converge too slowly to be of practical use, or a convenient formula for the remainder may be unobtainable. A class of nonconvergent series which is also useful in mathematical theory, for example in studying the properties of functions defined by differential equations, is the class of asymptotic series.[1] A series $\sum_{k=0}^{\infty} a_k x^{-k}$ is said to represent a function $f(x)$ **asymptotically** on the positive end of the x-axis in case

$$\lim_{x=+\infty} [f(x) - s_n(x)]x^n = 0 \quad \text{for } n = 0, 1, 2, \cdots,$$

where $s_n(x) = \sum_{k=0}^{n} a_k x^{-k}$. This definition may be generalized in various ways; in particular, by allowing the variable x to be complex.

[1] See Knopp [7], Chap. 14; Fort [6], Chap. 18; Ince, *Differential Equations*, pp. 169*ff.*; Schlesinger, *Einführung in die Theorie der gewöhnlichen Differentialgleichungen*, 3d Ed., 1922, pp. 257*ff.*

Exercise

State the theorems corresponding to Theorems 1, 6, 7, and 8 in terms of series.

4. The Space of Continuous Functions.—Let S be a set of points in k-dimensional space, and let $\mathfrak{C}$ denote the class of all real-valued functions f that are continuous on S. The class $\mathfrak{C}$ is a **linear set** in the sense that it contains the sum of every pair of its elements and the product of each of its elements by an arbitrary real number. It also contains the product of every pair of its elements and is closed under two additional operations which we shall introduce. If f_1 and f_2 are two functions, let $f_1 \vee f_2$ denote the function whose value for each x is the greater of $f_1(x)$ and $f_2(x)$, and let $f_1 \wedge f_2$ denote the function whose value for each x is the lesser of $f_1(x)$ and $f_2(x)$. The results of these two operations may be called "logical sum" and "logical product," respectively, following Daniell,[1] or "join" and "meet" following a usage of lattice theory. The class $\mathfrak{C}$ is easily seen to be closed under these operations.

It is frequently desirable to extend the domain of a function f which is continuous on S, *i.e.*, to determine a function g which is continuous on a set T including S and such that $g(x) = f(x)$ on S. Such a function g will be called an **extension of f to be continuous on T.**

A function $\phi(t)$ defined for $0 < t < \infty$ is called a **modulus of continuity** of a function $f(x)$ with domain S in case[2]

$$0 < t < \infty \,.\, x \text{ in } S \,.\, x' \text{ in } S \,.\, \|x - x'\| \leqq t \cdot \supset \cdot |f(x) - f(x')| \leqq \phi(t).$$

The **least modulus of continuity** of $f(x)$ is the function $\phi_0(t)$ whose value for each t is the greatest lower bound of the values of such functions $\phi(t)$. It is clear that the function $\phi_0(t)$ is nondecreasing and nonnegative. Moreover, $f(x)$ is uniformly continuous on S if and only if $\lim\limits_{t=0} \phi_0(t) = 0$.

A function $\phi(t)$ will be said to be **concave** in case the set of points of the (t, u)-plane for which ϕ is defined and $u \leqq \phi(t)$ is a

[1] See *Annals of Mathematics*, Vol. 19 (1918), p. 280.

[2] The notation $\|x\|$ for the norm or modulus of a point was introduced in Sec. 2 of Chap. V.

convex set. A concave function $\phi(t)$ defined for $t \geqq 0$ and having $\phi(0) \geqq 0$ has the property that

$$\phi(t_1 + t_2) \leqq \phi(t_1) + \phi(t_2). \tag{4:1}$$

For, assuming for definiteness $0 < t_1 < t_2$, the point $(t_1 + t_2, \phi(t_1 + t_2))$ must lie on or below the line joining the points $(t_1, \phi(t_1))$ and $(t_2, \phi(t_2))$, and also on or below the line joining the points $(0, 0)$ and $(t_1, \phi(t_1))$. Hence

$$(t_2 - t_1)\phi(t_1 + t_2) \leqq t_2\phi(t_2) - t_1\phi(t_1),$$
$$t_1\phi(t_1 + t_2) \leqq (t_1 + t_2)\phi(t_1).$$

If we add these two inequalities and divide by t_2, we obtain (4:1). It is easily seen that a concave function must be continuous, except possibly at the ends of its interval of definition, and hence the restriction that $0 < t_1 < t_2$ may be removed.

In order to prove our theorem on extension, we shall make use of the following preliminary result.

THEOREM 20. *Suppose that the function $\phi_0(t)$ is defined for $0 < t < \infty$, that there exist constants c and d such that $0 \leqq \phi_0(t) \leqq ct + d$, and that $\lim_{t=0} \phi_0(t) = 0$. Then there exists a function $\phi(t)$ which is (a) concave, (b) not less than $\phi_0(t)$, (c) such that $\lim_{t=0} \phi(t) = 0$. Such a function $\phi(t)$ is automatically continuous and nondecreasing.*

Proof.—The set of points of the (t, u)-plane for which $t > 0$, $u \leqq at + b$ is obviously a convex set. Consequently the product V of all such sets for which $\phi_0(t) \leqq at + b$ is convex. The upper boundary of V defines the desired function $\phi(t)$. It is clear that $\phi_0(t) \leqq \phi(t) \leqq ct + d$. To verify (c), we note that

$$\epsilon > 0 :\supset: \exists \delta > 0 \ni: 0 < t \leqq \delta \cdot\supset\cdot \phi_0(t) \leqq \epsilon,$$
$$\epsilon > 0 \,.\, \delta > 0 :\supset: \exists a > 0 \ni: t > \delta \cdot\supset\cdot at + \epsilon > ct + d.$$

Thus $\phi(t) < at + \epsilon$, and so $\phi(t) < 2\epsilon$ if $t \leqq \epsilon/a$. If ϕ were not monotonic, it would become negative for large values of t.

THEOREM 21. *Suppose that the function f is uniformly continuous on the set S. Then there exists an extension g of f to be continuous on the whole finite portion of space. This extension is uniquely determined on the closure $\bar{S}$ of S. If $\phi(t)$ is a modulus of continuity of f which is concave and approaches zero with t, then the extension g may be required to have $\phi(t)$ as a modulus of con-*

tinuity. If f is bounded, then the extension g may at the same time be required to have the same bounds as f.[1]

Proof.—Suppose first that f is bounded. Then its least modulus of continuity is bounded, so that by Theorem 20 it has a modulus of continuity $\phi(t)$ which is concave and approaches zero with t, and hence is continuous and nondecreasing. Let $\phi(0) = 0$, and

$$g(x) \equiv \text{l.u.b. } [f(y) - \phi(\|x - y\|)] \quad \text{for } y \text{ in } S.$$

Then when x is in S, $f(y) - \phi(\|x - y\|) \leqq f(x)$, so that $g(x) = f(x)$. The function g clearly has only finite values, and by Theorem 14 of Chap. IV,

$$g(x) - g(x') \leqq \text{l.u.b. } [\phi(\|x' - y\|) - \phi(\|x - y\|)] \quad \text{for } y \text{ in } S.$$

Now $\|x' - y\| \leqq \|x' - x\| + \|x - y\|$, and hence by (4:1), $\phi(\|x' - y\|) \leqq \phi(\|x' - x\|) + \phi(\|x - y\|)$, so that

$$g(x) - g(x') \leqq \phi(\|x' - x\|).$$

Thus ϕ is also a modulus of continuity for the extension g. It is clear that g has the same upper bound as f. Let g_1 be the function that is constant and equal to the lower bound of f, and let $g_2 = g \vee g_1$. Then g_2 satisfies all the requirements and has the same bounds as f.

In case f is unbounded, let us set $K_n = E[\|x\| \leqq n]$, $S_n = SK_n$. By the uniform continuity of f on S, the subset S_n may be divided into a finite number of pieces on each of which the oscillation of f is less than unity. Hence f is bounded on each S_n. Assuming for simplicity that the set S_2 is not null, let f_1 denote the section of the function f whose domain is S_2, and let g_1 denote the extension of f_1 which has the same bounds as f_1, obtained by the method of the first part of the proof. When $f_{n-1}(x)$ and $g_{n-1}(x)$ have been defined, let $f_n(x) = g_{n-1}(x)$ on $K_{n-1} + S_n$, $f_n(x) = f(x)$ on S_{n+1}, and let $g_n(x)$ be the extension of $f_n(x)$. Now let $g(x) = g_n(x)$ on K_n. Then $g(x)$ is seen to have the required properties. The uniqueness of the extension on $\bar{S}$ follows from Theorem 18 of Chap. IV.

If we may take $\phi(t) = Kt^\alpha$, where $0 < \alpha \leqq 1$, then f is said to satisfy a **Hölder condition** (**Lipschitz condition** when $\alpha = 1$).

[1] Compare McShane, "Extension of Range of Functions," *Bulletin of the American Mathematical Society*, Vol. 40 (1934), pp. 837–842.

Thus our theorem shows that a function satisfying such a condition has an extension that also satisfies it. Moreover, the proof in the last paragraph shows that a function f which is continuous on a closed set S has a continuous extension g to the whole of space. Such a function f need not be uniformly continuous on S, although it is so on every S_n.

Let us return to the consideration of the class $\mathfrak{C}$ of functions f continuous on S, and let us suppose hereafter that the set S is bounded and closed. Then we may define the **norm** of f by the formula

$$\|f\| \equiv \text{l.u.b. } |f(x)| \text{ on } S.$$

This norm has two important properties, expressed by the following formulas, which hold for all functions f and g in $\mathfrak{C}$ and all real numbers a.

$$(4{:}2) \qquad \|af\| = |a|\cdot\|f\|,$$

$$(4{:}3) \qquad \|f + g\| \leqq \|f\| + \|g\|.$$

For an easily discovered reason the last inequality is frequently called the "triangle inequality." In terms of the norm the **distance** from f to g is defined to be $\|f - g\|$. The **ϵ-neighborhood** $N(f; \epsilon)$ of a function f is defined to consist of all functions g such that $\|f - g\| < \epsilon$. Thus the class $\mathfrak{C}$ becomes a **linear space,** in which the notion of **function of accumulation** is defined in terms of neighborhoods in the usual way. Along with this are associated automatically the notions of **derived set, closed set, open set,** and so on. By Theorem 1 the space $\mathfrak{C}$ is **complete,** in the sense that every Cauchy sequence in $\mathfrak{C}$ has a limit in $\mathfrak{C}$. But not every bounded set of continuous functions has a function of accumulation, so that to obtain an analogue of the Weierstrass-Bolzano theorem we must introduce another condition.

If D is a subset of the space $\mathfrak{C}$, D is said to be **compact** in case every infinite subset of D has at least one function of accumulation. According to this definition, all finite sets D are compact.

The functions f of a set D are said to be **equicontinuous at a point** b of S in case

$$\lim_{x=b} f(x) = f(b) \text{ uniformly for } f \text{ in } D.$$

They are said to be **equicontinuous on** a subset T of S in case this relation holds for every point b of T. When T is bounded and closed, it is easily shown by means of the Heine-Borel theorem that then $\lim_{x=b} f(x) = f(b)$ uniformly for f in D and b in T. It is also clear that when S is bounded and closed, the functions f are equicontinuous on S if and only if they have a common modulus of continuity $\phi(t)$ which approaches zero with t.

We shall now find it useful to consider some conditions implying uniformity of convergence.

THEOREM 22. *Suppose that the functions $f_m(x)$ are real-finite-valued for x in S and $m = 1, 2, \cdots$, and that*

$$\lim_{x=a} f_m(x) = b_m, \qquad \lim_{\substack{x=a\\ m=\infty}} f_m(x) = c,$$

where b_m and c are also finite. Then $\lim_{x=a} f_m(x) = b_m$ uniformly with respect to m.

Proof.—By Theorem 3, $\lim_m b_m = c$, and thus

$$\epsilon > 0 : \supset : \exists p \,.\, \exists \delta > 0 \ni : m > p \,.\, x \text{ in } N(a;\delta) \cdot \supset \cdot$$
$$|f_m(x) - c| < \epsilon \,.\, |b_m - c| < \epsilon,$$

and hence $|f_m(x) - b_m| < 2\epsilon$. Also

$$\epsilon > 0 \,.\, p : \supset : \exists \beta > 0 \ni : m \leqq p \,.\, x \text{ in } N(a;\beta) \cdot \supset \cdot |f_m(x) - b_m| < 2\epsilon,$$

so that when x is in the smaller of the two neighborhoods $N(a;\beta)$, $N(a;\delta)$, $|f_m(x) - b_m| < 2\epsilon$ for all m.

THEOREM 23. *Suppose that the function $f(x, y)$ is real-finite-valued for x in the closed set S and y in T and suppose that*

$$\lim_{\substack{h=0\\ y=b}} f(x + h, y) = g(x) \text{ on } S,$$

where $g(x)$ is finite. Then

$$\lim_{\substack{h=0\\ y=b}} f(x + h, y) = g(x) \text{ uniformly on } S.$$

Proof.—Since we may take $h = 0$, we have $\lim_{y=b} f(x, y) = g(x)$ for each x in S. Then by Theorem 3, $g(x)$ is continuous on S and, if we set $f(x, b) = g(x)$, $f(x, y)$ is continuous on the closed set for which x is in S and $y = b$, and so is uniformly continuous on that set.

THEOREM 24. *Suppose that the functions $f_m(x)$ are continuous on S for $m = 1, 2, \cdots$, and that $\lim_m f_m(x) = g(x)$ uniformly on S. Then the functions $f_m(x)$ are equicontinuous on S.*

Proof.—By the Moore theorem (Theorem 2),

$$\lim_{\substack{h=0\\ m=\infty}} f_m(x+h) = g(x) \text{ on } S,$$

and then by Theorem 22, $\lim_{h=0} f_m(x+h) = f_m(x)$ uniformly with respect to m.

THEOREM 25. *Suppose that the functions $f_m(x)$ are equicontinuous on the bounded closed set S and that the sequence $(f_m(x))$ converges at each point of a set T whose closure $\bar{T} = S$. Then the sequence $(f_m(x))$ converges uniformly on S.*

Proof.—Let $g(x) = \lim_{m=\infty} f_m(x)$ wherever the limit exists. By the Moore theorem, the three limits

$$\lim_{\substack{h=0\\ m=\infty}} f_m(x+h), \qquad \lim_{h=0} g(x+h), \qquad \lim_{m=\infty} f_m(x),$$

all exist and are finite and equal, where x is in S and $x+h$ is restricted to be in the set T. Hence they also exist without this restriction. Then by Theorem 23 we obtain the desired conclusion.

Another theorem ensuring uniform convergence is due to Dini.

THEOREM 26. *Suppose that the functions $f_m(x)$ and $g(x)$ are continuous on the bounded closed set S. Suppose also that the sequence $f_m(x)$ is monotonic for each x in S, and that $\lim_m f_m(x) = g(x)$ on S. Then $\lim_m f_m(x) = g(x)$ uniformly on S.*

Proof.—It is sufficient to consider the case where $g(x) = 0$. For a fixed x, and $\epsilon > 0$,

$$\exists q \ni\cdot\, |f_q(x)| \leqq \epsilon,$$
$$\exists \delta > 0 \ni: \|h\| < \delta \cdot\supset\cdot\, |f_q(x+h)| \leqq |f_q(x)| + \epsilon,$$

and hence

$$m \geqq q \,.\, \|h\| < \delta \cdot\supset\cdot\, |f_m(x+h)| \leqq 2\epsilon.$$

Thus the hypotheses of Theorem 23 are fulfilled.

In both of the last two theorems, the variable m may be replaced by a more general variable, as is shown by applying Theorem 13 of Chap. IV to the function

$$F(y) = \text{l.u.b. } |f(x, y) - g(x)| \text{ for } x \text{ on } S.$$

The need in the last two theorems for the hypothesis that S is closed is shown by the following examples:

$$f_m(x) = \frac{m+1}{mx}, \qquad 0 < x < 1;$$

$$f_m(x) = \sin(1/x), \qquad 0 < x < 1/n\pi,$$
$$= 0, \qquad 1/n\pi \leqq x < 1.$$

From Theorem 24 we can easily derive a necessary condition that a subset B of the space $\mathfrak{C}$ of functions continuous on the bounded closed set S shall be compact.

THEOREM 27. *Suppose that B is a compact subset of $\mathfrak{C}$. Then the functions f in B are uniformly bounded and equicontinuous.*

Proof.—It is obvious that B must be bounded. Suppose the functions f are not equicontinuous at a point x of S. Then

$$(4{:}4) \quad \exists \epsilon > 0 \ni : m \cdot \supset \cdot \exists f_m \,.\, \exists h_m \ni \cdot \ \|h_m\| < 1/m \,. \\ |f_m(x + h_m) - f_m(x)| > \epsilon.$$

However, by hypothesis the sequence (f_m) has a subsequence (f_{m_p}) which converges uniformly on S, so that by Theorem 24 its functions are equicontinuous on S. But this contradicts (4:4).

That the conditions given in the last theorem are also sufficient for compactness was proved by Ascoli.

THEOREM 28. **Ascoli's theorem.** *Suppose that the functions f of a subset B of $\mathfrak{C}$ are uniformly bounded and equicontinuous on S. Then B is compact.*

Proof.—Let T be a denumerable subset of S whose closure $\bar{T} = S$, and let the points of T be denoted by x_i. The existence of such a set was proved in Theorem 9 of Chap. III. In case the set B is finite, it is compact by definition. If B is infinite, let (f_n) be a sequence of distinct functions chosen from B. By the Weierstrass-Bolzano theorem the sequence $(f_n(x_1))$ has a finite point of accumulation which we shall denote by $g(x_1)$, and there is a subsequence $(f_n^{(1)})$ such that $\lim_n f_n^{(1)}(x_1) = g(x_1)$. The sequence $(f_n^{(1)}(x_2))$ has a point of accumulation $g(x_2)$, and there is a subsequence $(f_n^{(2)})$ of $(f_n^{(1)})$ such that $\lim_n f_n^{(2)}(x_2) = g(x_2)$. Proceeding in this way, we obtain a sequence of values $g(x_i)$ and a sequence of subsequences such that $\lim_n f_n^{(i)}(x_j) = g(x_j)$ for $j \leqq i$. The "diagonal sequence" $(f_n^{(n)})$ will be denoted by (F_n). If the first i terms of (F_n) are omitted, the remainder forms a subsequence of $(f_n^{(i)})$, so that $\lim_n F_n(x_i) = g(x_i)$ for $i = 1, 2, 3, \cdots$, that is, the sequence $F_n(x)$ converges on T. Then by Theorem 25, it converges uniformly on the whole of S.

In the above proof of Ascoli's theorem we used the property that every subset S of the k-dimensional space $\mathfrak{R}$ is **separable,** in the sense that there exists a denumerable subset T whose closure $\bar{T} \supset S$. When $S = \mathfrak{R}$, the set T may be chosen to consist of all the points with rational coordinates. The space $\mathfrak{C}$ of continuous functions also has the property of being separable. This is a consequence of Theorem 29, due to Weierstrass, on the approximation of a continuous function by polynomials. For the class of polynomials with rational coefficients is denumerable, and every polynomial may be approximated uniformly on a bounded set S by polynomials with rational coefficients.

THEOREM 29. **Weierstrass' theorem.** *If $f(x)$ is continuous on the bounded closed set S, then there exists a sequence of polynomials $P_n(x)$ converging to $f(x)$ uniformly on S.*

Proof.—By a linear transformation of variables we may transform the set S into a set interior to the interval A consisting of the points x for which $0 \leqq x^{(i)} \leqq 1$, so we shall suppose that S is interior to A. By Theorem 21 we may suppose that $f(x)$ is actually defined and continuous on the whole interval A and has the same bounds on A as on S. We shall let $M = \|f\| = $ l.u.b. $|f(x)|$ on A, and let $\phi(t)$ be a modulus of continuity of f on A, which approaches zero with t. For convenience in writing the integrals below, we set $f = 0$ at points outside the interval A. Let B denote the interval consisting of the points for which $\|x\| \leqq 1$, and set

$$Q_n(x) = \prod_{i=1}^{k} (1 - x^{(i)2})^n,$$

$$(4{:}5) \quad \frac{1}{\mu_n} = \int_B Q_n(x)\,dx = \int_{-1}^{1} \cdots \int_{-1}^{1} Q_n(x)\,dx^{(1)} \cdots dx^{(m)},$$

$$P_n(x) = \mu_n \int_A f(z)Q_n(z - x)\,dz. \tag{4:6}$$

Then it is clear that $Q_n(x) \geqq 0$ on B, that $P_n(x)$ is a polynomial, and that for x in A we have $|P_n(x)| \leqq M$ and

$$P_n(x) = \mu_n \int_B f(x + v)Q_n(v)\,dv. \tag{4:7}$$

Now let $S_t \equiv [\text{all } x \ni: \|x\| < t]$. Then on the set $B - S_t$ we have

$$|Q_n(x)| \leqq (1 - t^2)^n. \tag{4:8}$$

Also if $\delta = n^{-\frac{1}{2}}$,

$$\frac{1}{\mu_n} \geqq \int_{S_\delta} Q_n(x)\,dx \geqq \int_{S_\delta} (1 - 1/n)^{kn}\,dx = [2\delta(1 - 1/n)^n]^k,$$

so that

$$\mu_n \leqq cn^{k/2}, \tag{4:9}$$

where c is a properly chosen constant. Now let α denote the minimum distance from the set S to the boundary of the interval A, and let $t < \alpha$. Then, by referring to (4:5) and (4:7) to (4:9), we see that on the set S,

$$\begin{aligned} |P_n(x) - f(x)| &= \mu_n \left| \int_B [f(x + v) - f(x)]Q_n(v)\,dv \right| \\ &\leqq \mu_n \int_{S_t} |f(x + v) - f(x)|Q_n(v)\,dv \\ &\qquad + \mu_n \int_{B - S_t} \{|f(x + v)| + |f(x)|\}Q_n(v)\,dv \\ &\leqq \phi(t) + 2M(1 - t^2)^n cn^{k/2}. \end{aligned}$$

For an arbitrary $\epsilon > 0$, we may choose t so that $\phi(t) < \epsilon$, and then there is an index q such that for $n > q$,

$$2M(1 - t^2)^n cn^{k/2} < \epsilon.$$

This completes the proof.

For other methods of proof for this famous theorem of Weierstrass, see D. V. Widder, *The Laplace Transform*, pages 152–153; also Hobson [1], Vol. 2, pages 228–234, 459–461, and references there. The proof given above is due to Landau.[1] It may be

[1] *Rendiconti del Circolo Matematico di Palermo*, Vol. 25 (1908), p. 337.

shown that when the function f is of class $C^{(p)}$ on the interval A, the derivatives of the polynomials $P_n(x)$ defined by (4:6), up to and including those of order p, will converge uniformly on S to the corresponding derivatives of f.[1]

The space $\mathfrak{C}$ contains functions that fail at every point to have a derivative, finite or infinite. To show this we cite the following example, due to Weierstrass, of a function of a single variable. For a more elaborate discussion of nondifferentiable functions and for other examples, see Hobson [1], Vol. 2, pages 401–412.

Let $0 < b < 1$, and let k be an odd integer such that

$$bk > 1 + 3\pi/2. \tag{4:10}$$

Then the series

$$f(x) = \sum_{n=0}^{\infty} b^n \cos (k^n \pi x) \tag{4:11}$$

converges uniformly and so defines a function f which is continuous for all x. We shall show that at every point the upper derivate of f on one side is $+\infty$ while the lower derivate on the other side has the value $-\infty$.

Let $f(x) = s_m(x) + r_m(x)$, where $s_m(x)$ denotes the sum of the first m terms of the series (4:11), and let

$$S_m = [s_m(x + h) - s_m(x)]/h, \qquad R_m = [r_m(x + h) - r_m(x)]/h.$$

Then by the theorem of mean value it follows readily that

$$|S_m| \leqq \frac{\pi[(bk)^m - 1]}{bk - 1} < \frac{\pi(bk)^m}{bk - 1}. \tag{4:12}$$

Now to each x and m there corresponds an integer p such that

$$|k^m x - p| \leqq \tfrac{1}{2}.$$

Let $q = k^m x - p$, $h = (\pm 1 - q)/k^m$. Then

$$|h| < 3/2k^m, \tag{4:13}$$

and h may be either positive or negative. Now $k^n(x + h) = k^{n-m}(p \pm 1)$, and k is odd, so that for $n \geqq m$,

$$\cos [k^n \pi (x + h)] = (-1)^{p+1}.$$

[1] See la Vallée Poussin, *Cours d'analyse*, 2d Ed., Tome 2 (1912), pp. 126–137; Graves, *Annals of Mathematics*, Vol. 42 (1941), pp. 281–292.

Also

$$\begin{aligned}\cos(k^n\pi x) &= \cos[k^{n-m}\pi(p+q)]\\ &= \cos(k^{n-m}\pi p)\cos(k^{n-m}\pi q)\\ &= (-1)^p\cos(k^{n-m}\pi q),\end{aligned}$$

so that

$$R_m = \frac{(-1)^{p+1}}{h}\sum_{n=m}^{\infty} b^n[1+\cos(k^{n-m}\pi q)]. \tag{4:14}$$

Every term of the series on the right side of this expression is nonnegative and, since $|q| \leqq \frac{1}{2}$, the first term (corresponding to $n = m$) is not less than b^m. Thus by (4:14) and (4:13),

$$|R_m| \geqq \frac{b^m}{|h|} > \frac{2(bk)^m}{3},$$

and hence with the help of (4:12)

$$|R_m| - |S_m| \geqq (bk)^m\left[\frac{2}{3} - \frac{\pi}{bk-1}\right].$$

By (4:10), the expression on the right tends to $+\infty$ with m, and by (4:13), h tends to zero. Since $[f(x+h) - f(x)]/h = S_m + R_m$, we see from (4:14) that if the integer p is odd for infinitely many values of m, then $D^+(x) = +\infty$, $D_-(x) = -\infty$, while if p is even for infinitely many values of m, then $D_+(x) = -\infty$, $D^-(x) = +\infty$.

The series (4:11) in the above example is a series of analytic functions of x which converges uniformly for x on the real axis. An elementary theorem of the theory of functions of a complex variable tells us that if this series converged uniformly in a region of the complex plane having a piece of the real axis in its interior, it would define a function $f(x)$ analytic in the interior of that region and hence having derivatives of all orders.[1]

***5. Discontinuous Functions.**—It is interesting to note that certain discontinuous functions may be defined by means of rather simple formulas. For example, let

$$\begin{aligned}\operatorname{sgn} x &= 1 \quad \text{for} \quad x > 0,\\ &= -1 \quad \text{for} \quad x < 0,\\ &= 0 \quad \text{for} \quad x = 0.\end{aligned}$$

[1] Compare the remark following Theorem 8 in Sec. 2.

Then

$$\operatorname{sgn} x = \frac{2}{\pi} \lim_n \tan^{-1} nx = \lim_n \tanh nx.$$

Moreover the function

$$(5:1) \qquad f(x) = a + (b - a) \lim_m \operatorname{sgn} (\sin^2 m!\pi x)$$

has the value a for x rational and the value b for x irrational.

In 1899 Baire introduced an interesting classification of discontinuous functions, which may be described as follows.[1] Let the functions continuous on the set S constitute the class 0. A function which is the limit on S of a sequence of continuous functions but which is not itself continuous is said to belong to the class 1. A function which is the limit on S of a sequence of functions of class less than α, but which is not itself of class less than α, is said to belong to the class α. When the set S is perfect and nonnull, it may be proved that there are functions of class α for each ordinal number α of the first or of the second class.[2] For example, the function sgn x is in the class 1, while the function $f(x)$ defined by (5:1) for $a \neq b$ is in the class 2.[3] It may also be shown that there are functions not in any of the Baire classes.[4]

We shall now show that every semicontinuous function is in Baire's class 1, and in fact may be approximated by a monotonic sequence of continuous functions. The theorem will be stated only for the case of lower semicontinuous functions.

THEOREM 30. *Suppose that $g(x)$ is lower semicontinuous on the set S. Then there exists a nondecreasing sequence $(f_m(x))$ of functions which are continuous on S, such that* $\lim_m f_m(x) = g(x)$ *on S. When the function $g(x)$ has a finite lower bound, the functions $f_m(x)$ may be required to be continuous and the sequence to be nondecreasing on the whole space.*

Proof.—By definition of lower semicontinuity, $g(x)$ has only finite values. We shall at first suppose that $g(x) \geqq L$ on S,

[1] See Baire, *Leçons sur les fonctions discontinues*, Paris, 1905.

[2] See la Vallée Poussin, *Intégrales de Lebesgue, Fonctions d'ensemble, Classes de Baire*, pp. 145–151.

[3] For a proof, see Hobson [1], pp. 264–274, 276.

[4] See Sierpinski, *Fundamenta Mathematicae*, Vol. 5 (1924), pp. 87–91.

where L is finite. Let

$$f_m(x) = \text{g.l.b. } [g(z) + m\|x - z\|] \text{ for } z \text{ in } S.$$

Then it follows at once that $L \leqq f_m(x) \leqq f_{m+1}(x)$ everywhere, and $f_m(x) \leqq g(x)$ on S, so that the sequence $(f_m(x))$ has a limit $f(x)$, and $f(x) \leqq g(x)$ on S. To show that f_m is continuous, let x and y be distinct points of space. Then for a properly selected point z in S,

$$g(z) + m\|x - z\| < f_m(x) + \|x - y\|,$$

$$f_m(y) \leqq g(z) + m\|y - z\| \leqq g(z) + m(\|y - x\| + \|x - z\|) < f_m(x) + (m + 1)\|x - y\|.$$

Since x and y may be interchanged in this argument, it follows that

$$|f_m(x) - f_m(y)| < (m + 1)\|x - y\|.$$

Finally, we wish to show that $\lim f_m(x) = g(x)$ on S. There exists a point z_m in S such that

$$g(z_m) + m\|x - z_m\| < f_m(x) + 1/m, \tag{5:2}$$

and hence

$$\|x - z_m\| < \frac{1}{m}\left[f_m(x) + \frac{1}{m} - g(z_m)\right] \leqq \frac{1}{m}[g(x) + 1 - L],$$

so that $\lim\limits_{m} z_m = x$. Therefore

$$g(x) \leqq \liminf_{m=\infty} g(z_m) \leqq \lim_{m=\infty} f_m(x)$$

by the lower semicontinuity of g and (5:2). But it was already known that $\lim\limits_{m} f_m(x) \leqq g(x)$ on S.

To care for the case when the function g is not bounded below, we make use of the transformation

$$v = V(t) = \frac{t}{1 + |t|},$$

which is continuous and increasing and transforms the interval $(-\infty, +\infty)$ into $(-1, 1)$. Obviously the inverse transformation

$t = T(v)$ is also continuous and increasing. If we set $\gamma(x) = V[g(x)]$, then $-1 < \gamma(x) < 1$ and γ is lower semicontinuous, so that by the first part of the proof there exists a nondecreasing sequence $(\phi_m(x))$ of continuous functions such that $\lim_m \phi_m(x) = \gamma(x)$ on S. Obviously we may also suppose that $-1 \leqq \phi_m(x) < 1$ everywhere. Now let $\sum e_m$ be a convergent series of numbers whose terms satisfy the conditions $0 < e_{m+1} < e_m < 1$, and set

$$\psi_m = \phi_m + e_1(\phi_{m+1} - \phi_m) + e_2(\phi_{m+2} - \phi_{m+1}) + \cdots .$$

This series converges uniformly, since $0 \leqq \phi_{n+1} - \phi_n \leqq 2$, and hence each ψ_m is continuous. Moreover $\phi_m \leqq \psi_m \leqq \psi_{m+1} \leqq \gamma$ on S, and $\psi_m(x) = \phi_m(x)$ when $\phi_m(x) = \gamma(x)$, $\psi_m(x) > \phi_m(x)$ when $\phi_m(x) < \gamma(x)$, so that we always have $-1 < \psi_m(x) < 1$ on S. Then the transformed functions $f_m(x) = T[\psi_m(x)]$ are all continuous and approximate to the function $g(x)$ in the required fashion.

We shall next consider a theorem that has as a corollary a converse of the last theorem.

THEOREM 31. *Let $f(x, y)$ have for its domain the Cartesian product ST, and let*

$$u(x) = \limsup_{y=b} f(x, y) \text{ on } S,$$
$$m(y) = \liminf_{x=a} f(x, y) \text{ on } T,$$

where $u(x)$ and $m(y)$ have finite values. Suppose, furthermore, that one of these relations holds uniformly. Then

$$\limsup_{y=b} m(y) \leqq \liminf_{x=a} u(x).$$

Proof.—Consider the case where

$$\limsup_{y=b} f(x, y) = u(x) \text{ uniformly on } S.$$

Let $\epsilon > 0$. Then

(5:3) $\exists \delta > 0 \ni : x \text{ in } S \,.\, y \text{ in } TN(b; \delta) \cdot \supset \cdot f(x, y) < u(x) + \epsilon,$
(5:4) $y \text{ in } T : \supset : \exists \gamma > 0 \ni : x \text{ in } SN(a; \gamma) \cdot \supset \cdot f(x, y) > m(y) - \epsilon.$

Hence we find in succession,

$$y \text{ in } TN(b;\,\delta)\,.\,x \text{ in } SN(a;\,\gamma)\cdot\supset\cdot\, m(y) < u(x) + 2\epsilon,$$

$$(5{:}5)\quad y \text{ in } TN(b;\,\delta)\cdot\supset\cdot\, m(y) \leqq \liminf_{x=a} u(x) + 2\epsilon,$$

$$\limsup_{y=b} m(y) \leqq \liminf_{x=a} u(x).$$

It is clear that in the theorem and the proof so far, the roles of x and y may be interchanged. Then the case when the uniformity holds for lim inf $f(x, y)$ may be obtained from the case already considered by replacing f by $-f$.

Theorem 31 has the following immediate corollaries.

THEOREM 32. *Let the functions $f_m(x)$ have domain S, and let the sequence $f_m(x)$ be nondecreasing and bounded for each x in S. Then*

$$\lim_{m=\infty} \liminf_{x=a} f_m(x) \leqq \liminf_{x=a} \lim_{m=\infty} f_m(x).$$

THEOREM 33. *Let the functions $f_m(x)$ be lower semicontinuous on S, and let $\lim_{m=\infty} f_m(x) = g(x)$ on S, where $g(x)$ is finite. Suppose also that the sequence $f_m(x)$ is nondecreasing or else that the convergence is uniform on S. Then $g(x)$ is lower semicontinuous on S.*

There are of course similar corollaries involving nonincreasing sequences and upper semicontinuous functions.

EXERCISE

This exercise provides a review of fundamental points in some of the preceding chapters.

Make up correct definitions and theorems from the following, by choosing the expression to be defined or the hypothesis of the theorem from A to Z, and the definition or the conclusion of the theorem from 1 to 30; for example, A $\cdot\equiv\cdot$ 1; A . B $\cdot\supset\cdot$ 2; C $\cdot\sim\cdot$ 3. Note that none of the statements given as examples is correct. It is understood in the following that the functions involved are real-valued. As usual, $[a, b]$ denotes a closed interval of the real axis, but the set S and the interval $[a, b]$ have no relation unless otherwise specified.

A. The ordered field $\mathfrak{R}$ has the Dedekind property.

B. The point c is interior to the set S.

1. $\epsilon > 0 :\supset: \exists b$ in $S \ni\cdot b$ in $N(c;\,\epsilon)\,.\,b \neq c$.

2. A real number $c \ni:.\ c \leqq S :\ \epsilon > 0 \cdot\supset\cdot \exists b$ in $S \ni\cdot b < c + \epsilon$.

C. The set S contains none of its accumulation points.
D. The set S is the sum of the open sets E_α.
E. The greatest lower bound of a set S of real numbers.
F. The set $S = A + B$, where A and B are nonnull and have no points in common, and A is closed.
G. The set S is connected.
H. The set $S = A + B$, where A and B are nonnull open sets and have no points in common.
I. The linearly ordered set Ω has the Dedekind property.
J. The point c is an accumulation point of the set S.
K. $\lim_{x=c} f(x)$ exists and is finite, where $f(x)$ is defined on S.
L. $\liminf_{x=c} f(x) = -\infty$.
M. S is bounded and closed, and $f(x)$ is continuous on S.
N. $f(x)$ has a continuous derivative on the interval $[a,b]$.
O. $f(x, y)$ has finite partial derivatives $\partial f/\partial x$ and $\partial f/\partial y$ at the point (x_1, y_1).
P. $f(x)$ is continuous on the interval $[a, b]$.
Q. $f(x)$ has an antiderivative on the interval $[a, b]$.
R. $f(a) < u < f(b)$.
S. $f(x)$ has only a denumerable infinity of discontinuities on the interval $[a, b]$.

3. The set S is disconnected.
4. All the points of S are isolated points.
5. The point c is not an exterior point of the set S.
6. Every subset S of Ω which has a lower bound has a greatest lower bound.
7. The ordered field $\mathfrak{R}$ is Archimedean.
8. $\exists \epsilon > 0 \ni\cdot N(c; \epsilon) \subset S$.
9. The set S is open.
10. The set A contains a point of accumulation of the set B.
11. $\epsilon > 0 :\supset: \exists \delta > 0 \ni: x$ in $SN(c; \delta) . x'$ in $SN(c; \delta) \cdot\supset\cdot |f(x) - f(x')| < \epsilon$.
12. $\epsilon > 0 :\supset: \exists \delta > 0 \ni: x$ in $S . x'$ in $SN(x; \delta) \cdot\supset\cdot |f(x) - f(x')| < \epsilon$.
13. There is a point x_0 between a and b such that $f(x_0) = u$.
14. $f(x)$ is Riemann-integrable on $[a, b]$.
15. $\epsilon > 0 \cdot\supset\cdot \exists x$ in $N(c; \epsilon) \ni\cdot f(x) \not> -1/\epsilon$.
16. $f(x)$ has a maximum and a minimum on the set S.
17. $\lim_{\substack{x=b \\ n=\infty}} f_n(x)$ exists and is finite.
18. The series $\sum_{n=1}^{\infty} |f_n(x)|$ converges uniformly for x in S.
19. $\lim_{x=b} g(x)$ and $\lim_{n=\infty} \lim_{x=b} f_n(x)$ exist and are equal.

T. $f(x)$ is bounded on $[a, b]$.

U. For each n, $f_n(x)$ is continuous in x for x in S.

V. For each n, $f_n(x)$ is continuous in x uniformly with respect to x in S.

W. $f_n(x)$ converges to $g(x)$ as n approaches ∞, uniformly for x in S.

X. $f_n(x)$ is continuous in x on S, uniformly with respect to n.

Y. For each n, $\lim_{x=b} f_n(x)$ exists and is finite.

Z. Every rearrangement of the series $\sum_{n=1}^{\infty} f_n(x)$ converges uniformly for x in S.

20. If S is an interval $[a, b]$, and each $f_n(x)$ is Riemann-integrable on $[a, b]$, then $g(x)$ is Riemann-integrable on $[a, b]$, and
$$\lim_{n=\infty} \int_a^b f_n\, dx = \int_a^b g\, dx.$$

21. $\lim_{x=b} \sum_{n=1}^{\infty} f_n(x)$ exists and is finite.

22. $g(x)$ is continuous on S.

23. $f(x, y)$ has a differential at (x_1, y_1).

24. $\exists M \ni : x$ in $[a, b] . x'$ in $[a, b] \cdot \supset \cdot |f(x) - f(x')| \leqq M|x - x'|$.

25. The sum of the series $\sum_{n=1}^{\infty} f_n(x)$ is continuous on S.

26. x in $S . \epsilon > 0 : \supset : \exists \delta > 0 \ni : n . x'$ in $SN(x;\ \delta) \cdot \supset \cdot |f_n(x') - f_n(x)| < \epsilon$.

27. $\epsilon > 0 : \supset : \exists p \ni : n > p . x$ in $S \cdot \supset \cdot |f_n(x) - g(x)| < \epsilon$.

28. $\epsilon > 0 : \supset : \exists p \ni : m > p . n > p . x$ in $S \cdot \supset \cdot |f_m(x) - f_n(x)| < \epsilon$.

29. $n . x$ in $S . \epsilon > 0 : \supset : \exists \delta > 0 \ni : x'$ in $SN(x;\ \delta) \cdot \supset \cdot |f_n(x') - f_n(x)| < \epsilon$.

30. $n . \epsilon > 0 : \supset : \exists \delta > 0 \ni : x$ in $S . x'$ in $SN(x;\ \delta) \cdot \supset \cdot |f_n(x') - f_n(x)| < \epsilon$.

REFERENCES

1. Hobson, *The Theory of Functions of a Real Variable*, Vol. 1, Chap. 5; Vol. 2, Chaps. 1 to 6.
2. Pierpont, *The Theory of Functions of Real Variables*, Vol. 1, Chaps. 6, 13; Vol. 2, Chaps. 3 to 7, 14, 16.

3. Goursat, *Mathematical Analysis*, Vol. 1, Chaps. 8, 9.
4. Jordan, *Cours d'analyse*, Vol. 1, Chap. 3.
5. Bromwich, *An Introduction to the Theory of Infinite Series.*
6. Fort, *Infinite Series.*
7. Knopp, *Theory and Application of Infinite Series.*
8. Reid, *Infinite Series and Definite Integrals* (Mimeographed, University of Chicago, 1939), Chaps. 2 to 4, 8.
9. Smail, *Elements of the Theory of Infinite Processes.*

CHAPTER VIII

FUNCTIONS DEFINED IMPLICITLY

1. Introduction.—The need for theorems justifying the existence and properties of functions defined implicitly by means of an equation or a system of equations is illustrated by the following examples in which the desired properties fail to hold. If $g(x, y) = x^2 + y^2 - x^3$, then $g(0, 0) = 0$, but the equation $g(x, y) = 0$ has no real solution for y when x has a value different from zero and less than one. If $g(x, y) = (y - x^2)^2 - x^5$, we find that the equation $g(x, y) = 0$ has two real solutions for y when x is positive and none at all when x is negative.

In Sec. 2 we shall give conditions justifying the existence and uniqueness of the solution $y = \phi(x)$ of an equation or system of equations $g(x, y) = 0$, near a given initial solution such as the point $(0, 0)$ in the above examples. The method of proof we shall use is an extension of Newton's method for the solution of numerical equations, with a slight modification. If y_0 is a first approximation to a root of the equation $g(y) = 0$, then under certain conditions a better approximation is given by the formula

$$y_1 = y_0 - \frac{g(y_0)}{g'(y_0)},$$

and the sequence (y_m), where

$$y_{m+1} = y_m - \frac{g(y_m)}{g'(y_0)}, \tag{1:1}$$

converges to a root of the equation. It is convenient to set

$$f(y) = y - \frac{g(y)}{g'(y_0)}. \tag{1:2}$$

Then the formula (1:1) becomes $y_{m+1} = f(y_m)$, and in terms of the function f the method becomes one of successive substitution. This method of successive substitution is very widely applicable, since it may also be used to show the existence of solutions of differential equations, integral equations, and systems of equations with infinitely many unknowns, and the variables in these cases may be either real or complex. However, other methods could be used equally well to obtain the theorems of the present chapter. When the variables are complex and the functions involved are all analytic, the theorems obtained by the method of successive substitution show that the solutions are also analytic functions. These solutions may therefore be expressed as power series whose coefficients may be determined by the usual formal methods without any need for a supplementary proof of convergence by the use of dominant series.

Sections 3 and 4 contain theorems on the extent of the domain of definition of implicit functions, and Sec. 5 contains theorems in which neither a Lipschitz condition nor differentiability are assumed.

2. Solutions Defined near an Initial Solution.—The first theorem we shall give is concerned with conditions under which the method of successive substitution yields a sequence converging to a solution. In it the function f is supposed to have values in the same space as its argument y, and this space may have any finite number of dimensions. The points at infinity are omitted from space throughout this chapter. The notation $\|y\|$ of Chap. V, Sec. 2, is used for max $|y^{(i)}|$.

THEOREM 1. *Let $f(y)$ be defined on a neighborhood $N(y_0; a)$, and suppose there is a number $K < 1$ such that for every pair of points y_1 and y_2 in $N(y_0; a)$,*

$$\|f(y_1) - f(y_2)\| \leqq K\|y_1 - y_2\|. \tag{2:1}$$

Suppose also that

$$\|f(y_0) - y_0\| < (1 - K)a. \tag{2:2}$$

Then there is a unique point y in the neighborhood $N(y_0; a)$ such that $y = f(y)$.

Proof.—Let $y_1 = f(y_0)$, $y_{m+1} = f(y_m)$. Then

$$\|y_{m+1} - y_m\| \leqq K\|y_m - y_{m-1}\| \leqq K^m\|y_1 - y_0\|, \tag{2:3}$$

provided all the approximations up to y_m lie in the neighborhood $N(y_0; a)$. But then we have

$$(2:4)\quad \|y_{m+1} - y_0\| \leqq \sum_{i=0}^{m} \|y_{i+1} - y_i\| \leqq \|y_1 - y_0\| \sum_{i=0}^{m} K^i < \frac{\|y_1 - y_0\|}{1 - K} < a,$$

so that y_{m+1} lies in the neighborhood and may be used to define the next approximation. From (2:3) we see that the series $\sum (y_{m+1} - y_m)$ is dominated by a geometric series which converges. Hence the sequence (y_m) converges to a limit y, which lies in $N(y_0; a)$ by (2:4). Since f is continuous by (2:1), $f(y_m)$ converges to $f(y)$, and so $y = f(y)$. If there were another solution $\bar{y}$ in $N(y_0; a)$, we should have by (2:1),

$$\|y - \bar{y}\| \leqq K\|y - \bar{y}\| < \|y - \bar{y}\|,$$

which is impossible.

A function satisfying (2:1) is said to satisfy a **Lipschitz condition** with constant K. From the Theorem of the Mean it is clear that this condition is satisfied when each component of f has continuous first partial derivatives with respect to the k variables $y^{(i)}$ each of which is not greater than K/k in absolute value for y on the neighborhood $N(y_0; a)$.

In case the space of the variable y is one-dimensional, the solution of the equation $y = f(y)$ corresponds to finding the point of intersection of the curve $z = f(y)$ and the line $z = y$. Some of the possibilities that may occur are indicated in the accompanying figures. The line AC in Figs. 1 to 3 has slope K

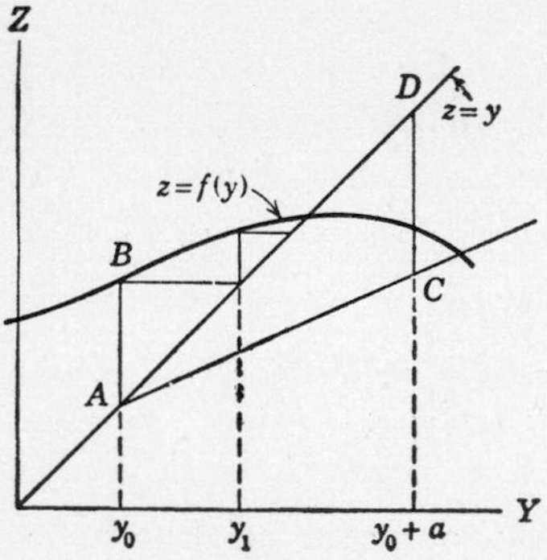

Fig. 1

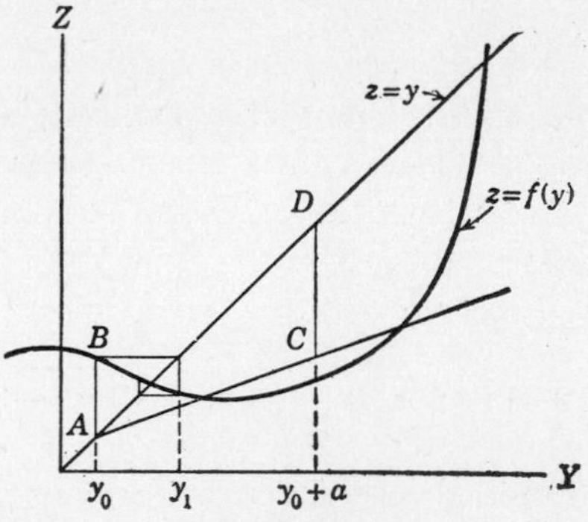

Fig. 2

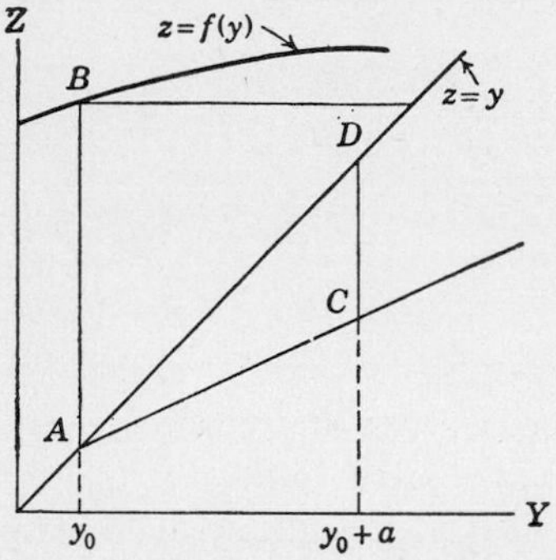

Fig. 3

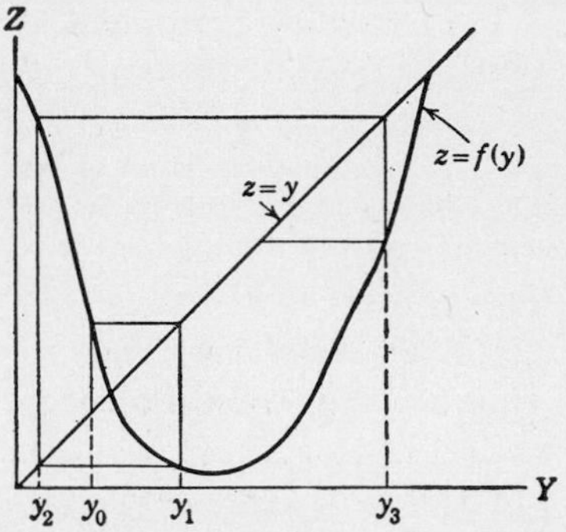

Fig. 4

and, in case the function $f(y)$ has a derivative, the Lipschitz condition (2:1) in the theorem implies that the slope of $z = f(y)$ is numerically not greater than K on the interval $(y_0 - a, y_0 + a)$. This condition fails to hold in Fig. 4. The condition (2:2) of the theorem requires that the segment AB shall be less than CD.

Note that in case $a = +\infty$, the condition (2:2) may be omitted.

The following examples illustrate possible determinations of the constants a and K in Theorem 1.

A. $y = y^3 - y^2 + 0.1$. Here we may take $y_0 = 0.1$, $a = 0.1$, $K = 0.4$.

B. $y = \cos y - 0.8$. Here we may take $y_0 = 0$, $a = \pi/6$, $K = 0.5$.

C. $y = e^y - 2$. Here we may take $y_0 = -2$, $a = 1$, $K = 1/e$.

D. $y = \frac{1}{2}\cos y$. Here $a = +\infty$, $K = \frac{1}{2}$, and we may take y_0 arbitrarily.

In case the function $g(y)$ has a continuous second derivative, let $M(d)$ denote the maximum of $|g''(y)|/|g'(y_0)|$ on the interval $y_0 - d \leqq y \leqq y_0 + d$. Suppose d can be so chosen that

$$\frac{2}{d} \leqq 4M(d) < \frac{|g'(y_0)|}{|g(y_0)|}. \tag{2:5}$$

Then since $f'(y) = 1 - g'(y)/g'(y_0) = (y_0 - y)g''(\bar{y})/g'(y_0)$, where $\bar{y}$ lies between y_0 and y, the function f defined by (1:2) satisfies the conditions of Theorem 1 with $a = 1/2M(d)$, $K = \frac{1}{2}$, and hence the sequence defined by (1:1) converges to a solution of the equation $g(y) = 0$.

If we modify example A to

$$y = y^3 - y^2 - 3,$$

we find that Theorem 1 is not applicable directly. However, conditions (2:5) are fulfilled by $g(y) = y^3 - y^2 - y - 3$ with $y_0 = 2$, $d = \frac{1}{3}$, $M(d) = \frac{12}{7}$, $a = \frac{7}{24}$.

We are now prepared to prove what is properly called an "implicit function theorem." In its statement, x and y are variables in spaces of one or more dimensions, and $g(x, y)$ is a function with values in the same space as its argument y. The symbol $g_y(x, y)$ then stands for the square matrix whose elements are the partial derivatives of the components of g with respect to the components of y. Similarly the symbol $g_x(x, y)$ also stands for a matrix of partial derivatives, but it need not be square. We shall use the usual notation of matrix theory for matrix multiplication, treating x, y, and g as matrices each consisting of one column. Thus, for example, the notation $g_y(y_1 - y_2)$ stands for the matrix the elements of whose only column are $\sum_{j=1}^{k} \frac{\partial g^{(i)}}{\partial y^{(j)}} (y_1^{(j)} - y_2^{(j)})$. The determinant of the matrix g_y will be denoted by det g_y.

THEOREM 2. *Suppose that $g(x, y)$ is of class $C^{(m)}$ on an open set W of xy-space, and that $g(x_0, y_0) = 0$ while* det $g_y(x_0, y_0) \neq 0$ *at a point (x_0, y_0) of W. Then there exist neighborhoods $N(x_0; b)$ and $N(y_0; a)$ and a function $\phi(x)$ defined on $N(x_0; b)$ such that for every x in $N(x_0; b)$,* det $g_y(x, \phi(x)) \neq 0$, *and $\phi(x)$ is the only solution in the neighborhood $N(y_0; a)$ of the equation $g(x, y) = 0$. Moreover, $\phi(x)$ is of class $C^{(m)}$ on $N(x_0; b)$.*

Proof.—For simplicity we shall first take up the case when both variables x and y lie in one-dimensional spaces. Let

$$f(x, y) = y - \frac{g(x, y)}{g_y(x_0, y_0)}. \tag{2:6}$$

Then the equation $y = f(x, y)$ has the same solutions as $g(x, y) = 0$. Also f has a partial derivative with respect to y which is continuous and vanishes at (x_0, y_0). Hence there exist positive numbers K, a, b, and c, with $K < 1$, such that for x in $N(x_0; b)$ and y, y_1, y_2 in $N(y_0; a)$, (x, y) is in W, and

$$(2:7)\qquad |g_y(x, y)| \geqq c,$$

$$(2:8)\qquad \begin{aligned} |f(x, y_1) - f(x, y_2)| &= |f_y(x, y_2 + \theta(y_1 - y_2))||y_1 - y_2| \\ &\leqq K|y_1 - y_2|, \\ |f(x, y_0) - y_0| &< (1 - K)a. \end{aligned}$$

Thus the existence and uniqueness of the function $\phi(x)$ follow from Theorem 1. We may show that $\phi(x)$ is continuous without assuming the existence of the partial derivative g_x. For, with the help of the Theorem of the Mean, we have

$$(2:9)\qquad \begin{aligned} 0 &= g(x_1, \phi(x_1)) - g(x, \phi(x)) \\ &= g(x_1, \phi(x_1)) - g(x_1, \phi(x)) + g(x_1, \phi(x)) - g(x, \phi(x)) \\ &= g_y(x_1, \phi(x) + \theta\,\Delta\phi)\,\Delta\phi + g(x_1, \phi(x)) - g(x, \phi(x)), \end{aligned}$$

where $\Delta\phi = \phi(x_1) - \phi(x)$ and $0 < \theta < 1$. Since $|g_y(x, y)| \geqq c > 0$ and $g(x, y)$ is continuous, $\phi(x)$ is also continuous. If the partial derivative g_x exists and is continuous, then from (2:9), writing Δx for $x_1 - x$, we have

$$(2:10)\qquad 0 = g_y(x_1, \phi(x) + \theta\,\Delta\phi)\,\Delta\phi + g_x(x + \theta_1\,\Delta x, \phi(x))\,\Delta x.$$

Hence $\Delta\phi/\Delta x$ has the limit

$$(2:11)\qquad \phi'(x) = -\frac{g_x(x, \phi(x))}{g_y(x, \phi(x))},$$

and $\phi(x)$ is of class C'. If g is of class $C^{(m)}$ and ϕ is of class $C^{(m-1)}$, then the right-hand side of (2:11) is of class $C^{(m-1)}$, by Theorem 15 of Chap. V, and hence ϕ is of class $C^{(m)}$.

The meaning of the theorem for the case just considered may be visualized by considering the graph of the equation $z = g(x, y)$. When this graph intersects the xy-plane at a point (x_0, y_0) where the tangent plane is not parallel to the y-axis, then the graph intersects the xy-plane in a curve passing through (x_0, y_0) which defines y as a single-valued function of x.

Let us return now to the general case, and set[1]

$$A(x, y_1, y_2) = \int_0^1 g_y(x, y_2 + t(y_1 - y_2))\,dt.$$

At points where the matrix $A(x, y_1, y_2)$ is nonsingular, let $B(x, y_1, y_2)$ denote its inverse or reciprocal. By Theorem 17 of

[1] In this formula involving the integration of a matrix, it is understood that each element of the matrix is integrated separately.

Chap. VI,

$$g(x, y_1) - g(x, y_2) = A(x, y_1, y_2)(y_1 - y_2).$$

Then in the preceding proof let us replace formula (2:6) by

$$f(x, y) = y - B(x_0, y_0, y_0)g(x, y)$$

and make corresponding alterations in the remainder of the proof. Inequality (2:7) is replaced by

$$|\det A(x, y_1, y_2)| \geqq c, \tag{2:12}$$

and we note that then the elements of the matrix $B(x, y_1, y_2)$ are continuous and bounded for x in $N(x_0; b)$ and y_1 and y_2 in $N(y_0; a)$. Formula (2:8) is replaced by

$$\begin{aligned}\|f(x, y_1) - f(x, y_2)\| = \|y_1 - y_2 \\ - B(x_0, y_0, y_0)A(x, y_1, y_2)(y_1 - y_2)\| \\ \leqq K\|y_1 - y_2\|,\end{aligned}$$

and (2:9) is replaced by

$$0 = A(x_1, \phi(x_1), \phi(x))\, \Delta\phi + g(x_1, \phi(x)) - g(x, \phi(x)),$$

from which we obtain

$$\Delta\phi = -B(x_1, \phi(x_1), \phi(x))[g(x_1, \phi(x)) - g(x, \phi(x))]. \tag{2:13}$$

If we set

$$C(x_1, x, y) = \int_0^1 g_x(x + t(x_1 - x), y)\, dt,$$

we obtain

$$\Delta\phi = -B(x_1, \phi(x_1), \phi(x))C(x_1, x, \phi(x))\, \Delta x \tag{2:14}$$

from (2:13), so that (2:11) is replaced by the matrix formula

$$\phi_x(x) = -B(x, \phi(x), \phi(x))C(x, x, \phi(x)). \tag{2:15}$$

Since the elements of the matrix B are rational functions of the elements of A, with denominator bounded from zero by (2:12), the argument that ϕ is of class $C^{(m)}$ is completed as before. Note that formula (2:15) is equivalent to the system of equations

$$g_x(x, \phi(x)) + g_y(x, \phi(x))\phi_x(x) = 0.$$

It is clear that the above proof proceeds on the basis of the fact that for each x near x_0, y_0 is a sufficiently close approximation to a solution for Theorem 1 to be applicable. Thus we see that it is not essential to have an exact initial solution (x_0, y_0).

In the following examples the variables x and y are both in one-dimensional space. In each case except G an initial solution corresponding to $x = 0$ may be considered.

E. $g(x, y) = x^2 + y^2 - 1 = 0.$
F. $g(x, y) = x^2 + y^2 = 0.$
G. $g(x, y) = x^2 + y^2 + 1 = 0.$
H. $g(x, y) = \sin^2 y - x + \cos^2 y - 1 = 0.$
I. $g(x, y) = y^3 - x \sin (1/x) = 0.$
J. $g(x, y) = y^3 - x \sin (1/x) - 1 = 0.$

In these examples the question of the existence of a solution and its properties when it exists may be settled by elementary considerations. To some of them Theorem 2 is applicable, to others not. We recall that the proof of Theorem 2 shows that everything but the differentiability of the solution may be secured without the existence of the partial derivative g_x. In the next three examples the existence and properties of the solution would not be obvious without the help of Theorem 2.

K. $g(x, y) = \sin (x + y) - e^{xy} + 1 = 0.$
L. $g(x, y) = \sin (x + y) - e^{xy} + 1 + xy \sin (1/x) = 0.$
M. $g(x, y) = \log (1 + x + y) - \tanh xy = 0.$

3. Maximal Sheets of Solutions.—It is sometimes desirable to have information about the extent to which a solution $y = \phi(x)$ of an equation $g(x, y) = 0$ may be continued. The theorems to be proved in this section are designed to give information of this type. In Theorem 3 we shall be considering equations $g(x, y) = 0$ of the same type as those considered in Theorem 2, but for its statement we shall need to define some additional concepts.

A **sheet of points** in xy-space is defined to be a connected set W_0 of points $w = (x, y)$ with finite coordinates such that, for every point $w_0 = (x_0, y_0)$ of W_0, there exists a neighborhood $N(w_0; a)$ such that no two points of W_0 in $N(w_0; a)$ have the same projection x; and for every w_0 in W_0 and every $a > 0$, there is a neighborhood $N(x_0; b)$ each of whose points x is the projection of a point w of W_0 in $N(w_0; a)$.[1] It is clear that in a

[1] This definition of a sheet of points is somewhat more restrictive than the one introduced in Bliss [4], p. 22. It corresponds to his "connected sheet consisting only of interior points."

sufficiently small neighborhood of each of its points a sheet determines y as a single-valued continuous function of x. Conversely, if $y = \phi(x)$ is continuous on an open connected set, then its graph is a sheet. Furthermore, a sheet is necessarily arcwise connected.

For example, in case x and y represent points in spaces of one dimension, a sheet of points according to the above definition corresponds to a single-valued continuous function $y = f(x)$ defined on an open interval $c < x < d$. The set of points on the circle $x^2 + y^2 = 1$ is not a sheet, but removal of the points of intersection with the x-axis divides the set into two sheets. In case the x-space has two dimensions and the y-space has one dimension, the helicoidal surface $y = c \tan^{-1} (x_1/x_2)$ is a sheet. The sphere $x_1^2 + x_2^2 + y^2 = 1$, on the other hand, is not a sheet, but is divided into two sheets by removal of its intersection with the plane $y = 0$.

A **boundary point of a sheet** W_0 is a point not belonging to W_0, but every neighborhood of which contains points of W_0. This concept is not the same as that of boundary point of a set, since every point of a sheet is a boundary point of the set of points composing the sheet.

If the function $g(x, y)$ is defined and of class C' for (x, y) in an open set W, then a point $w = (x, y)$ is called an **ordinary point** for $g(x, y)$ in case w is in W and the matrix $g_y(x, y)$ is nonsingular. All other points are called **exceptional points.**

THEOREM 3. *Let $w_0 = (x_0, y_0)$ be an ordinary point for $g(x, y)$ and a solution of the equation*

$$g(x, y) = 0.$$

Then there is a unique sheet W_0 of solutions of this equation with the properties

A. *W_0 contains w_0;*
B. *Every point of W_0 is an ordinary point;*
C. *The only finite boundary points of W_0 are exceptional points.*

Proof.—The existence of a sheet W_1 having properties A and B follows from Theorem 2. Let W_0 be the logical sum of all such sheets W_1. Then W_0 is connected and is a set of solutions having properties A and B. Moreover, from property B and Theorem 2 it follows that W_0 is a sheet. Let $w_1 = (x_1, y_1)$ be a boundary point of W_0 and an ordinary point for $g(x, y)$. Since g is continuous, $g(x_1, y_1) = 0$. Hence by Theorem 2, the sheet W_0 could be extended to include the point w_1, and properties A and B would still hold. This contradicts the definition of W_0, and consequently W_0 has property C. To show that there is only one sheet having these properties, suppose another sheet W_2 has the same properties. Then W_2 must be contained in W_0. If $A = W_0 - W_2$ is not null, we find that $W_2A' = 0$ by Theorem 2, and $AW_2' = 0$ by property B for W_0 and property C for W_2. But this contradicts the connectedness of W_0.

As an example, consider the equations

$$y_1^2 - y_2^2 - x_1 = 0,$$
$$2y_1y_2 - x_2 = 0.$$

The functional determinant is

$$\begin{vmatrix} 2y_1 & -2y_2 \\ 2y_2 & 2y_1 \end{vmatrix} = 4(y_1^2 + y_2^2),$$

which equals zero only for $y_1 = y_2 = 0$, $x_1 = x_2 = 0$. There is only one maximal sheet of solutions, corresponding to the Riemann surface for the function $y = \sqrt{x}$, where $y = y_1 + iy_2$, $x = x_1 + ix_2$. However, if in the consideration of the equation $y^2 - x = 0$, x and y are restricted to real values, there are two maximal sheets of solutions, corresponding, respectively, to positive and to negative values of y, and the point (0, 0) is a boundary point of each. For the equation $y^2 - x^2 - 1 = 0$, there are also two maximal sheets of solutions, having no finite boundary points, when x and y are restricted to real values. For another example, consider the equation

$$x_1^2 + x_2^2 + y^2 - 1 = 0.$$

The exceptional points are those for which $y = 0$. The maximal sheet of solutions through the point (0, 0, 1) is the upper hemisphere while the maximal sheet of solutions through (0, 0, -1) is the lower hemisphere.

A more general application of Theorem 3 is that to an equation of the form

$$g(x, y) = a_0(x)y^n + a_1(x)y^{n-1} + \cdot \cdot \cdot + a_n(x) = 0,$$

where the functions $a_i(x)$ are polynomials. If x and y are permitted to be complex variables and the polynomial $g(x, y)$ is irreducible, there is only one maximal sheet of solutions, and its only finite boundary points correspond to the solutions of the equation $D(x) = 0$, where $D(x)$ is the discriminant of $g(x, y)$ regarded as a polynomial in y. One or more of the values of y becomes infinite at the points where $a_0(x) = 0$. A variety of situations may arise when x and y are restricted to be real, as has been indicated by some of the preceding examples. Let us suppose, for instance, that the coefficients of $g(x, y)$ are real, that the equation $a_0(x)\,D(x) = 0$ has no real roots, and that there are exactly k distinct real solutions (x_1, y_1), (x_1, y_2), . . . , (x_1, y_k), corresponding to a particular initial value of x. Then, when x and y are restricted to be real, there are k maximal sheets of solutions each of which determines a single-valued function of x defined on the whole x-axis. A special example of this is afforded by the equation

$$(x^2 + 1)y^3 - (x^2 + 3)y + 1 = 0,$$

which has three distinct real roots for each real value of x. Its graph consists of three curves which do not intersect.

4. An Extended Implicit Function Theorem.—(Compare Bliss [4], pages 19–21; Bolza [5]). There are cases in which one wishes to apply an implicit function theorem when an initial curve of solutions is given. Such an occasion will arise in the next chapter, when we consider an embedding theorem for systems of differential equations that are not solved for the derivatives.

THEOREM 4. *Let W^* be a bounded closed set in the xy-space with projection X^* on the x-space, and suppose each point x in X^* is the projection of only one point (x, y) in W^*. Suppose also that each point of W^* is an ordinary point for $g(x, y)$, and that $g(x, y) = 0$ on W^*. Then there exist positive numbers a and b and a function $\phi(x)$ such that*

(a) $\phi(x)$ is of class C' on the neighborhood $N(X^*; b)$;

(b) For every x in $N(X^*; b)$ the point $(x, \phi(x))$ is the unique solution in the neighborhood $N(W^*; a)$ of $g(x, y) = 0$.

Proof.—We first show that there is a neighborhood $N(W^*; a)$ in which there do not exist two solutions with the same x. If not, there would exist distinct solutions (x_n, y_n), (x_n, y'_n), in every neighborhood $N(W^*; a_n)$ with $a_n = 1/n$, and the two sequences (x_n, y_n) and (x_n, y'_n) would have a common accumulation point (x, y) in W^*. But by Theorem 2 there is a neighborhood of (x, y) in which the solution is unique. To show that the solution $\phi(x)$ is certainly defined on a neighborhood $N(X^*; b)$, we may apply the Heine-Borel theorem, since the projection X^* is also bounded and closed. By Theorem 2 the solution ϕ is defined and of class C' on a neighborhood $N(x; c)$ of each point x of X^*, but the value of c may vary with x. Since the family of neighborhoods $N(x; c/2)$ covers X^*, there is a finite subset $N(x_1; c_1/2), \ldots, N(x_k; c_k/2)$, which also covers X^*. Let b be the least of the positive numbers $c_1/2, \ldots, c_k/2$. Then each point x in $N(X^*; b)$ is in one of the neighborhoods $N(x_i; c_i)$ where the solution ϕ is surely defined.

As a simple example, we may consider the equation

$$y^2 + x_1x_2 - 1 = 0,$$

where the variables are all regarded as real. Each maximal sheet of solutions is single-valued, and its projection is bounded by the hyperbola $x_1x_2 = 1$. As an initial set W^*, we may take a segment $c_1 \leqq x_1 \leqq d_1$, $x_2 = 0$, $y = 1$. The size of the neighborhoods $N(X^*; b)$ and $N(W^*; a)$ guaranteed by Theorem 4 obviously depends on c_1 and d_1, and it is clear from this example why the set W^* in the theorem is assumed to be bounded and closed. Another example in which the properties are not obvious is afforded by the equation

$$\sin (x_1 + y) - e^{x_2 y} + x_1x_2 + 1 = 0,$$

with the initial set of solutions $c_1 \leqq x_1 \leqq d_1$, $x_2 = 0$, $y = -x_1$.

*The following extension of Theorem 4 is readily proved, again with the help of the Borel theorem:

*THEOREM 5. *Suppose that $g(x, y) = 0$ on the bounded closed set W^* in xy-space and that each point of W^* is an ordinary point for g. Then there is a finite number h of maximal sheets of solutions $W_1, \cdots, W_h$ such that $W^* \subset W_1 + \cdots + W_h$. Moreover, for every positive number a there is a positive number b such that $N(x; b)$ is contained in the projection of the part of one of the maximal sheets $W_1, \cdots, W_h$ contained in $N(w; a)$ whenever $w = (x, y)$ is a point of W^*. When W^* is also connected, $h = 1$.*

***5. Implicit Function Theorems without Differentiability.**— Theorem 1 was concerned with the existence and uniqueness of a fixed point or invariant point for a transformation $f(y)$. The next theorem yields the existence of a fixed point (but not its uniqueness) on the basis of weaker conditions than those of Theorem 1. The proof is somewhat more complicated and involves some elementary concepts of topology.

A **simplex** S in k-dimensional space R^k is determined by a set of $k + 1$ **vertices** $p_0, p_1, \cdots, p_k$, which do not lie in a $(k - 1)$-dimensional hyperplane, and S consists of all points

$$(5{:}1) \qquad y = \sum_{i=0}^{k} c_i p_i,$$

for which

$$c_i \geqq 0, \qquad \sum_{i=0}^{k} c_i = 1.$$

When $k = 1$, a simplex is a closed interval $[p_0, p_1]$. For $k = 2$, a simplex consists of the points within and on a triangle. For $k = 3$, a simplex consists of the points within and on a tetrahedron.

A **side** of S is determined by choosing a subset of its vertices and consists of the points given by (5:1) for which certain of the c_i are kept equal to zero. A side will be denoted by its vertices, and the simplex S itself will be regarded as a side when convenient. Thus when $k = 3$, the sides of a tetrahedron consist of its vertices, edges, faces, and the tetrahedron itself.

Any point $q = \sum d_i p_i$ of S, not a vertex, determines a **simplicial partition** of S into subsimplices T_j, where T_j has q as a vertex in place of p_j. (When q is on a side of S not containing p_j, the corresponding T_j is not present.) It is clear that a point belonging to a subsimplex T_j also belongs to S. To show that every point y of S given by (5:1) belongs to some subsimplex T_j, let $v = \text{minimum } (c_i/d_i)$, and let $u_i = c_i - vd_i$. Then $vq + \sum u_i p_i = \sum c_i p_i$, $u_i \geqq 0$, $v + \sum u_i = 1$, and at least one $u_i = 0$. This subdividing process may be repeated as often as is desired, with the proviso that each new vertex q is to be used to subdivide each simplex to which it belongs. The result of a finite succession of such subdivisions will also be called a **simplicial partition** and will be denoted by π. It is clear that the maximum diameter of a subsimplex of S may be made arbitrarily small by choice of a suitable simplicial partition π.

For two-dimensional space, Fig. 1 illustrates a partition that is not simplicial because q_1 and q_2 are not vertices of every subsimplex to which they belong, while a simplicial partition using the same vertices is given in Fig. 2.

We shall be interested in the properties of a function $\mu(q)$ defined for every vertex q of a partition π of S, taking only the values $0, 1, \ldots, k$, and such that whenever q lies on a side

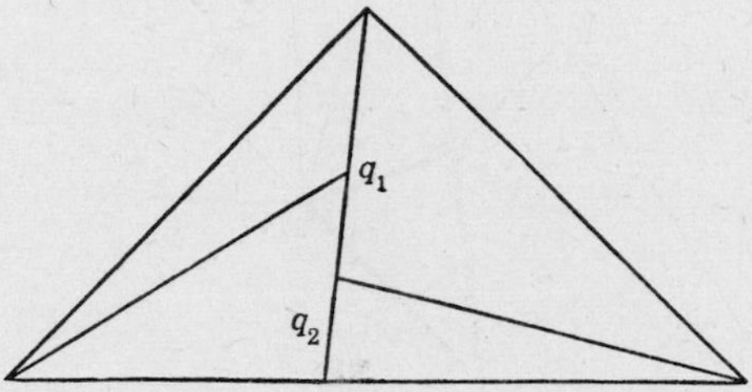

FIG. 1.

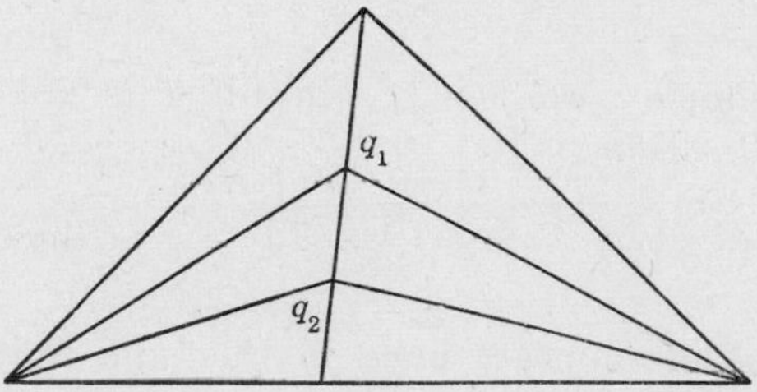

FIG. 2.

$(p_{i_0}, p_{i_1}, \ldots, p_{i_m})$ of S, $\mu(q)$ has one of the values $i_0, i_1, \ldots, i_m$. A subsimplex T in π is called a μ-**simplex** in case the set of values of $\mu(q)$ for q ranging over the vertices of T is $[0, 1, \ldots, k]$. A $(k - 1)$-dimensional side U of a subsimplex in π is called a μ-**side** in case the set of values of $\mu(q)$ for q ranging over the vertices of U is $[0, 1, \cdots, k - 1]$. In Fig. 3 is shown a simplicial partition of a triangle S, with vertices labeled with the values of a function $\mu(q)$, and with the single μ-simplex present shown by the heavy line. There are two μ-sides, but only one of these lies on the boundary of S. This figure illustrates some of the possibilities that must be considered in the proof of Lemma 1.

LEMMA 1. *For every simplicial partition π of S the number of μ-simplices is odd.*

Proof.—The statement is easily seen to be true for one-dimensional space. Now let ρ be the number of μ-simplices, let σ be the number of μ-sides lying on the boundary of S, and let $\alpha(T)$ be the number of μ-sides of an arbitrary subsimplex T of π.

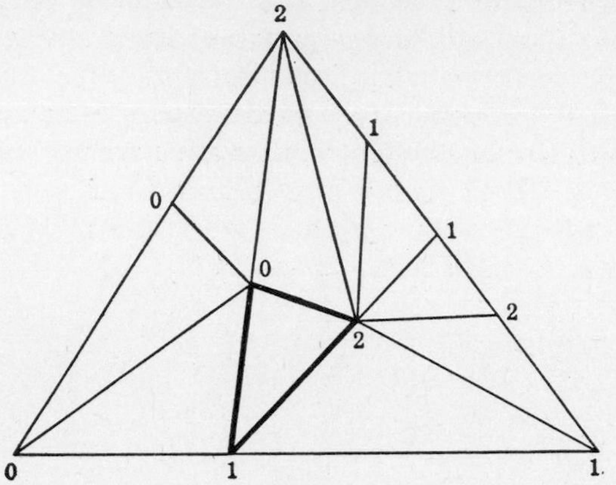

FIG. 3.

If T is a μ-simplex, $\alpha(T) = 1$, while if T is not a μ-simplex, $\alpha(T) = 0$ or 2. Hence

$$\rho \equiv \sum_{\pi} \alpha(T) \qquad (\text{mod } 2).$$

Since every μ-side appears once in this sum if it lies on the boundary of S, and twice if it does not, we have also

$$\sigma \equiv \sum_{\pi} \alpha(T) \qquad (\text{mod } 2).$$

Since all μ-sides on the boundary of S must lie on the side $(p_0, p_1, \ldots, p_{k-1})$, it follows that, if the statement holds for $(k - 1)$-dimensional space, it holds for k-dimensional space.

LEMMA 2. *Let $A_0, A_1, \ldots, A_k$ be closed sets such that every m-dimensional side $(p_{i_0}, p_{i_1}, \ldots, p_{i_m})$ of the simplex S is contained in the sum $A_{i_0} + A_{i_1} + \cdots + A_{i_m}$, for $m = 0, 1, \cdots, k$. Then the sets A_i have a common point.*

Proof.—For an arbitrary integer n, there is a simplicial partition π of S for which each subsimplex has diameter less than $1/n$. For each vertex q of π, there is a side $(p_{i_0}, p_{i_1}, \ldots, p_{i_m})$ of S of lowest dimension containing q. Then q is in one of the sets $A_{i_0}, A_{i_1}, \cdots, A_{i_m}$, say in A_{i_j}. Then if we set $\mu(q) = i_j$, the function μ has the properties required for Lemma 1, so that there is a μ-simplex $(q_0^n, q_1^n, \ldots, q_k^n)$ in π. We may suppose the notation for the vertices chosen so that $\mu(q_i^n) = i$, and thus q_i^n is in the set A_i. The sequence (q_0^n) has a point of accumulation y, which is also a point of accumulation of each sequence (q_i^n), since the diameter of $(q_0^n, q_1^n, \ldots, q_k^n)$ is less than $1/n$. So the point y is in each set A_i.

THEOREM 6. *Suppose the function f on S to R^k is continuous on the k-dimensional simplex S and transforms the boundary of S into part of S. Then there is a point y in S such that $y = f(y)$.*

Proof.—If S has vertices $p_0, p_1, \ldots, p_k$, every point y of the space R^k may be represented in the form

$$(5:2) \qquad y = \sum_{i=0}^{k} c_i p_i, \qquad \sum_{i=0}^{k} c_i = 1,$$

the points of S being characterized by the additional conditions $c_i \geqq 0$. Moreover, the coefficients c_i are continuous functions of y, since the equations (5:2) have the determinant of the coefficients of the c_i different from zero when the points p_i determine a k-dimensional simplex. Hence the equations

$$f(y) = \sum_{i=0}^{k} c_i' p_i, \qquad \sum_{i=0}^{k} c_i' = 1,$$

determine the c_i' as continuous functions of y. Thus if we let A_i denote the set of all points y for which $c_i' \leqq c_i$, each set A_i is closed. If y is a point of a side $(p_{i_0}, p_{i_1}, \ldots, p_{i_m})$, then $\sum_{j=0}^{m} c_{i_j} = 1$, and also $\sum_{j=0}^{m} c_{i_j}' \leqq 1$ since $c_i' \geqq 0$ when y is on the boundary of S, and $m = k$ and $\sum_{j=0}^{m} c_{i_j}' = \sum_{i=0}^{k} c_i' = 1$ when y is interior to S. Thus $c_{i_j}' \leqq c_{i_j}$ for at least one value of j, so that the sets A_i satisfy the conditions of Lemma 2. A common point of all the sets A_i must have $c_i' = c_i$, since $\sum_{i=0}^{k} c_i = \sum_{i=0}^{k} c_i' = 1$.

Theorem 6 has an immediate extension to the case when f is on a bounded closed set T to R^k, and there exists a continuous function g on $T + f(T)$ to R^k, having a single-valued inverse, and such that $g(T)$ is a simplex S. Extensions of the theorem to more general metric spaces than R^k have been obtained by various writers.[1] Existence theorems for differential equations follow from such a fixed-point theorem for the space $\mathfrak{C}$ of continuous functions.[2] There are also more complicated theorems on fixed points for continuous transformations of manifolds that are not topologically equivalent to a simplex.[3]

In case the transformation f in Theorem 6 depends also on a parameter x, the equation $y = f(x, y)$ determines a function $y = \phi(x)$, which may however be multiple-valued, so that nothing can be proved about its continuity. However, when the solution $y = \phi(x)$ of an equation $g(x, y) = 0$ is known to be single-valued, its continuity may be proved under rather general conditions, given in the following theorem:

THEOREM 7. *If the function $g(x, y)$ is continuous on the bounded closed set W_0 in xy-space and if for each x in the bounded closed set S, $y = \phi(x)$ is the unique solution of the equation $g(x, y) = 0$ having (x, y) in W_0, then ϕ is continuous on S.*

Proof.—By the first condition in Theorem 25 of Chap. IV, the set of all solutions of $g(x, y) = 0$, lying in W_0 and having x in S, is bounded and closed. By the third condition of the same theorem, $\phi(x)$ is continuous.

If, for example, f is continuous on a bounded closed set S and has a single-valued inverse, then f^{-1} is also continuous. When S is one-dimensional and f is properly monotonic, f^{-1} is obviously single-valued. Examples, such as $f(y) = 1/y$ for $1 \leqq y < \infty$, $f(0) = 0$, or $f(y) = y$ for $0 < y < 1$, $f(-1) = 0$, $f(2) = 1$, show that f^{-1} need not be continuous when S is not closed.

REFERENCES

1. Goursat, *Mathematical Analysis*, Vol. 1, Chaps. 2, 9.
2. Hobson, *The Theory of Functions of a Real Variable*, Vol. 1, pp. 432–443.
3. Pierpont, *The Theory of Functions of Real Variables*, Vol. 1, Chap. 9.
4. Bliss, "Fundamental Existence Theorems," *Princeton Colloquium Lectures, American Mathematical Society.*
5. Bolza, *Vorlesungen über Variationsrechnung*, pp. 158–168.
6. Moulton, *Differential Equations*, Chap. 6.

[1] See, for example, Schauder, "Der Fixpunktsatz in Funktionalräumen," *Studia Mathematica*, Vol. 2 (1930), p. 171.

[2] See Birkhoff and Kellogg, "Invariant Points in Function Space," *Transactions of the American Mathematical Society*, Vol. 23 (1922), p. 96.

[3] See, for example, Alexandroff and Hopf, *Topologie*, Vol. 1 (1935), Chap. 14.

CHAPTER IX

ORDINARY DIFFERENTIAL EQUATIONS

1. Conditions Ensuring the Existence of Solutions.—In the following we shall let x denote the single real independent variable, and let y denote the dependent variables, of which there may be any finite number. Derivatives with respect to x will be denoted by accents. Thus a system of differential equations involving only first derivatives may be written in the form

$$F(x, y, y') = 0. \tag{1:1}$$

An equation or a system of equations involving derivatives of higher orders may always be reduced to a system of the form (1:1) by the introduction of new dependent variables. For example, consider the equation

$$y'' + a^2 y = 0. \tag{1:2}$$

If we set $y_1 = y$, $y_2 = y'$, equation (1:2) is equivalent to the system

$$\begin{aligned} y_1' &= y_2, \\ y_2' &= -a^2 y_1. \end{aligned} \tag{1:3}$$

We shall begin by considering systems of the form

$$y' = f(x, y), \tag{1:4}$$

in which the derivatives are expressed explicitly as functions of x and y. Here it is understood that the number of equations is the same as the number of dependent variables y which are to be determined as functions of x. If there is only one equation and one variable y, the equation (1:4) may be pictured as attaching to each point in a region of the xy-plane a line whose slope is $f(x, y)$. The problem of solving the differential equation is that of finding a curve having as its tangent at each point the line attached to that point. The extension of this geometrical interpretation to more dimensions is immediate.

By a **solution** of (1:4) we shall mean a differentiable function $y(x)$ defined on an (open or closed) interval (a, b) and such that $y'(x) = f(x, y(x))$ identically on (a, b). The set of all points $(x, y(x))$ with x on (a, b) is called the **graph** of the solution. There will in general be infinitely many solutions. If we adjoin to the differential equation (1:4) initial conditions of the form $y(\xi) = \eta$, then the solution on an interval (a,b) containing ξ is uniquely determined, provided the function f has suitable properties. The requirement that the solution shall satisfy the initial condition $y(\xi) = \eta$ is expressed geometrically by saying that the graph of the solution shall pass through the point (ξ, η). We shall be interested in studying the properties of the solution as a function $y(x, \xi, \eta)$ of x and these initial values. The variables ξ and η constitute a special choice of the constants of integration, convenient for theoretical purposes. In a sufficiently restricted domain the complete family of solutions is obtained with the value of ξ fixed. In the first theorem to be proved the domain of the function f is assumed to have a special shape.

THEOREM 1. *Suppose that $f(x, y)$ is continuous in x and that there exists a constant K such that*

$$\|f(x, y) - f(x, y_1)\| \leqq K\|y - y_1\| \tag{1:5}$$

for all values of x, y, and y_1 with $a \leqq x \leqq b$. Then there exists a unique family $y(x, \xi, \eta)$ of solutions of the differential equations (1:4), defined for all x and ξ on the interval $[a, b]$ and for all η, and such that

$$y(\xi, \xi, \eta) = \eta.$$

Moreover, the functions $y(x, \xi, \eta)$ and $y'(x, \xi, \eta)$ are continuous.

Proof.—It is clear that f is continuous in x and y together, since by the Lipschitz condition (1:5) it is continuous in y uniformly with respect to x. Now define a sequence of functions by successive substitutions as follows:

$$\begin{aligned} y_0(x, \xi, \eta) &= \eta, \\ y_{m+1}(x, \xi, \eta) &= \eta + \int_\xi^x f(x, y_m)\, dx, \quad m = 0, 1, 2, \cdots . \end{aligned} \tag{1:6}$$

By Theorem 9 of Chap. VII, the functions $y_m(x, \xi, \eta)$ are continuous for x and ξ on $[a, b]$ and η arbitrary. For each number N there exists a Q such that

$$\|y_1(x, \xi, \eta) - y_0(x, \xi, \eta)\| \leqq Q$$

on the region R_N consisting of all x and ξ on $[a, b]$ and all η with $\|\eta\| \leqq N$. Then it may be shown by use of the Lipschitz condition (1:5) and induction that

$$\|y_{m+1} - y_m\| \leqq QK^m|x - \xi|^m/m!$$

on R_N. Since the series $\sum QK^m(b - a)^m/m!$ converges, it follows from Theorem 17 of Chap. VII that the sequence $(y_m(x, \xi, \eta))$ converges uniformly on R_N. Since N may be chosen arbitrarily large, the limit $y(x, \xi, \eta)$ is defined for all values of η and is a continuous function of its arguments, by Theorem 6 of Chap. VII. Also $f(x, y_m(x, \xi, \eta))$ converges uniformly to $f(x, y(x, \xi, \eta))$ on R_N, and so by (1:6) and Theorem 7 of Chap. VII,

$$\begin{aligned} y(x, \xi, \eta) &= \eta + \lim \int_\xi^x f(x, y_m(x, \xi, \eta))\, dx \\ &= \eta + \int_\xi^x f(x, y(x, \xi, \eta))\, dx. \end{aligned} \tag{1:7}$$

By Theorem 9 of Chap. VI we may differentiate (1:7) to obtain (1:4), from which the continuity of $y'(x, \xi, \eta)$ is obvious. The uniqueness of the solution may be proved by supposing there are two solutions $y(x)$ and $z(x)$ corresponding to the same initial values (ξ, η). Then

$$y = \eta + \int_\xi^x f(x, y)\, dx, \qquad z = \eta + \int_\xi^x f(x, z)\, dx.$$

Let $P = \max \|y(x) - z(x)\|$ on $[a, b]$. Then by the Lipschitz condition (1:5),

$$\|y(x) - z(x)\| \leqq K \int_\xi^x \|y - z\|\, dx \leqq PK|x - \xi|,$$

and by induction we find that

$$\|y(x) - z(x)\| \leqq PK^m|x - \xi|^m/m!$$

for every m, so that $y(x) = z(x)$.

It is clear from the preceding proof that an arbitrary continuous function of (x, ξ, η) may be taken as the initial approximation $y_0(x, \xi, \eta)$ in place of the special choice indicated in (1:6). When this method of approximation is being used for numerical computation of a solution, a suitable choice of $y_0(x)$ may save much labor.

Before proceeding to an extension of Theorem 1, we consider

some examples. A most important class of equations to which Theorem 1 is applicable is the class of linear equations. We shall write a system of linear equations in the matrix notation

$$y' = A(x)y + c(x), \tag{1:8}$$

where A is a square matrix of continuous functions of x, defined for x on the interval $[a, b]$, c is a matrix of only one column whose elements have the same properties, and y and y' are likewise regarded as matrices having only one column. The maximum of the sum of the absolute values of the elements of A is effective as a Lipschitz constant K in Theorem 1, though it is not in general the smallest one.

In the following examples, the conclusions of Theorem 1 are not all fulfilled. In each there is a single variable y, and the explicit solutions are easily obtained by elementary means. The square roots indicated are all understood to be the positive roots.

A. $y' = 2y^{1/2}$.
B. $y' = 2|y|^{1/2} \sin x$.
C. $y' = (1 - y^2)^{1/2}$.
D. $y' = (1 - y^2)^{3/2}$.
E. $y' = y^2$.

In example A the right-hand side is defined only for $y \geqq 0$, and fails to satisfy a Lipschitz condition on this domain. There are infinitely many continuous solutions proceeding to the right from any point on the x-axis, each composed of a piece of that axis and the right half of a parabola $y = (x - c)^2$, but there is only one solution proceeding to the left from such a point. In example B the right-hand side is defined and continuous for all values of x and y, and the solution fails to be uniquely determined either to the right or to the left if it ever becomes tangent to the x-axis. Example C is somewhat similar to A. We note that distinct solutions can meet only at points where the Lipschitz condition fails. In example D the right-hand side has a continuous derivative, and so a Lipschitz condition is satisfied in the domain between the lines $y = \pm 1$, and there is a unique solution in the form

$$y = \frac{x - c}{[1 + (x - c)^2]^{1/2}},$$

through each point between these lines. None of these solutions ever reaches either of the lines $y = \pm 1$. The conclusion of Theorem 1 holds with the restriction that η shall lie in the strip bounded by the lines $y = \pm 1$, but this conclusion cannot be deduced from the fact that the hypotheses hold in this strip, as is shown by example E. Here the function y^2 satisfies a Lipschitz condition on every finite interval of the y-axis, but each solution $y = 1/(c - x)$ has a discontinuity. According to Theorem 1 this could not happen if the right-hand side satisfied a Lipschitz condition on the whole y-axis.

The next two theorems are preliminary results useful in securing the continuity in the initial values and parameters of the solutions described in Theorem 4. They also have applications in more general situations.

THEOREM 2. *Suppose that $y(x)$ and $z(x)$ are continuous functions with piecewise continuous derivatives on the interval $a \leqq x \leqq b$. Suppose also that $f(x, y)$ is continuous in x and satisfies a Lipschitz condition in y, with constant K, on a domain D containing the graphs of $y(x)$ and $z(x)$. Suppose finally that*

$$\|y'(x) - z'(x) - f(x, y(x)) + f(x, z(x))\| \leqq \epsilon \tag{1:9}$$

at the points of $[a, b]$ where $y'(x)$ and $z'(x)$ exist and are continuous. Then for each ξ and x on the interval $[a, b]$, we have

$$\|y(x) - z(x)\| \leqq \|y(\xi) - z(\xi)\| e^{K|x-\xi|} + \frac{\epsilon}{K}(e^{K|x-\xi|} - 1).$$

Proof.—Let $p(x) = y(x) - z(x)$. When $x < \xi$, we may use the substitution $x = -u$, so it is only necessary to consider the case $\xi \leqq x$. Then with the help of the Lipschitz condition and (1:9), we find that

$$\|p(x) - p(\xi)\| \leqq K \int_\xi^x \|p\| \, dx + \epsilon(x - \xi),$$

and so

$$\|p(x)\| \leqq \|p(\xi)\| + K \int_\xi^x \left\{ \|p\| + \frac{\epsilon}{K} \right\} dx. \tag{1:10}$$

Let $M = \max \|p(x)\|$ on $[a, b]$, and assume that

$$\|p(x)\| \leqq \|p(\xi)\| + \left\{ \|p(\xi)\| + \frac{\epsilon}{K} \right\} \{e^{K(x-\xi)} - 1\} + \frac{MK^n(x - \xi)^n}{n!}. \tag{1:11}$$

This holds for $n = 1$, by (1:10), since $e^{K(x-\xi)} - 1 \geqq K(x - \xi)$. By substituting (1:11) in (1:10) and integrating, we obtain (1:11) with n replaced by $n + 1$. By letting n approach infinity in (1:11), we obtain the desired conclusion.

THEOREM 3. *Suppose that the functions $y(x)$ and $z(x)$ are of class C' on the interval $a \leqq x \leqq b$, and that the functions $f(x, y)$ and $g(x, y)$ are continuous on a domain D containing the graphs of $y(x)$ and $z(x)$. Suppose also that on D, $f(x, y)$ satisfies a Lipschitz condition in y, with constant K, and that*

$$\|f(x, y(x))\| \leqq M,$$
$$\|f(x, z(x)) - g(x, z(x))\| \leqq \epsilon,$$
$$y'(x) = f(x, y(x)), \qquad z'(x) = g(x, z(x)),$$

on $[a, b]$. Then for each ξ, ξ, and x on the interval $[a, b]$, we have

$$\|y(x) - z(x)\| \leqq \{\|y(\xi) - z(\xi)\| + M|\xi - \xi|\}e^{K|x-\xi|} + \frac{\epsilon}{K}(e^{K|x-\xi|} - 1).$$

This theorem follows immediately from Theorem 2. From it we see at once that (granting the existence of the solutions) a solution of $y' = g(x, y)$ will be near a solution of $y' = f(x, y)$ taking the same initial values, provided $g(x, y)$ differs but little from $f(x, y)$. Thus, for sufficiently small values of x, a solution of the equation $y' = \sin xy$ differs but little from the solution $y = Ce^{x^2/2}$ (taking the same initial value) of the equation $y' = xy$. Likewise for sufficiently small values of x, a solution of the equation $y' = e^{xy+y}$ with $y(0) = \eta$ differs but little from the solution with the same initial value of the equation $y' = e^{x\eta+y}$.

The next theorem is concerned with the maximal extent of a solution of a system of differential equations, with somewhat relaxed conditions on $f(x, y)$. It is convenient at this point to introduce parameters α in the differential equations. If R denotes a set in (x, y, α)-space, the notation R_α will be used to denote the **section** of R consisting of all points (x, y) for which (x, y, α) is in R.

THEOREM 4. *Let $f(x, y, \alpha)$ be defined and continuous on an open set R in (x, y, α)-space and suppose in addition that each point of R has a neighborhood on which f satisfies a Lipschitz condition* (1:5) *with respect to y. Then for each (ξ, η, α) in R there exists a unique* *solution* $y(x, \xi, \eta, \alpha)$ *of the differential equations*

$$y' = f(x, y, \alpha), \tag{1:12}$$

defined and continuous for all x *on an open interval* $(a(\xi, \eta, \alpha), b(\xi, \eta, \alpha))$, *whose graph lies in the section* R_α *of* R, *passes through* (ξ, η), *and has all its finite limiting points, as* x *approaches* $a(\xi, \eta, \alpha)$ *or* $b(\xi, \eta, \alpha)$, *on the boundary of* R_α. *Moreover, the solution* $y(x, \xi, \eta, \alpha)$ *is continuous in all its arguments.*

Proof.—Let I be an interval in R, with edges parallel to the coordinate axes, on which f satisfies a uniform Lipschitz condition. Then by Theorem 21 of Chap. VII, there exists a function $g(x, y, \alpha)$, defined for the same interval of values of x and α and for all y, satisfying the same Lipschitz condition, and equal to f on I.[1] This function g is easily seen to be continuous. Thus by Theorem 1 the differential equations $z' = g(x, z, \alpha)$ have a unique solution $z(x, \xi, \eta, \alpha)$, which is continuous in all its arguments by Theorem 3. If (ξ, η, α) is interior to the interval I, the portion of this solution which lies interior to I will be denoted by $y(x, \xi, \eta, \alpha)$. It is a solution of the original differential equation (1:12) defined on an interval $a_1(\xi, \eta, \alpha) < x < b_1(\xi, \eta, \alpha)$, and extending from boundary to boundary of I. Now let $(a(\xi, \eta, \alpha), b(\xi, \eta, \alpha))$ be the logical sum of all intervals containing ξ on which a solution $y(x, \xi, \eta, \alpha)$ is defined, lies in R_α, passes through (ξ, η), and is continuous in all its arguments. Clearly the solution is uniquely determined on the interval $(a(\xi, \eta, \alpha), b(\xi, \eta, \alpha))$, since a Lipschitz condition holds near each point on the graph. If (x_n, y_n) is a sequence of points on the graph such that $\lim_{n=\infty} x_n = a = a(\xi, \eta, \alpha)$, $\lim_{n=\infty} y_n = u$, we can show by an indirect proof that the point (a, u) is on the boundary of R_α. For if (a, u) is in R_α, then there is a neighborhood $N(a, u, \alpha; \epsilon)$ whose closure is contained in R and on which $f(x, y, \alpha)$ satisfies a Lipschitz condition with respect to y. Let $M = \text{l.u.b.}\ \|f(x, y, \alpha')\|$ for (x, y, α') in $N(a, u, \alpha; \epsilon)$, and suppose $\delta < \epsilon/(2M + 1)$. When (x_n, y_n) is in $N(a, u; \delta)$, the solution $y(x, \xi, \eta, \alpha)$, which passes through (x_n, y_n), must satisfy

[1] For extension of the domain of f from an interval a simpler method than that of Theorem 21 may be employed. For example, if there is only one component of y, and the interval I is defined by $a \leqq x \leqq b$, $c \leqq y \leqq d$, we may set $g(x, y) = f(x, c)$ for $y < c$, $g(x, y) = f(x, d)$ for $y > d$.

$$\|y - u\| \leqq \|y - y_n\| + \|y_n - u\| \leqq M|x - x_n| + \delta$$
$$\leqq (2M + 1)\delta < \epsilon$$

for $a - \delta \leqq x \leqq x_n$, and since that solution extends from boundary to boundary of $N(a, u; \epsilon)$ it must be defined for $a - \delta \leqq x < b$. The solution $y(x, \xi, \eta, \alpha)$ is also continuous in all its arguments on the extended interval $a - \delta \leqq x < b$, since $y_n = y(x_n, \xi, \eta, \alpha)$ is continuous in (ξ, η, α) for x_n fixed, and $y(x, x_n, y_n, \alpha)$ is continuous in (x, y_n, α). Thus we have obtained a contradiction with the definition of the interval $(a(\xi, \eta, \alpha), b(\xi, \eta, \alpha))$, so that the point (a, u) cannot be in R_α.

The hypotheses of Theorem 4 are clearly fulfilled in case $f(x, y, \alpha)$ and the partial derivatives $f_y(x, y, \alpha)$ are continuous on R. Consequently, Theorem 4 is applicable in the examples A to E listed above, provided the region R is suitably restricted. In example A, for instance, we would suppose $y > 0$. In example D, the domain of the function f may be extended by setting $f = 0$ for $|y| > 1$, and then the hypotheses of Theorem 1 are satisfied. That a solution may have infinitely many limiting values on the boundary of the region R is shown by the example

$$y' = y(\cos \log x)/x,$$

whose general solution is

$$y = Ce^{\sin \log x}.$$

However, when $f(x, y)$ is continuous on R plus its boundary, there cannot be more than one finite limiting point at either end of the interval (a, b).

The method of successive substitutions may be used to prove that, when the functions of the set denoted by $f(x, y)$ are all analytic functions of their arguments, then the solutions of the differential equations (1:4) are analytic functions. For this purpose the variables must be regarded as complex variables, and care must be taken to restrict the independent variable x to a neighborhood of ξ so small that the successive approximations $y_m(x, \xi, \eta)$ all lie in the domain where the functions $f(x, y)$ are analytic. The line of development explicitly outlined in Theorems 1 and 4 is not applicable. The reader may consult Picard [8], pages 379–381.

*When the function $f(x, y)$ is only assumed to be continuous on the open set R, we may prove the existence (though not the uniqueness) of a solution through each point of R, extending from boundary to boundary of R, with the help of the preceding theorems and some theorems from Chap. VII, as follows:

*THEOREM 5. *Let $f(x, y)$ be continuous on an open set R in (x, y)-space. Then through each point (ξ, η) in R there passes at least one solution $y(x)$ of the differential equation $y' = f(x, y)$, which is defined and continuous on an open interval (a, b), has its graph in R, and has all its finite limiting points, as x approaches a or b, on the boundary of R.*

Proof.—Consider an interval I contained in R, defined by inequalities of the form $|x - \xi| \leqq h_1$, $\|y - \eta\| \leqq h_2$, and let $M = \text{l.u.b.}\ \|f(x, y)\|$ on I. By Theorem 29 of Chap. VII, there is a sequence (P_n) of polynomials such that $\|P_n(x, y) - f(x, y)\|$ approaches zero uniformly on I, and $\|P_n(x, y)\| \leqq M$ on I. By Theorem 4, there is a unique solution $y_n(x)$ of the equation $y' = P_n(x, y)$, passing through the point (ξ, η). This solution lies in the interval I at least for $|x - \xi| \leqq h$, where h is the smaller of h_1 and h_2/M. The functions $y_n(x)$ are bounded and have bounded derivatives for $|x - \xi| \leqq h$, and so they are equicontinuous. Hence by Theorem 28 of Chap. VII, there is a subsequence (y_{n_j}) which converges uniformly on the interval $|x - \xi| \leqq h$ to a function $y(x)$. Then with the help of an elementary inequality (or from Theorem 4 of Chap. VII) it follows that $y'_{n_j}(x) = P_{n_j}(x, y_{n_j}(x))$ converges uniformly to $f(x, y(x))$, and so $y(x)$ has a derivative $y'(x) = f(x, y(x))$ for $|x - \xi| \leqq h$, by Theorem 8 of Chap. VII.

To show the existence of a solution with the properties described in the theorem, we now consider the set of all open intervals (β, γ) containing ξ, with β and γ rational, on which a continuous solution through the point (ξ, η) is defined. This set is denumerable, and we may let (β_n, γ_n) denote a denumeration of it. Let y_1 be a solution on the interval (β_1, γ_1), and take the smallest integer $n_1 > 1$, if one exists, such that the interval $(\beta_{n_1}, \gamma_{n_1})$ is not contained in (β_1, γ_1), and such that there is a solution $\bar{y}_2$ on $(\beta_{n_1}, \gamma_{n_1})$ equal to y_1 on the common part of the two intervals. Such a solution $\bar{y}_2$ defines an extension y_2 of the solution y_1 to the sum of the intervals (β_1, γ_1) and $(\beta_{n_1}, \gamma_{n_1})$. Next take the smallest integer $n_2 > n_1$ such that a solution $\bar{y}_3$ on $(\beta_{n_2}, \gamma_{n_2})$ defines in a similar way an extension y_3 of y_2. Proceeding in this way, we obtain a finite or denumerable increasing sequence of solutions, whose logical sum defines a solution $y(x)$ on an open interval (a, b). If a limiting point $(x, y) = (a, u)$ were interior to R, there would be a solution containing $y(x)$ and defined on an interval extending to the left of a, by an argument somewhat similar to that used in the proof of Theorem 4. Such a solution would have a section defined on an interval (β_n, γ_n) with $\beta_n < a$. But this contradicts the definition of the solution $y(x)$.

A direct proof of the existence of a solution without the use of the Lipschitz condition, using the Cauchy polygon method, is given, for example, in Kamke [3], pages 59–66, 126–130.

*With the help of an additional hypothesis it may be proved that the graph of the solution described in Theorem 5 cannot have any limiting points at infinity except for $x = \infty$, as indicated below.

*THEOREM 6. *Let $L(u)$ be a positive continuous function defined for $0 \leqq u < \infty$, such that $\int_0^\infty \frac{du}{L(u)}$ diverges. Suppose that $\|f(x, y)\| < L(\|y\|)$ for all values of x and y for which f is defined. Let $y(x)$ be a continuous function having a derivative $y'(x) = f(x, y(x))$ on the interval $a < x < b$. Then the graph of $y(x)$ has no limiting points at infinity unless a or b is infinite.*

Proof.—Let $u_0 = \|y(\xi)\|$, where ξ is an arbitrary point of the interval (a, b). The function

$$x = \psi(u) = \int_{u_0}^{u} \frac{du}{L(u)} + \xi$$

is continuous and increasing for $u \geqq 0$, and $\lim_{u=+\infty} \psi(u) = +\infty$, and so ψ has a single-valued inverse $u = \phi(x)$ which is defined and continuous at least for $\xi \leqq x < \infty$, and satisfies the differential equation $u' = L(u)$. We shall show by an indirect proof that $\|y(x)\| \leqq \phi(x)$ on the interval $\xi \leqq x < b$, so that $y(x)$ cannot have any limiting point at infinity as x approaches b unless b itself is infinite. If there is a point x_1 such that $\|y(x_1)\| > \phi(x_1)$, there is a point x_0 such that $\xi \leqq x_0 < x_1$, $\|y(x_0)\| = \phi(x_0)$, and $\|y(x)\| > \phi(x)$ for $x_0 < x < x_1$. Then $\|y'(x_0)\| = \|f(x_0, y(x_0))\| < L(\|y(x_0)\|) = \phi'(x_0)$, and hence $\|y(x) - y(x_0)\| < \phi(x) - \phi(x_0)$ on a small interval $x_0 < x < x_0 + \delta$. From this we find immediately $\|y(x)\| \leqq \|y(x_0)\| + \phi(x) - \phi(x_0) = \phi(x)$ for $x_0 < x <$

$x_0 + \delta$, but this contradicts a preceding inequality. The corresponding result for the interval $a < x \leqq \xi$ follows from the above by the transformation $x = -t$.

Another existence theorem, for the case when $f(x, y)$ is continuous in y but merely integrable in the Lebesgue sense with respect to x, is discussed in Caratheodory's *Vorlesungen über reelle Funktionen*, pages 665–688.[1] A résumé of a number of other existence theorems and their applications has been published by W. M. Whyburn.[2] Both the method of successive substitutions and the Cauchy polygon method may be extended to apply to a rather general type of integral equations.[3] They may be used, of course, for the actual computation of solutions of particular equations. For a discussion of convenient methods in the numerical solution of differential equations, see Moulton [1], Chaps. 12, 13; Bennett, Milne, and Bateman [7]; and Scarborough [9].

2. Special Properties of Linear Homogeneous Differential Equations.—In this section we wish to consider the special case

$$y' = A(x)y \tag{2:1}$$

of equation (1:8) in which there are no terms independent of y, and $A(x)$ is a matrix of k rows and k columns whose elements are continuous on $a \leqq x \leqq b$. As before, y is regarded as a matrix having only one column. If $Y(x)$ is a matrix of several columns each of which is a solution of (2:1), we write

$$Y' = A(x)Y$$

and call Y a **matrix solution** of (2:1). The columns of a matrix solution Y form a **fundamental set of solutions** of (2:1) in case (*a*) these columns are linearly independent and (*b*) every solution of (2:1) is expressible linearly in terms of these columns. In

[1] See also McShane, *Integration*, Chap. 9.

[2] See *Existence Theorems for Ordinary Differential Equations*, Publications of the University of California at Los Angeles in Mathematical and Physical Sciences, Vol. 1, No. 2, pp. 115–133.

[3] See A. M. Killen, *An Application of the Cauchy-Lipschitz Method to a System of Functional Equations*, M.S. Thesis, University of Chicago, 1930; H. H. Bishop, *Existence Theorems for a Class of Integral Equations*, M.S. Thesis, University of Chicago, 1935; Graves, "Implicit Functions and Differential Equations in General Analysis," *Transactions of the American Mathematical Society*, Vol. 29 (1927), pp. 514–552.

case $k = 1$, equation (2:1) may be explicitly solved, and in this case it is seen at once that every solution is a constant multiple of a particular solution. The proofs of the next two theorems are obvious.

THEOREM 7. *The class of solutions of* (2:1) *is a linear set, that is, every linear combination with constant coefficients of solutions is also a solution.*

THEOREM 8. *If a solution of* (2:1) *has* $y(\xi) = 0$ *at a point* ξ, *then* $y(x)$ *vanishes identically on* $[a, b]$.

This is so since $y(x) = 0$ is always a solution, and by Theorem 1 there is only one solution with given initial values.

THEOREM 9. *If* Y *is a matrix solution of* (2:1) *then the columns of* Y *form a fundamental set of solutions if and only if* Y *is square and has a determinant not zero at one point. In this case the determinant of* Y *does not vanish on* $[a, b]$.

Proof.—Since the initial values $\eta = y(\xi)$ of a solution may be chosen arbitrarily, it is clear that Y must have at least k columns. If Y had more than k columns, then corresponding to a particular point ξ we could determine a matrix c of one column (and more than k rows) such that $Y(\xi)c = 0$. Then by Theorems 7 and 8 we should have $Y(x)c = 0$ on $[a, b]$, that is, the columns of Y would not be linearly independent. Hence Y is square. The argument just made applies also to show that det $Y(x)$ cannot vanish on $[a, b]$. To prove the converse, suppose that

$$\det Y(\xi) \neq 0.$$

Then the columns of Y are clearly linearly independent. Corresponding to an arbitrary solution $y(x)$ of (2:1), there is a matrix c of one column such that

$$Y(\xi)c = y(\xi).$$

Since the two solutions $Y(x)c$ and $y(x)$ have the same initial values at ξ, they must be identical on $[a, b]$ by Theorem 1.

THEOREM 10. *There exists a matrix* $Y(x)$ *whose columns form a fundamental set of solutions of* (2:1).

To see this, it is only necessary to take for the matrix $Y(\xi)$ of initial values the identity matrix I. Any other nonsingular matrix of initial values would do as well.

From these theorems we see that the solutions of (2:1) form a k-dimensional linear subspace of the space of all continuous functions on $[a, b]$ with values in k-dimensional space. The solutions of a single linear homogeneous equation of the nth order

$$\frac{d^n y}{dx^n} + p_1(x)\frac{d^{n-1}y}{dx^{n-1}} + \cdots + p_n(x)y = 0$$

form an n-dimensional linear subspace of the space $\mathfrak{C}$ of continuous real-valued functions.

When the coefficients are constant, that is, when the matrix A is independent of x, explicit formulas for the solutions may be determined. For an excellent discussion of this case, see W. D. MacMillan, *Dynamics of Rigid Bodies,* pages 419–429. The method used there is due to W. Bartky.

The following examples may serve as illustrations of the meaning of these theorems. Numerous other examples may be found in any elementary text on differential equations.

F. $xy' = y.$

G. $y'' + \mu^2 y = 0.$

H. $x^2y'' = 2xy' - (x^2 + 2)y.$

When G and H are written as systems of first-order equations, using the substitution $y_1 = y$, $y_2 = y'$, we find that a matrix of solutions of G is

$$\begin{pmatrix} \cos \mu x & \sin \mu x \\ -\sin \mu x & \cos \mu x \end{pmatrix},$$

and a matrix of solutions of H is

$$\begin{pmatrix} x \cos x & x \sin x \\ -x \sin x + \cos x & x \cos x + \sin x \end{pmatrix}.$$

The conclusion of Theorem 9 is violated in H as well as in F, but the hypotheses of this theorem are not fulfilled on any interval containing the point $x = 0$.

3. An Embedding Theorem, and the Differentiability of Solutions.—It is frequently desirable to know that a given solution of a differential equation is embedded in a family of solutions and that the family is differentiable with respect to the constants of integration. The following embedding theorem is an easy corollary of Theorem 4.

THEOREM 11. *Suppose that $f(x, y, \alpha)$ satisfies the hypotheses of Theorem* 4, *and that for $a_0 \leqq x \leqq b_0$, $y = y_0(x)$ is a solution of*

(1:12) *corresponding to* $\alpha = \alpha_0$, *whose graph* E *lies in the section* R_{α_0} *of* R. *Then there exists a positive number* δ *such that the family of solutions* $y(x, \xi, \eta, \alpha)$ *of* (1:12) *is defined and continuous for* (ξ, η) *in the neighborhood* $N(E; \delta)$, α *in* $N(\alpha_0; \delta)$ *and* $a_0 - \delta \leqq x \leqq b_0 + \delta$.

Proof.—Since the set R is open, the solution $y_0(x)$ has by Theorem 4 an extension defined on an interval $a_0 - \gamma \leqq x \leqq b_0 + \gamma$. Let E_1 denote the graph of this extended solution. Since the set of points (x, y, α_0) with (x, y) on E_1 is bounded and closed and interior to R, the Cartesian product of the neighborhoods $N(E_1; \epsilon)$ and $N(\alpha_0; \epsilon)$ lies in R when ϵ is sufficiently small. The family of solutions $y(x, \xi, \eta, \alpha)$ given by Theorem 4 is continuous, so by Theorem 23 of Chap. IV it is uniformly continuous for (ξ, η) on E, $\alpha = \alpha_0$, $a_0 - \gamma \leqq x \leqq b_0 + \gamma$. Then there is a number $\delta < \epsilon$ such that the graph of $y(x, \xi, \eta, \alpha)$ lies in $N(E_1; \epsilon)$ for (ξ, η) in $N(E; \delta)$, α in $N(\alpha_0; \delta)$, and $a_0 - \delta \leqq x \leqq b_0 + \delta$.

For convenience we shall say that a function such as $f(x, y, \alpha)$ is of class $C^{(p)}$ in y on a region R in case f and all its partial derivatives with respect to the components of y up to and including those of order p are defined and continuous in (x, y, α) throughout the region R. Partial derivatives will be indicated by subscripts, except that derivatives with respect to x will usually be indicated by accents as before. Thus the symbols f_y and y_η denote square matrices of partial derivatives, while f, y, z, y_t, y_ξ denote matrices of one column only. The proofs of the following theorems are based on a simple preliminary result, in the statement of which it is convenient to omit the parameters α.

LEMMA. *Suppose that* $f(x, y)$ *is of class* C' *in* y *on the open set* R, *and suppose that* $y(x, t)$ *is a family of solutions of the differential equations* $y' = f(x, y)$, *continuous in* (x, t) *and lying in* R *for* $a_0 \leqq x \leqq b_0$, $|t| < \delta$. *Suppose in addition that the partial derivative* $y_t(\xi, 0)$ *exists and is finite, where* ξ *is a fixed point of* $[a_0, b_0]$. *Then the derivative* $y_t(x, 0)$ *exists and is finite for* $a_0 \leqq x \leqq b_0$, *and is a solution of the linear differential equations*

$$z' = f_y(x, y(x, 0))z. \tag{3:1}$$

Proof.—If we set $\Delta y = y(x, t) - y(x, 0)$, and

$$A(x, t) = \int_0^1 f_y(x, y(x, 0) + \theta\, \Delta y)\, d\theta,$$

we see that $\Delta y/t$ is a solution of the linear differential equations

$$z' = A(x, t)z. \tag{3:2}$$

This system of equations has by Theorems 1 and 3 a unique continuous family of solutions $z(x, \xi, \zeta, t)$ defined for $a_0 \leqq x \leqq b_0$, $|t| < \delta$, ζ arbitrary, and having $z(\xi, \xi, \zeta, t) = \zeta$. Thus

$$\frac{\Delta y}{t} = z\left(x, \xi, \frac{\Delta y(\xi)}{t}, t\right),$$

and, since by hypothesis $\Delta y(\xi)/t$ has a finite limit $y_t(\xi, 0)$, we see that $\Delta y(x)/t$ likewise has a finite limit

$$y_t(x, 0) = z(x, \xi, y_t(\xi, 0), 0)$$

for $a_0 \leqq x \leqq b_0$, satisfying (3:2) for $t = 0$, that is, satisfying (3:1).

THEOREM 12. *Suppose that $f(x, y, \alpha)$ is of class $C^{(p)}$ in y on the open set R. Then the family $y(x, \xi, \eta, \alpha)$ of solutions of the differential equations* (1:12), *given by Theorem* 4, *has the property that the partial derivatives*

$$\begin{aligned} &y_\xi(x, \xi, \eta, \alpha),\ y_\eta(x, \xi, \eta, \alpha), \\ &y'_\xi(x, \xi, \eta, \alpha),\ y'_\eta(x, \xi, \eta, \alpha), \end{aligned} \tag{3:3}$$

are defined and continuous and of class $C^{(p-1)}$ in η for (ξ, η, α) in R and $a(\xi, \eta, \alpha) < x < b(\xi, \eta, \alpha)$. Moreover y_ξ and y_η satisfy the linear differential equations

$$z' = f_y(x, y(x, \xi, \eta, \alpha), \alpha)z \tag{3:4}$$

with the initial values

$$y_\xi(\xi, \xi, \eta, \alpha) = -f(\xi, \eta, \alpha), \qquad y_\eta(\xi, \xi, \eta, \alpha) = I,$$

where I is the identity matrix, and hence they are related by the formula

$$y_\xi(x, \xi, \eta, \alpha) = -y_\eta(x, \xi, \eta, \alpha)f(\xi, \eta, \alpha). \tag{3:5}$$

Proof.—We may clearly restrict attention to a closed interval $[a_0, b_0]$ to which ξ and x are interior, and such that $a(\xi, \eta, \alpha) < a_0 < b_0 < b(\xi, \eta, \alpha)$. On such an interval the preceding lemma is at once applicable to show the existence of $y_\eta(x, \xi, \eta, \alpha)$, since $y(\xi, \xi, \eta, \alpha) = \eta$ and hence $y_\eta(\xi, \xi, \eta, \alpha) = I$. Moreover, by the lemma, $y_\eta(x, \xi, \eta, \alpha)$ is a matrix solution of the equations

(3:4), and by Theorem 4 this solution must be a continuous function of x and the parameters (ξ, η, α). To show the existence of y_ξ, we take $t = \Delta\xi$ in the lemma. We have (omitting η and α),

$$\frac{y(\xi, \xi + \Delta\xi) - y(\xi, \xi)}{\Delta\xi} = \frac{\int_{\xi+\Delta\xi}^{\xi} f(x, y(x, \xi + \Delta\xi))\, dx}{\Delta\xi}$$

and by the Theorem of the Mean for integrals and the continuity of $f(x, y, \alpha)$ this has the limit $-f(\xi, \eta, \alpha)$. Thus by the lemma the derivative $y_\xi(x, \xi, \eta, \alpha)$ exists and satisfies (3:4). Since $y_\eta(\xi, \xi, \eta, \alpha) = I$, the columns of the matrix y_η form a fundamental set of solutions of (3:4), and since (3:5) holds for $x = \xi$, it holds for all values of x on $[a_0, b_0]$. The continuity of $y_\xi(x, \xi, \eta, \alpha)$ follows from (3:5), and the continuity of y'_ξ and y'_η follows from (3:4).

The proof may be completed by induction. Suppose that, whenever f is of class $C^{(p)}$ in y, the functions (3:3) are of class $C^{(p-1)}$ in η. Suppose also that the function f is of class $C^{(p+1)}$ in y. Then the right-hand sides of the equations

$$z' = f_y(x, y(x, v, w, \alpha), \alpha)z,$$
$$w' = 0,$$

are of class $C^{(p)}$ in (z, w), and hence by the induction hypothesis their solutions $z = z(x, \xi, \zeta, \eta, v, \alpha)$, $w = \eta$, are such that z_ζ and z_η are of class $C^{(p-1)}$ in (ζ, η), that is, z is of class $C^{(p)}$ in (ζ, η). It follows at once that $y_\xi(x, \xi, \eta, \alpha) = z(x, \xi, -f(\xi, \eta, \alpha), \eta, \xi, \alpha)$ is of class $C^{(p)}$ in η, and likewise for $y_\eta(x, \xi, \eta, \alpha)$. Since y_ξ and y_η are solutions of (3:4), it follows also that y'_ξ and y'_η are of class $C^{(p)}$ in η.

COROLLARY. *In case $f(x, y, \alpha)$ is of class $C^{(p)}$ in (y, α), then not only the partial derivatives* (3:3) *but also $y_\alpha(x, \xi, \eta, \alpha)$, $y'_\alpha(x, \xi, \eta, \alpha)$ are defined and continuous and of class $C^{(p-1)}$ in (η, α).*

Proof.—If we adjoin to the differential equations (1:12) the equations $\alpha' = 0$, we have a system satisfying all the conditions of the theorem with y and α as the dependent variables, and consequently the solutions have the asserted differentiability properties with respect to the initial values η and α.

THEOREM 13. *Suppose that $f(x, y, \alpha)$ is of class $C^{(p)}$ in (x, y, α) on R. Then the family $y(x, \xi, \eta, \alpha)$ of solutions of the differential* *equation* (1:12) *and its derivative* $y'(x, \xi, \eta, \alpha)$ *are of class* $C^{(p)}$ *in* (x, ξ, η, α).

Proof.—By the preceding theorem and its corollary, $y(x, \xi, \eta, \alpha)$ is of class C' in (x, ξ, η, α). Since

$$(3:6) \qquad y'(x, \xi, \eta, \alpha) = f(x, y(x, \xi, \eta, \alpha), \alpha),$$

$y'(x, \xi, \eta, \alpha)$ is also of class C'. To complete the proof we have to show that, when the statement holds for $p = q$, it must hold also for $p = q + 1$. If f is of class $C^{(q+1)}$ and $y(x, \xi, \eta, \alpha)$ is of class $C^{(q)}$, then the right-hand sides of the two systems of differential equations

$$(3:7) \quad z' = f_y(x, y(x, v, \eta, \alpha), \alpha)z,$$
$$(3:8) \quad z' = f_y(x, y(x, v, \eta, \alpha), \alpha)z + f_\alpha(x, y(x, v, \eta, \alpha), \alpha),$$

are of class $C^{(q)}$ in (x, z, v, η, α). If the statement holds for $p = q$, then the families of solutions $z(x, \xi, \zeta, v, \eta, \alpha)$ of each of these systems will be of class $C^{(q)}$ in $(x, \xi, \zeta, v, \eta, \alpha)$. Now the partial derivatives y_ξ and y_η satisfy (3:7) with $v = \xi$ and the initial values $\zeta = -f(\xi, \eta, \alpha)$ and $\zeta = I$, respectively, and y_α satisfies (3:8) with $v = \xi$ and $\zeta = 0$, so that y_ξ, y_η, and y_α are of class $C^{(q)}$. By (3:6), $y'(x, \xi, \eta, \alpha)$ is also of class $C^{(q)}$, so that y is of class $C^{(q+1)}$, and by another reference to (3:6), y' is also of class $C^{(q+1)}$. This completes the induction.

As examples let us consider the following:

J. $y' = 2|y|^{1/2}$.
K. $y' = y^2(x + y + xy^2)$.
L. $y'' = -g \sin y$.

Example J is a slight modification of example A in Sec. 1. It has the solution $y \equiv 0$. However, the solution $y(x, \xi, \eta)$ has $y(1, 0, \eta) > 1$ whenever $\eta > 0$, and the conclusion of Theorem 11 fails. In example E in Sec. 1, every solution $y(x, \xi, \eta)$ with $\eta \neq 0$ becomes infinite at one end of its interval of definition, and $y(x, \xi, 0) = 0$, but nevertheless the preceding theorems are applicable. Since $y(x, \xi, \eta) = \eta/[1 + \eta(\xi - x)]$ in this example, we can verify directly that the following statement holds:

$$(3:9) \quad M > 0 \,.\, \epsilon > 0 : \supset : \exists \delta > 0 \ni : |\eta| < \delta \,.\, |x| < M \cdot \supset \cdot |y(x, 0, \eta)| < \epsilon.$$

By Theorem 11 we know that the solutions are defined and that

(3:9) also holds in example K, although in this case we have no explicit formula for the solutions. Example L is the differential equation for the motion of a simple pendulum of unit length, where y is the angular displacement from the vertical and x is the time. If we denote the family of solutions by $y(x, \xi, \eta, \eta')$, we see that $y(x, 0, \pi, 0) = \pi$. This solution corresponds to the position of unstable equilibrium when the pendulum bob is at rest at its highest point. In this case the following statement holds by virtue of Theorem 11:

$$M > 0 \,.\, \epsilon > 0 :\supset: \exists \delta > 0 \ni: |\eta'| < \delta \,.\, |x| \leqq M \cdot\supset\cdot |y(x, 0, \pi, \eta') - \pi| < \epsilon.$$

This means that the pendulum will remain within an angular distance ϵ of the vertically upward position for M units of time, provided its initial velocity is sufficiently small.

4. First Integrals.—By definition a **first integral** of the system of differential equations (1:4) is a function $G(x, y)$ which is of class C' on an open subset T of the set R, is not constant on T, and is such that for every solution $y = \phi(x)$ of (1:4) whose graph lies in T the function $G(x, \phi(x))$ is constant.[1] Some results concerning first integrals follow immediately from the preceding sections. For convenience we shall now denote the family of solutions $y(x, \xi, \eta)$ given by Theorem 4 by $\phi(x, \xi, \eta)$, and denote its components by $\phi_i(x, \xi, \eta)$ for $i = 1, \cdots, k$. Let J denote the projection of the region R on the x-axis. For definiteness assume that $f(x, y)$ is of class C' in y.

THEOREM 14. *For each i and each fixed ξ in J, $\phi_i(\xi, x, y)$ is a first integral.*

Proof.—$\phi(\xi, x, \phi(x, \xi_0, \eta)) = \phi(\xi, \xi_0, \eta)$, and this is independent of x.

THEOREM 15. *For each fixed ξ in J, the k first integrals $\phi_i(\xi, x, y)$ are independent. Moreover, any nonconstant differentiable function of these first integrals is also a first integral.*

Proof.—The Jacobian of these first integrals as functions of y is the determinant of the matrix ϕ_η, which is never zero by Theorems 9 and 12. Hence if $H(y)$ is differentiable but not constant, $H(\phi(\xi, x, y))$ cannot be independent of y, so that there

[1] Some writers drop the adjective "first," but other writers use the term "integral" where we have used "solution." To avoid confusion we retain the classic terminology "first integral."

can be no relation existing between the first integrals $\phi_i(\xi, x, y)$. It is obvious that $H(\phi(\xi, x, y))$ is also a first integral.

THEOREM 16. *If $G(x, y)$ is a first integral on an open subset T of R, and ξ is in the projection A of T on the x-axis, then on a suitable subset of T, G may be expressed as a function of the first integrals $\phi_i(\xi, x, y)$, so that these latter may be regarded as a fundamental set.*

Proof.—Let $H(\xi, \eta) = G(x, \phi(x, \xi, \eta))$. Then

$$\begin{aligned} H(\xi, \phi(\xi, x, y)) &= G(x, \phi(x, \xi, \phi(\xi, x, y))) \\ &= G(x, \phi(x, x, y)) \\ &= G(x, y). \end{aligned}$$

THEOREM 17. *Let $G_i(x, y)$, $(i = 1, \cdots, k)$, be a set of first integrals defined on an open subset T of R, whose Jacobian with respect to y is not zero on T. Then if the equations*

$$G_i(x, y) = c_i \tag{4:1}$$

have an initial solution (ξ, η) in T, they define a solution $y = y(x)$ of the differential equations (1:4), passing through the point (ξ, η), and extending from boundary to boundary of T.

Proof.—By Theorem 3 of Chap. VIII, the equations (4:1) have a unique solution $y = \bar{y}(x)$ through the point (ξ, η) and extending from boundary to boundary of T. The differential equations (1:4) likewise have a unique solution $y = y(x)$ through (ξ, η). Since by definition a first integral is constant on each solution of (1:4), these two functions $y(x)$ and $\bar{y}(x)$ must coincide on their common interval of definition.

THEOREM 18. *A function $G(x, y)$, of class C' and not constant on an open subset T of R, is a first integral of (1:4) if and only if it is a solution of the linear homogeneous partial differential equation*

$$\frac{\partial G}{\partial x} + \sum_{i=1}^{k} \frac{\partial G}{\partial y_i} f_i(x, y) = 0 \tag{4:2}$$

on T.

This follows immediately from the definition of first integral.

From the theorems of this chapter it follows that the problems of finding the general solution of the system of ordinary differential equations (1:4) and of finding the general solution of the partial differential equation (4:2) are equivalent problems.

Moreover, a knowledge of one or more first integrals may theoretically be used to reduce the order of the system (1:4). This is sometimes but not always an advantage in the practical determination of the solutions of this system.[1]

The following examples are taken from problems of dynamics and the independent variable x represents the time, while G and H are first integrals.

M. $y'' = -g;\ G = 2gy + y'^2,\ H = -gx^2/2 - y'x + y.$

N. $y'' = -g \sin y;\ G = -2g \cos y + y'^2.$

P. $y'' = -k^2y;\ G = k^2y^2 + y'^2.$

Q. $r'' = r\theta'^2 - k^2/r^2,\ \theta'' = -2r'\theta'/r;\ G = r'^2 + r^2\theta'^2 - 2k^2/r,$
$H = r^2\theta'.$

In each of these examples the first integral G is proportional to the sum of the kinetic and potential energies. In example Q the differential equations are those for the motion of a particle in a central field of force, in which the force is inversely proportional to the square of the distance, and r and θ are polar coordinates. The first integral H in this case is the rate at which the radius vector sweeps over area. In examples M and P the solutions are readily obtained in explicit form, and so other first integrals may be written down at once, by virtue of Theorems 14 and 15.

5. Equations in the Form $F(x, y, y') = 0$.—Differential equations frequently arise which are not solved for the derivatives. Theorems concerning their solutions can be obtained by combining the results of the preceding sections with the implicit function theorems of Chap. VIII.

We shall consider a function $F(x, y, z)$, which is of class $C^{(p)}$ on an open set R in (x, y, z)-space, where $p \geqq 1$. The function F and the variables y and z are each supposed to have the same number of components. Following the terminology of Chap. VIII, Sec. 3, an **ordinary point** for F is defined to be a point (x, y, z) in R such that the matrix of partial derivatives $F_z(x, y, z)$ is nonsingular. All other points are **exceptional points.**

THEOREM 19. *For every ordinary point (ξ, η, ζ) for the function F, with $F(\xi, \eta, \zeta) = 0$, there is a unique continuous solution $y(x, \xi, \eta, \zeta)$ of the differential equations*

$$F(x, y, y') = 0 \tag{5:1}$$

[1] See, for example, Moulton [1], Chap. 5.

and initial conditions

$$y(\xi, \xi, \eta, \zeta) = \eta, \qquad y'(\xi, \xi, \eta, \zeta) = \zeta,$$

defined on an interval $a < x < b$ *such that on this interval the point*

$$P_x: \ (x, y(x, \xi, \eta, \zeta), y'(x, \xi, \eta, \zeta))$$

of $(2k + 1)$*-dimensional space is always an ordinary point for* F, *while the only finite limiting values of* P_x *as* x *approaches* a *or* b *are exceptional points for* F. *When* $\zeta = \zeta(\xi, \eta)$ *is a continuous solution of* $F(\xi, \eta, \zeta) = 0$ *composed of ordinary points for* F, $y(x, \xi, \eta, \zeta(\xi, \eta))$ *and* $y'(x, \xi, \eta, \zeta(\xi, \eta))$ *are of class* $C^{(p)}$ *in* (x, ξ, η).

Proof.—By Theorem 2 of Chap. VIII, the equations $F(x, y, z) = 0$ have one and only one solution $z = f(x, y)$ defined near the point (ξ, η) and having values near ζ, and this solution is of class $C^{(p)}$. Then the differential equations $y' = f(x, y)$ have a unique continuous solution $y(x, \xi, \eta)$ defined for x near ξ, and $y(x, \xi, \eta)$ and $y'(x, \xi, \eta)$ are of class $C^{(p)}$ in all their arguments, by Theorem 13. When the equation $F(\xi, \eta, \zeta) = 0$ has more than one solution for ζ, the solution $y(x, \xi, \eta)$ of the differential equations (5:1) depends also on ζ, and we may indicate this by writing $y(x, \xi, \eta, \zeta)$. The above argument shows that a continuous solution $y(x)$ of (5:1), all of whose elements $(x, y(x), y'(x))$ are ordinary points for F, is uniquely determined by its initial values. Now let $y(x, \xi, \eta, \zeta)$ be the logical sum of all continuous solutions passing through the initial element (ξ, η, ζ), satisfying the last statement of the theorem, and with no elements that are exceptional points for F. This function is defined for x on an open interval (a, b), and it remains only to show that the only finite limiting points of P_x as x approaches a or b are exceptional points for F. This is accomplished as in the proof of Theorem 4.

THEOREM 20. *Suppose that* $F(x, y, z)$ *is of class* $C^{(p)}$ *on an open set* R, *and that*

$$E: \ y = y_0(x), \qquad a_0 \leqq x \leqq b_0,$$

is a solution of class C' *of the differential equations* (5:1), *along which the matrix* F_z *is nonsingular. Let* E_1 *denote the set of points* $(x, y_0(x), y_0'(x))$, $a_0 \leqq x \leqq b$. *Then there exist positive numbers* ϵ *and* δ *and a unique function* $y(x, \xi, \eta)$ *defined for* $a_0 - \delta \leqq x \leqq b_0 + \delta$ *and* (ξ, η) *in the neighborhood* $N(E; \delta)$, *such that* $(x, y(x, \xi, \eta), y'(x, \xi, \eta))$ *lies in* $N(E_1; \epsilon)$ *and satisfies the differential equations* (5:1). *The functions* $y(x, \xi, \eta)$ *and* $y'(x, \xi, \eta)$ *are of class* $C^{(p)}$.

Proof.—By Theorem 4 of Chap. VIII, there exist positive numbers ϵ and δ_1 and a function $f(x, y)$ such that f is of class $C^{(p)}$ on $N(E; \delta_1)$, and for each (x, y) in this neighborhood $(x, y, f(x, y))$ is the unique solution in $N(E_1; \epsilon)$ of $F(x, y, z) = 0$. Then by Theorem 11, the conclusion stated must hold for a sufficiently small $\delta < \delta_1$. The differentiability follows from Theorem 13.

In the following examples there are singular solutions which correspond to exceptional points for the function F.

R. $y'^2 + y^2 - 1 = 0.$

S. $y_1'^2 - y_2'^2 + y_1^2 - y_2^2 - 1 = 0,\ y_1'y_2' + y_1y_2 = 0.$

T. $y_1'^2 - y_2'^2 + 4y_1 \cos 2x - 4y_2 \sin 2x = 0,\ 2y_1'y_2' + 4y_1 \sin 2x + 4y_2 \cos 2x = 0.$

The solutions of R guaranteed by Theorem 19 are the arcs of the curves $y = \sin (x + C)$ between the points of contact with the singular solutions $y = \pm 1$. The solutions of S are given by the formulas $y_1 = (1 + C_2^2)^{1/2} \sin (x + C_1)$, $y_2 = C_2 \cos (x + C_1)$. For $C_2 \neq 0$ the solutions extend from $x = -\infty$ to $x = +\infty$ without approaching an exceptional point, but for $C_2 = 0$ the situation reduces essentially to that of example R. If we set $C_1 = \pi/2 + \epsilon \cos t$, $C_2 = \sinh (\epsilon \sin t)$, and take $\xi = 0$, then as t varies through an interval of length π, the initial values η_1 and η_2 return to their original values, but ζ_1 and ζ_2 become the negatives of their original values. The interval (a,b) of definition of the solution, described in Theorem 19, becomes finite whenever $\sin t = 0$. The solutions of T are given by the formulas

$$y_1 = (\cos x + c_1)^2 - (\sin x + c_2)^2,$$
$$y_2 = 2(\cos x + c_1)(\sin x + c_2).$$

One of these solutions meets the singular solution $y_1 = y_2 = 0$ if and only if $c_1^2 + c_2^2 = 1$.

REFERENCES

1. Moulton, *Differential Equations*, 1930.
2. Ince, *Ordinary Differential Equations*, 1926.
3. Kamke, *Differentialgleichungen reeller Funktionen*, 1930.
4. Goursat, *Mathematical Analysis*, Vol. 2, part 2.
5. Bolza, *Vorlesungen über Variationsrechnung*, pp. 168*ff*.
6. Bliss, "Fundamental Existence Theorems," *Princeton Colloquium Lectures*, pp. 86–98.
7. Bennett, Milne, and Bateman, "Numerical Integration of Differential Equations," *Bulletin of the National Research Council*, No. 92.
8. Picard, *Traité d'analyse*, Vol. 2 (3d Ed., 1925), Chap. 11.
9. Scarborough, *Numerical Mathematical Analysis*, 1930, Chaps. 11 to 13.

CHAPTER X

THE LEBESGUE INTEGRAL

1. Introduction.—The theory of Lebesgue integrals will be developed here from the point of view originally expounded by F. Riesz [8]. This makes it possible to prove the important convergence and approximation theorems for integrals at the very outset, in a simple way, on the basis of only a rudimentary theory of point sets and measure. The general theory of measure becomes a corollary of the theorems on integrals. The method of Riesz also makes possible a simple and brief treatment of the differentiation of indefinite integrals of functions of one variable.

The theory will be phrased in terms of functions of a single real variable. However many of the definitions and theorems, especially in the earlier sections, are equally valid for integrals of functions of any finite number of variables, and for a generalized measure function replacing the ordinary length, area, volume, etc., but having the properties specified in Sec. 2. When a general measure function is used, the integral usually known as the Lebesgue-Stieltjes integral is obtained. Those theorems which are not known to be valid for the Lebesgue-Stieltjes integral in several dimensions are marked with a †. Occasionally indications will be given, in paragraphs marked with a *, of the necessary modifications in terminology and proofs for the case of functions of several variables or for the Lebesgue-Stieltjes integral. These paragraphs may well be omitted at a first reading. The reader who wishes to gain a knowledge of the Lebesgue-Stieltjes integral should restudy this chapter in connection with Chap. XII.

The method of Riesz for the definition of the integral is extensible to the case when the independent variable ranges over a topological space in which a suitable measure is defined, and the functional values lie in a Banach space.[1]

[1] For the second aspect of the generalization, see Bochner, "Integration von Funktionen deren Werte die Elemente eines Vektorraumes sind," *Fundamenta Mathematicae*, Vol. 20 (1933), pp. 262–276.

2. Point Sets and Functions of Intervals.—An **interval** is a set of points of the real axis defined by one of the following types of conditions:

$$
\begin{aligned}
a &\leqq x \leqq b, \\
a &\leqq x < b, \\
a &< x \leqq b, \\
a &< x < b.
\end{aligned}
$$

An interval of the first type is **closed,** one of the fourth is **open,** while an interval of the second or third type may be called **half-open.** An interval of the first type with $a = b$ is a **degenerate interval** or a point. For convenience the null set will also be considered as an interval.

*In a space of more than one dimension, an interval would be defined by taking an inequality of one of the four types for each coordinate. In this case there are various degrees of degeneracy of intervals.

All point sets E to be considered in this chapter are subsets of a *nondegenerate finite closed fundamental interval* I. All complements of sets are then taken with respect to I, that is, the complement of a set E, denoted by cE, is defined to be $I - E$. A set E is **open relative** to I in case its complement is closed. Hereafter the term "open" is understood to mean "relative to I."

The sets of a family are said to be **disjoint** in case no two of them have an element in common.

We shall be interested in an **interval function** $m(i)$ which is defined for all subintervals i of I. Such a function m is said to be **additive** in case

$$m(i_1) = m(i_2) + m(i_3),$$

whenever i_1 is the sum of disjoint intervals i_2 and i_3. We suppose that the interval function $m(i)$ is *nonnegative, finite, and additive,* and that it has the additional properties

$$
\begin{aligned}
m(i) &= \text{g.l.b. } m(i_1) \text{ for all open } i_1 \supset i, \\
m(i) &= \text{l.u.b. } m(i_2) \text{ for all closed } i_2 \subset i.
\end{aligned}
\tag{2:1}
$$

The simplest example of such a function is the length of the interval. With it we obtain the ordinary Lebesgue integral in the developments that follow.

*For intervals in two dimensions, length is to be replaced by area. Other examples of additive interval functions of the above type are obtained by using the increments of nondecreasing bounded functions $f(x)$. If i is the open interval $a < x < b$, we should then set

$$m(i) = f(b - 0) - f(a + 0),$$

where $f(a + 0)$, for example, denotes the right-hand limit of $f(x)$ at a. If i is the closed interval $a \leqq x \leqq b$, we set

$$m(i) = f(b + 0) - f(a - 0).$$

For a function $f(x_1, x_2)$ of two variables which is nondecreasing in a suitable sense, and an open interval

$$i\colon a_1 < x_1 < b_1, \qquad a_2 < x_2 < b_2,$$

we set

$$m(i) = f(b_1 - 0, b_2 - 0) - f(a_1 + 0, b_2 - 0) \\ - f(b_1 - 0, a_2 + 0) + f(a_1 + 0, a_2 + 0).$$

When these more general interval functions $m(i)$ are admitted, we obtain the generalization of the Lebesgue integral usually known as the Lebesgue-Stieltjes integral.

We shall be interested in certain special classes of point sets in I. The class $\mathfrak{A}$ consists of all point sets A, each of which is the sum of a finite number of disjoint intervals. The class $\mathfrak{C}$ consists of all sets C, each of which is the sum of a finite or denumerable number of disjoint intervals. If $A = \sum_{h=1}^{q} i_h$, $C = \sum i_h$, we set

$$m(A) = \sum_{h=1}^{q} m(i_h), \qquad m(C) = \sum m(i_h).$$

Here and in the following the summation sign $\sum$ without any attached index of summation will be used to indicate summation over all possible values of the variable, and so may indicate either a finite sum or an infinite series. The justification for the definition of $m(A)$ is obtained by considering any two representations $\sum i_h$ and $\sum i'_j$ of A as a sum of disjoint intervals, and a third representation $\sum i''_k$ such that each interval i_h or i'_j is a sum of certain intervals i''_k, and the sum of any two adjacent intervals i''_k and i''_l is again an interval. The justification of the definition given for $m(C)$ is provided by the Corollary of Lemma 2.

Since the product of two intervals is obviously an interval and the complement of an interval is in $\mathfrak{A}$, we can readily verify the following properties of the class $\mathfrak{A}$:

LEMMA 1. *The class $\mathfrak{A}$ is closed with respect to the operations of taking complements, differences, and finite sums and products. If*

$$A = \sum_1^q A_i,$$

$$m(A) \leqq \sum_1^q m(A_i). \tag{2:2}$$

When the sets A_i are disjoint, the inequality in (2:2) *should be replaced by equality.*

In order to justify the definition of $m(C)$ we need the following proposition:

LEMMA 2. *Let $C = \sum i_h$ be a subset of $E = \sum i'_h$, where the intervals i'_h are not required to be disjoint. Then*

$$\sum m(i_h) \leqq \sum m(i'_h).$$

Proof.—By (2:1), for an arbitrary positive ϵ, each interval i'_h can be enlarged into an interval i''_h in such a way that every point of C is interior to some i''_h, and

$$\sum m(i''_h) \leqq \sum m(i'_h) + \epsilon.$$

Likewise each interval i_h contains a closed interval i^0_h such that

$$\sum m(i^0_h) \geqq \sum m(i_h) - \epsilon.$$

Then for each q the set $A = \sum_1^q i^0_h$ is a bounded closed set covered by the family of intervals i''_h. By the Borel theorem, A is covered by a finite number $i''_1, \ldots, i''_p$ of these intervals. Thus

$$\sum_1^q m(i_h^0) \leqq \sum_1^p m(i_h'') \leqq \sum m(i_h''),$$

$$\sum m(i_h^0) \leqq \sum m(i_h''),$$

$$\sum m(i_h) \leqq \sum m(i_h') + 2\epsilon,$$

and since ϵ is arbitrary, the desired inequality follows.

COROLLARY. *Let* $\sum i_h = \sum i_h'$ *be two representations of a set* C *as a sum of disjoint intervals. Then*

$$\sum m(i_h) = \sum m(i_h').$$

The following result is easily obtained by use of Lemma 1.

LEMMA 3. *If* E *is a denumerable sum of intervals, then* E *is in* $\mathfrak{C}$.

LEMMA 4. *The class* $\mathfrak{C}$ *is closed with respect to the operations of taking denumerable sums and finite products. If* $C_1 \subset C_2$, $m(C_1) \leqq m(C_2)$. If $C = \sum C_j$,

$$m(C) \leqq \sum m(C_j). \tag{2:3}$$

When the sets C_j *are disjoint, the inequality in* (2:3) *should be replaced by equality.*

Proof.—The closure of $\mathfrak{C}$ with respect to sums follows from Lemma 3, and that with respect to products from the formula

$$\sum_h i_h \sum_k i_k' = \sum_{hk} i_h i_k'.$$

The remaining statements follow from Lemma 2.

LEMMA 5. *Every open set* E *is in* $\mathfrak{C}$. *When the fundamental interval* I *is one-dimensional, an open set* E *has a unique representation (apart from order) as a sum of disjoint open intervals.*

Proof for the One-dimensional Case.—Let (x_n) be a denumerable set dense on I. Then each point x_n is contained in a maximum open interval i_n contained in E. (This interval i_n is null when x_n is not in E.) Let $n_1 = 1$ and let n_2 be the least integer such that x_{n_2} is not in i_{n_1}, n_3 the least integer such that x_{n_3} is not in $i_{n_1} + i_{n_2}$, and so on. Then

$$E = \sum i_{n_j}.$$

**Proof for the General Case.*—As before, let (x_n) be a denumerable set dense on I. Let i_{nk} denote the "cube" with center x_n and edge $1/k$. Then E is the sum of the intervals i_{nk} which are contained in E, and hence is in $\mathfrak{C}$ by Lemma 3.

A set Z is a **set of measure zero** in case for every $\epsilon > 0$ there is a set C in $\mathfrak{C}$ such that $C \supset Z$ and $m(C) < \epsilon$. The following properties are easily proved:

LEMMA 6. *Every subset of a set of measure zero is also of measure zero.*

LEMMA 7. *The sum of a denumerable number of sets of measure zero is also of measure zero.*

We shall need also the following fundamental result:

LEMMA 8. *Let (C_n) be a sequence of sets in $\mathfrak{C}$ such that*

$$\limsup C_n = Z,$$

where Z is a set of measure zero. Then

$$\lim m(C_n) = 0.$$

Proof.—Let $\bar{C}_k = \sum_{n \geqq k} C_n$. Then $Z = \prod_k \bar{C}_k$, $\bar{C}_{k+1} \subset \bar{C}_k$, $m(C_k) \leqq m(\bar{C}_k)$, by Lemma 4. Thus it suffices to consider the case when the sequence (C_n) is nonincreasing. If the lemma is false in this case, there exists a positive number δ such that $m(C_n) > \delta$ for every n. Let ϵ be positive but less than δ. Let $C_n = \sum_h i_{nh}$ be a representation of C_n as a sum of disjoint intervals. By (2:1) each interval i_{nh} contains a closed interval i'_{nh} such that $m(i'_{nh}) > m(i_{nh}) - \epsilon/2^{n+h+1}$. Then if

$$A_n = \sum_{h=1}^{p_n} i'_{nh}$$

with p_n sufficiently large, we shall have

$$m(A_n) > m(C_n) - \epsilon/2^n. \tag{2:4}$$

Now let $\bar{A}_n = \prod_{k=1}^{n} A_k$. Then $\bar{A}_{n+1} \subset \bar{A}_n \subset A_n \subset C_n \subset C_{n-1}$, and

$$\prod_{n=1}^{\infty} \bar{A}_n = \prod_{n=1}^{\infty} A_n \subset \prod_{n=1}^{\infty} C_n = Z. \tag{2:5}$$

We shall prove by induction that

$$(2:6) \qquad m(\bar{A}_n) > m(C_n) - \epsilon\left(1 - \frac{1}{2^n}\right).$$

For $n = 1$, this inequality is the same as (2:4). Now since $\bar{A}_n$ and A_{n+1} are both subsets of C_n, we have

$$m(A_{n+1}) + m(\bar{A}_n - A_{n+1}) \leqq m(C_n),$$
$$m(\bar{A}_n) = m(\bar{A}_n A_{n+1}) + m(\bar{A}_n - A_{n+1}).$$

By adding the last two statements and transposing the term $m(C_n)$, we obtain

$$m(\bar{A}_{n+1}) = m(\bar{A}_n A_{n+1}) \geqq m(\bar{A}_n) + m(A_{n+1}) - m(C_n).$$

From this and (2:6), and (2:4) with n replaced by $n + 1$, we find that

$$m(\bar{A}_{n+1}) > m(C_n) - \epsilon\left(1 - \frac{1}{2^n}\right) + m(C_{n+1}) - \frac{\epsilon}{2^{n+1}} - m(C_n)$$
$$= m(C_{n+1}) - \epsilon\left(1 - \frac{1}{2^{n+1}}\right),$$

and this is (2:6) with n replaced by $n + 1$. Thus we have for every n,

$$(2:7) \qquad m(\bar{A}_n) > \delta - \epsilon.$$

Now let C be a sum of intervals enclosing Z, and such that

$$(2:8) \qquad m(C) < (\delta - \epsilon)/2.$$

By (2:1) we may suppose that the intervals composing C are open. From (2:7) and (2:8) and Lemma 2 it follows that the set $(\bar{A}_n - C)$ is nonnull for every n. Each of these sets is bounded and closed, and they form a decreasing sequence. Hence they have at least one point in common by Corollary 3 of Theorem 12 in Chap. IV. But this contradicts (2:5), and thus the lemma is proved.

†Two examples of sets of measure zero were mentioned on page 89. Another example may be constructed by selecting from the interval [0, 1] the points x in whose decimal representation $x = \sum a_j 10^{-j}$ the sequence (a_{2j+1}) of odd-numbered digits is ultimately periodic. The set of all points $z = \sum a_{2j} 10^{-2j}$ is con-

tained in intervals remaining after removing a set of intervals with length sum 0.9, 0.99, 0.999, . . . , and hence has measure zero. The points $y = \sum a_{2j-1}10^{-(2j-1)}$ are rational, and so the set of all points of the form $x = y + z$ is the sum of a denumerable infinity of sets of measure zero.

† From a two-dimensional interval I we may select two sets of measure zero as follows. Let E_1 consist of all points (x, y) with x and y both rational and having the same denominator. (It is understood that all rational numbers are represented in their lowest terms.) Let E_2 consist of all (x, y) with x rational and y irrational, or y rational with a different denominator from that of x. Each of these two sets is of two-dimensional measure zero, and each is dense on I. The set E_1 has only a finite number of points on each parallel to a coordinate axis.

3. Definition and Properties of the Integral.—Let $\mathfrak{Q}$ be an arbitrary class and let P denote a property that may be possessed by some subclasses of $\mathfrak{Q}$. The property P is said to be **extensionally attainable** in $\mathfrak{Q}$ in case for every subclass $\mathfrak{Q}_0$ of $\mathfrak{Q}$ there exists a subclass $\mathfrak{Q}_1$ containing $\mathfrak{Q}_0$ and having the property P, and such that every other subclass $\mathfrak{Q}_2$ containing $\mathfrak{Q}_0$ and having the property P contains $\mathfrak{Q}_1$. The class $\mathfrak{Q}_1$ may be described as the minimum class containing $\mathfrak{Q}_0$ and having the property P, and when it exists it is called **the extension of $\mathfrak{Q}_0$ to have property** P. In case $\mathfrak{Q}$ is the interval I, the property of being an open set is not extensionally attainable, while the property of being a closed set is extensionally attainable. The following necessary and sufficient condition for extensional attainability is easily proved.

LEMMA 9. *A property* P *is extensionally attainable in* $\mathfrak{Q}$ *if and only if*

(i) $\mathfrak{Q}$ *itself has the property* P;

(ii) *The logical product of a family of subsets, each having the property* P, *itself always has the property* P.

Now let $\mathfrak{Q}$ be the class of all functions ψ which are single-real-valued in the interval I. We shall be interested in the following operations on functions in $\mathfrak{Q}$:

I. Addition: $\psi_1 + \psi_2$.
II. Multiplication by a constant: $a\psi$.
III. Multiplication: $\psi_1\psi_2$.

IV. Logical addition: $\psi_3 = \psi_1 \vee \psi_2$, where for each x the value $\psi_3(x)$ is the greater of $\psi_1(x)$ and $\psi_2(x)$,

V. Logical multiplication: $\psi_3 = \psi_1 \wedge \psi_2$, where for each x the value $\psi_3(x)$ is the lesser of $\psi_1(x)$ and $\psi_2(x)$.

We shall sometimes wish to admit functions ψ which have infinite values, and we could adopt conventions as to the values obtained by adding and multiplying infinite values, but this will not be necessary.

It is clear that the property of being closed with respect to an arbitrary one of the operations I to V is extensionally attainable in $\mathfrak{Q}$. Moreover the extension of a class $\mathfrak{Q}_0$ is the class of all functions obtainable from those in $\mathfrak{Q}_0$ by a finite number of applications of the operation in question. A class which is closed with respect to both the operations I and II is called **linear.**

We note that a class $\mathfrak{Q}_0$ which is closed with respect to the operations II and IV is also closed with respect to the operation of taking the absolute value, since

$$|\psi| = \psi \vee (-\psi).$$

A very convenient concept is that of the **characteristic function** ϕ_E of a set E, which is defined to have the value unity at elements x of E, and the value zero elsewhere.

Let $\mathfrak{Q}_0$ be the class of all characteristic functions ϕ_A of sets A in $\mathfrak{A}$, and let the extension of $\mathfrak{Q}_0$ to be linear be denoted by $\mathfrak{S}$. The functions in the class $\mathfrak{S}$ are frequently called **step functions.** We shall use the notation $\alpha(x)$ for step functions. It is easily seen that the class $\mathfrak{S}$ is also closed with respect to the operations III to V. The integrals of step functions are defined in the obvious way as finite sums. Let the fundamental interval I be represented as a sum of disjoint intervals i_h in any way such that the function α has the constant value a_h on i_h. Then

$$\int_I \alpha(x)\, dx \equiv \sum a_h m(i_h).$$

When convenient, we may also use the notations

$$\int_a^b \alpha(x)\, dx \qquad \text{or} \qquad \int \alpha\, dx$$

for this integral. It is easy to see that the value obtained for the integral is the same for all decompositions of the interval I subject to the conditions stated.

An operator $K(\psi)$ with domain $\mathfrak{Q}_0$ is said to be **linear** in case $\mathfrak{Q}_0$ is linear, and

$$\begin{aligned} K(\psi_1 + \psi_2) &= K(\psi_1) + K(\psi_2), \\ K(a\psi_1) &= aK(\psi_1), \end{aligned}$$

for every ψ_1 and ψ_2 in $\mathfrak{Q}_0$ and every constant a. An operator $K(\psi)$ is said to be **positive** in case $K(\psi) \geqq 0$ whenever $\psi(x) \geqq 0$ for all x in I. A positive linear operator has the following additional properties:

$$\begin{aligned} &K(\psi_1) \leqq K(\psi_2) \qquad \text{whenever} \qquad \psi_1(x) \leqq \psi_2(x); \\ &|K(\psi)| \leqq K(|\psi|) \qquad \text{whenever} \qquad |\psi| \text{ is also in } \mathfrak{Q}_0. \end{aligned}$$

The integral

$$K(\alpha) = \int \alpha \, dx$$

is obviously a positive linear operator on the class $\mathfrak{S}$ of step functions.

*In case the interval function $m(i)$ is not the length of the interval, it is more appropriate to replace the symbol dx occurring in the notation for the integral by dm, in order to indicate the dependence of the integral on the choice of m. In this chapter and the next we shall use the notations indicated above. But when immediate generalization to the case of an arbitrary interval function satisfying the conditions stated in Sec. 2 is not possible, that fact will be indicated by a dagger (†).

*Note that a step function α may be such that it takes a particular value a at only a single point. When the value of the interval function m is zero for every degenerate interval, an arbitrary change in the value of α at a finite number of points does not affect the value of the integral, but in other cases it may affect it.

The notation $E[\ .\ .\ .\ ]$ is used to denote the set of all points of the interval I at which the property in the brackets holds.

A property P of points x is said to hold **almost everywhere** in case there exists a set Z of zero measure such that P holds on the complement of Z. For example, a function ψ is finite almost everywhere in case the set $E[\psi(x) = \pm\infty]$ is a set of measure zero. Also, $\lim_n \psi_n = \psi$ almost everywhere in case $\lim_n \psi_n(x) = \psi(x)$ with the possible exception of the points x in a set Z of measure zero.

A function μ is said to be **measurable** in case there exists a sequence (α_n) of step functions such that $\lim_n \alpha_n = \mu$ almost everywhere. The class of all measurable functions μ will be denoted by $\mathfrak{M}$. We note that a measurable function μ may have infinite values. We show later (Theorem 4, Corollary) that the class $\mathfrak{M}$ is the extension of the class $\mathfrak{S}$ to be closed with respect to the operation of taking limits in the sense of "almost everywhere."

A function ψ is said to be **essentially bounded** or **almost bounded** in case there exists a set Z of measure zero such that ψ is bounded on the complement of Z. The subclass of $\mathfrak{M}$ consisting of those functions μ which are essentially bounded will be denoted by $\mathfrak{M}_B$. The subclass consisting of those functions μ which are finite almost everywhere will be denoted by $\mathfrak{M}_F$. Then $\mathfrak{M}_B \subset \mathfrak{M}_F \subset \mathfrak{M}$. If μ is in $\mathfrak{M}_B$, and k and K are constants such that $k \leqq \mu(x) \leqq K$ almost everywhere, then there exists a sequence (α_n) of step functions such that $k \leqq \alpha_n(x) \leqq K$ for all x and $\lim_n \alpha_n = \mu$ almost everywhere. This is easily verified since the class $\mathfrak{S}$ of step functions is closed with respect to the operations IV and V.

A sequence of functions (ψ_n) is said to **converge almost uniformly** to a function ψ in case for every positive ϵ there exists a set C in $\mathfrak{C}$ such that $m(C) < \epsilon$ and $\lim_n \psi_n = \psi$ uniformly on the complement of C. Here it is understood that ψ has finite values on the complement of C. The relation of this useful type of convergence with convergence almost everywhere is partly indicated in the following two theorems, the second of which is a special case of a theorem of Egoroff.

THEOREM 1. *If* $\lim_n \psi_n = \psi$ *almost uniformly, then* $\lim_n \psi_n = \psi$ *almost everywhere.*

Proof.—Let C_q correspond to $\epsilon = 1/q$ in the definition of almost uniform convergence, and let $E = \prod C_q$. Then $\lim_n \psi_n = \psi$ on the complement of E. Since $E \subset C_q$ and $m(C_q) < 1/q$ for every q, E is a set of measure zero.

THEOREM 2. *Let (α_n) be a sequence of step functions converging almost everywhere to a function μ which is finite almost everywhere. Then $\lim_n \alpha_n = \mu$ almost uniformly.*

Proof.—Let Z denote the set of points at which either the limit μ is infinite or the convergence of α_n to μ fails. Let

$$C_{kq} = \sum_{h,j=k}^{\infty} E[|\alpha_h(x) - \alpha_j(x)| > 1/q].$$

The sequence (C_{kq}) is nonincreasing with respect to k, and $\prod_{k=1}^{\infty} C_{kq} \subset Z$ for every q. Hence by Lemma 8, $\lim_k m(C_{kq}) = 0$. Thus for an arbitrary positive number ϵ and for each q there exists an integer k_q such that $m(C_{k_q q}) < \epsilon/2^q$. Let C_0 be a set in $\mathfrak{C}$ including Z, with $m(C_0) < \epsilon$. If we set $C = C_0 + \sum C_{k_q q}$, we have $m(C) < 2\epsilon$ by Lemma 4, and $|\alpha_h(x) - \mu(x)| \leqq 1/q$ on the complement of C for $h > k_q$.

COROLLARY. *Let (α_n) be a sequence of step functions converging almost everywhere to a function μ and let $E_+ = E[\mu(x) = +\infty]$, $E_- = E[\mu(x) = -\infty]$. Then for every $\epsilon > 0$ there exists a set C in $\mathfrak{C}$ with $m(C) < \epsilon$, and such that for every $\delta > 0$ there exists an integer q such that when $n > q$, $\alpha_n(x) > \delta$ on $E_+ - C$, and $\alpha_n(x) < -\delta$ on $E_- - C$.*

Proof.—Let

$$(3{:}1) \qquad \bar{\alpha}_n(x) = \frac{\alpha_n(x)}{1 + |\alpha_n(x)|}, \qquad \bar{\mu}(x) = \frac{\mu(x)}{1 + |\mu(x)|}.$$

Then the hypotheses of the theorem are fulfilled by $(\bar{\alpha}_n)$ and $\bar{\mu}$, so that when q is sufficiently great, and $n > q$, and x is in $E_+ - C$, we have

$$\frac{1}{1 + \alpha_n(x)} = 1 - \bar{\alpha}_n(x) < \frac{1}{\delta + 1},$$

and hence $\alpha_n(x) > \delta$. A similar manipulation gives the corresponding inequality on $E_- - C$.

The following theorem gives the definition of the integral and its justification, for essentially bounded measurable functions. This case is taken up first because it is somewhat simpler than the general case. But Theorems 3 to 5 could be omitted.

THEOREM 3. *Let* (α_n) *be an essentially bounded sequence of step functions converging almost everywhere to a function* μ. *Then the sequence of integrals*

$$\int_I \alpha_n \, dx \tag{3:2}$$

has a finite limit which depends only on the function μ *and is denoted by* $\int_I \mu \, dx$.

Proof.—Suppose $|\alpha_n(x)| \leqq K$, and let ϵ be an arbitrary positive number. Then by Theorem 2, there exists a set C in $\mathfrak{C}$ and an integer n such that $m(C) < \epsilon/4K$, and $|\alpha_p(x) - \alpha_q(x)| \leqq \epsilon/2m(I)$ whenever $p > n$, $q > n$, except on a subset of C. Hence from the definition of the integral for step functions it follows that

$$\left|\int_I \alpha_p \, dx - \int_I \alpha_q \, dx\right| \leqq \epsilon,$$

whenever $p > n$, $q > n$. This establishes the existence of the limit of the sequence (3:2). To show that it depends only on the function μ, let (α_n') and (α_n'') be two sequences satisfying the conditions of the theorem, and converging almost everywhere to the same function μ. Form a new sequence (α_n) by taking terms alternately from (α_n') and (α_n''). Then the sequences

$$\int_I \alpha_n \, dx, \qquad \int_I \alpha_n' \, dx, \qquad \int_I \alpha_n'' \, dx$$

all converge, and since the second and third are subsequences of the first, they all have the same limit.

The next theorem gives a sufficient condition for term-by-term integration of sequences of functions in the class $\mathfrak{M}_B$.

THEOREM 4. *Let* (μ_n) *be an essentially bounded sequence of measurable functions converging almost everywhere to a function* ψ. *Then* ψ *is measurable and essentially bounded, and*

$$\lim \int_I \mu_n \, dx = \int_I \psi \, dx.$$

Proof.—Let K be a constant such that $|\mu_n(x)| \leqq K$ almost everywhere, for all values of n. For each n there is a sequence of step functions (α_{kn}) such that $\lim_k \alpha_{kn} = \mu_n$ almost everywhere, and $|\alpha_{kn}(x)| \leqq K$. Corresponding to a sequence of integers (k_n), let $\alpha_{k_n n}$ be denoted by $\bar{\alpha}_n$. By Theorems 2 and 3, for every

n there exists a set C_n in $\mathfrak{C}$ and an integer k_n such that

$$m(C_n) < 1/2^n,$$
$$|\bar{\alpha}_n(x) - \mu_n(x)| < 1/2^n \text{ on } I - C_n,$$
$$\left|\int_I \bar{\alpha}_n \, dx - \int_I \mu_n \, dx\right| < 1/2^n. \tag{3:3}$$

Let

$$\bar{C}_q = \sum_{n=q+1}^{\infty} C_n,$$

so that $m(\bar{C}_q) < 1/2^q$. Then

$$\lim_n (\bar{\alpha}_n - \mu_n) = 0 \tag{3:4}$$

on $I - \bar{C}_q$ for every q, and hence (3:4) holds almost everywhere, and $\lim_n \bar{\alpha}_n = \psi$ almost everywhere. Thus ψ is in $\mathfrak{M}_B$ and $\lim_n \int_I \bar{\alpha}_n \, dx = \int_I \psi \, dx$ by Theorem 3, and from this and (3:3) the final conclusion follows.

COROLLARY. *If (μ_n) is a sequence of measurable functions whose limit is almost everywhere a function ψ, then ψ is also measurable.*

This follows from the theorem by the use of the same type of transformation (3:1) as was used in the proof of the Corollary of Theorem 2.

THEOREM 5. *The class $\mathfrak{M}_B$ of essentially bounded measurable functions is closed with respect to the operations* I *to* V. *The class $\mathfrak{M}_F$ of measurable functions which are finite-valued almost everywhere is also closed with respect to these operations, provided it is agreed that the values of sums and products may be arbitrarily assigned at points where they may be undefined. The integral is a positive linear operator on the class $\mathfrak{M}_B$.*

These statements follow readily from the fact that the operation of taking limits is commutative with each of the operations I to V. A sum or a product in the class $\mathfrak{M}_F$ may lead to one of the indeterminate forms $\infty - \infty$ or $0 \cdot \infty$, but this can happen only at the points of a set of measure zero.

It is clear from the definitions that changing the value of a function at a set of measure zero cannot alter its measurability, integrability, nor the value of its integral. A function μ may even remain undefined on a set Z of measure zero, but we shall still use the symbol

$$\int_I \mu \, dx$$

when μ is integrable. In this situation, many authors prefer to make the agreement that μ shall be set equal to some convenient value (say zero) on the set Z.

We now proceed to the case when the assumption of boundedness is omitted. However, another hypothesis must take its place. In order to introduce this we find the following notation convenient, namely,

$$\int_A \alpha \, dx = \int \alpha\phi_A \, dx,$$

where the set A is in $\mathfrak{A}$, and ϕ_A is its characteristic function. The product $\alpha\phi_A$ is then also a step function. When the set A is regarded as variable, $\int_A \alpha \, dx$ is called the **indefinite integral** of α. It is evidently always **absolutely continuous** as a function of A, in the sense that

$$\lim_{m(A)=0} \int_A \alpha \, dx = 0.$$

The integrals $\int \alpha_n \, dx$ of a sequence are said to be **absolutely continuous uniformly with respect to** n in case

$$\lim_{m(A)=0} \int_A \alpha_n \, dx = 0$$

uniformly with respect to n. This definition will later be extended to more general functions and sets. The phrase "equiabsolutely continuous" is sometimes used for this notion, which is related to the notion of equicontinuous functions described in Chap. VII. We shall need two preliminary results before proceeding to the generalization of Theorem 3 to the unbounded case.

†LEMMA 10. *If the integrals* $\int_A \alpha_n \, dx$ *are absolutely continuous uniformly with respect to n, then they are bounded uniformly with respect to A and n.*

*This lemma and its proof hold also for generalized measure functions in any number of dimensions, *provided* that the measure function m satisfies the condition that *the fundamental interval I* *can be divided into a finite number of subintervals of arbitrarily small measure.* When the interval I is one-dimensional and the measure $m(i)$ is obtained from a nondecreasing function $f(x)$, the preceding condition is satisfied if and only if $f(x)$ is continuous.

Proof.—Suppose that δ is such that $\left|\int_A \alpha_n \, dx\right| < 1$ whenever $m(A) < \delta$. Let the fundamental interval I be divided into K subintervals each of measure less than δ. Then K is a bound for the integrals.

LEMMA 11. *Suppose that the integrals* $\int_A \alpha_n \, dx$ *are bounded uniformly with respect to* A *and* n, *and that* $\lim \alpha_n = \mu$ *almost everywhere. Then* μ *is finite almost everywhere.*

Proof.—Suppose that the set $E_+ = E[\mu(x) = +\infty]$ is not of measure zero, that is, suppose that there exists a positive ϵ such that $m(C) > 2\epsilon$ for every set C in $\mathfrak{C}$ including E_+. Corresponding to ϵ let C_0 be a set in $\mathfrak{C}$ satisfying the conditions of the Corollary of Theorem 2, so that $m(C_0) < \epsilon$. For an arbitrarily large number δ the set of points at which $\alpha_n(x) > \delta$ is a set A_n which includes $(E_+ - C_0)$ for n sufficiently large, and hence $m(A_n) > \epsilon$, and

$$\int_{A_n} \alpha_n \, dx > \epsilon\delta.$$

This contradicts the boundedness of the integrals. A similar proof shows that the set $E[\mu(x) = -\infty]$ is of measure zero.

†THEOREM 6. *Suppose that* (α_n) *is a sequence of step functions converging almost everywhere to a function* μ, *and that the integrals*

$$\int_A \alpha_n \, dx \tag{3:5}$$

are absolutely continuous uniformly with respect to n. *Then the sequence* (3:5) *converges uniformly for sets* A *in* $\mathfrak{A}$, *and the value of the limit depends only on the function* μ *and the set* A, *and is denoted by the symbol* $\int_A \mu \, dx$. *Moreover,* μ *is finite almost everywhere.*

*The preceding theorem *holds also for general measure functions* with the added hypothesis that *the function* μ *is finite almost everywhere,* or that *the sequence* (3:5) *is uniformly bounded.* Compare also the remark following Lemma 10.

Proof.—Let ϵ be an arbitrary positive number, and let δ correspond to ϵ as in the definition of uniform absolute continuity.

By Lemmas 10 and 11, the function μ is finite almost everywhere, so that by Theorem 2 there exists a set C in $\mathfrak{C}$ and an integer n such that $m(C) < \delta$ and the set $A_{pq} = E[|\alpha_p(x) - \alpha_q(x)| > \epsilon]$ is included in C whenever p and q are both greater than n. For an arbitrary set A in $\mathfrak{A}$ and $p > n, q > n$, let us set $B_{pq} = A \cdot A_{pq}$, $D_{pq} = A - A_{pq}$. Then $m(B_{pq}) < \delta$, and

$$\begin{aligned}\left|\int_A \alpha_p\,dx - \int_A \alpha_q\,dx\right| &\leqq \left|\int_{B_{pq}} \alpha_p\,dx\right| + \left|\int_{B_{pq}} \alpha_q\,dx\right| \\ &\qquad + \left|\int_{D_{pq}} (\alpha_p - \alpha_q)\,dx\right|, \\ &\leqq 2\epsilon + \epsilon m(A) \leqq \epsilon[2 + m(I)].\end{aligned}$$

Thus the Cauchy condition for the uniform convergence of the sequence of integrals is satisfied. That the value of the limit depends only on the function μ and the set A is shown by the same device as in the proof of Theorem 3.

Functions μ satisfying the hypotheses of Theorem 6 will be called **integrable** (or **integrable in the sense of Lebesgue**). They are frequently called **summable** functions. The class of all such functions will be denoted by $\mathfrak{L}$, and the functions themselves will sometimes be denoted by the letter λ. It was shown in the proof of the theorem that an integrable function λ is finite almost everywhere. It is clear that the indefinite integral $\int_A \lambda\,dx$ is always absolutely continuous, and that the definition of uniform absolute continuity applies at once to sequences $\left(\int_A \lambda_n\,dx\right)$ of integrals of integrable functions.

In order to justify the use of the symbol $\int_A \lambda\,dx$, we should note that its value is independent of the choice of the fundamental interval I in which the set A is contained. Let I^* be an interval containing I, and let the measure function m be defined on I^* consistently with its values on I. Let ϕ_A be the characteristic function of A, and let (α_n) be a sequence of step functions converging to λ almost everywhere on I. Then $(\alpha_n\phi_A)$ converges to $\lambda\phi_A$ almost everywhere on I^*, and in this statement it does not matter what values are assigned to α_n and λ on $I^* - I$. Since

$$\int_I \alpha_n\phi_A\,dx = \int_{I^*} \alpha_n\phi_A\,dx,$$

it follows that the value of $\int_A \lambda \, dx$ is independent of the choice of the fundamental interval I containing A.

*The preceding conditions are not satisfied in the following example. Let $f(x) = x$ on $0 \leqq x \leqq 1$, $f(x) = 2x$ on $1 < x \leqq 2$. Let $I = [0, 1]$, $I^* = [0, 2]$. Then the value of the interval function $m(I)$ obtained from the nondecreasing function f when I^* is the fundamental interval is 2, but when I itself is the fundamental interval, $m(I) = 1$.

It should be remarked that the class $\mathfrak{L}$ of Lebesgue-integrable functions is not obtained, either from the class $\mathfrak{S}$ of step functions or from the class $\mathfrak{C}$ of continuous functions, by taking the limits of sequences which converge everywhere, even though this process is indefinitely repeated. Compare the references in Chap. VII, Sec. 5.

†THEOREM 7. *Suppose that* (λ_n) *is a sequence of integrable functions converging almost everywhere to a function* μ, *and that the integrals*

$$\int_A \lambda_n \, dx \tag{3:6}$$

are absolutely continuous uniformly with respect to n. *Then* μ *is integrable, and the sequence* (3:6) *converges to* $\int_A \mu \, dx$ *uniformly for sets* A *in* $\mathfrak{A}$.

*As before, *the theorem holds also for general measure functions* with the added hypothesis that *μ is finite almost everywhere*, or that *the sequence* (3:6) *is uniformly bounded.*

Proof.—For every n there is a sequence (α_{kn}) such that $\lim_k \alpha_{kn} = \lambda_n$ almost everywhere, and such that the hypotheses of Theorem 6 are satisfied. Corresponding to a sequence of integers (k_n) let $\alpha_{k_n n}$ be denoted by $\bar{\alpha}_n$. By Theorems 2 and 6, for every n there exists a set C_n in $\mathfrak{C}$ and an integer k_n such that

$$m(C_n) < 1/2^n,$$
$$|\bar{\alpha}_n(x) - \lambda_n(x)| < 1/2^n \text{ on } I - C_n,$$
$$\left|\int_A \bar{\alpha}_n \, dx - \int_A \lambda_n \, dx\right| < 1/2^n \text{ for every set } A \text{ in } \mathfrak{A}. \tag{3:7}$$

As in the proof of Theorem 4, it follows that $\lim (\bar{\alpha}_n - \lambda_n) = 0$ almost everywhere, and hence $\lim \bar{\alpha}_n = \mu$ almost everywhere. By hypothesis, for every positive ϵ there exists a positive δ such that $\left|\int_A \lambda_n\, dx\right| < \epsilon$ for every n and every set A with $m(A) < \delta$. Thus by (3:7), we have

$$\left|\int_A \bar{\alpha}_n\, dx\right| < 2\epsilon, \tag{3:8}$$

whenever $m(A) < \delta$ and $1/2^n < \epsilon$. Since only a finite number of values of n fail to satisfy the last condition, there exists a positive $\delta_1 \leqq \delta$ such that (3:8) holds for all values of n provided only that $m(A) < \delta_1$. Thus the hypotheses of Theorem 6 are satisfied by the function μ and the sequence $(\bar{\alpha}_n)$, so that μ is integrable, and the final conclusion of the theorem is obtained by use of (3:7).

THEOREM 8. *Under the same agreement as in Theorem* 5, *the class* $\mathfrak{L}$ *of integrable functions is closed with respect to the operations* I, II, IV, *and* V, *and in particular the absolute value of an integrable function is integrable. The product of an integrable function by an essentially bounded measurable function is integrable. Moreover, the integral is a positive linear operator on the class* $\mathfrak{L}$.

Proof.—The proof is like that of Theorem 5, except that now the preservation of the property of uniform absolute continuity under the operations in question must be verified. To show this for the operation IV of taking the logical sum, we note that

$$\int_A (\alpha_1 \vee \alpha_2)\, dx = \int_{A_1} \alpha_1\, dx + \int_{A_2} \alpha_2\, dx.$$

To show this for the operation of multiplying by a bounded function, let the integrals $\int_A \alpha_n\, dx$ be absolutely continuous uniformly with respect to n, and let the sequence $(\bar{\alpha}_n)$ be uniformly bounded, $|\bar{\alpha}_n(x)| \leqq K$. Then if $\left|\int_A \alpha_n\, dx\right| < \epsilon$ whenever $m(A) < \delta$, $\left|\int_A \alpha_n \bar{\alpha}_n\, dx\right| \leqq 2K\epsilon$ whenever $m(A) < \delta$.

*For the case of a general measure function it is necessary also to verify the preservation of the property of uniform boundedness of the integrals under the operations in question.

The fact that the absolute value of an integrable function is integrable means that the Cauchy improper integral of elementary calculus is not included as a special case of the Lebesgue integral. A discussion of nonabsolutely convergent integrals may be found in Saks [1], Chaps. 6 to 8, or Hobson [3], Vol. I, Chap. 8.

THEOREM 9. *If λ is integrable, there exists a sequence (α_n) of step functions such that $\lim_{n=\infty} \alpha_n = \lambda$ almost everywhere, and*

$$\lim_{n=\infty} \int_I |\alpha_n - \lambda|\, dx = 0.$$

Proof.—We can in fact prove that any sequence (α_n) used in the definition of $\int \lambda\, dx$ satisfies the requirement stated. For, since

$$\int_A |\alpha_n - \lambda|\, dx \leqq \int_A |\alpha_n|\, dx + \int_A |\lambda|\, dx,$$

it is easily seen that the integrals on the left are absolutely continuous uniformly with respect to n, and then it is only necessary to apply Theorem 7.

THEOREM 10. *If λ is an integrable function and μ is a measurable function such that $|\mu(x)| \leqq \lambda(x)$ almost everywhere, then μ is also integrable.*

Proof.—Since by Theorem 8, μ is integrable if and only if the functions $\mu \vee 0$ and $\mu \wedge 0$ are both integrable, it is sufficient to consider the case when $\mu \geqq 0$. Let $\lim_n \alpha_n = \lambda$ almost everywhere, and let the sequence (α_n) satisfy the conditions of Theorem 6. Let $\lim_n \bar{\alpha}_n = \mu$ almost everywhere, and let $\alpha_n \geqq 0$, $\bar{\alpha}_n \geqq 0$. Set $\beta_n = \alpha_n \wedge \bar{\alpha}_n$. Then $\lim_n \beta_n = \mu$ almost everywhere, and the sequence (β_n) satisfies the conditions of Theorem 6.

As an immediate corollary of Theorem 8 we have the following useful criterion for the uniform absolute continuity of a sequence of integrals.

THEOREM 11. *Let λ_0 and each λ_n be integrable, and suppose that $|\lambda_n(x)| \leqq \lambda_0(x)$ almost everywhere. Then the integrals $\int_A \lambda_n\, dx$ are absolutely continuous uniformly with respect to n.*

The following example shows that the hypotheses of Theorem 7 may hold when there does not exist an integrable dominating function $\lambda_0(x)$ as described in Theorem 11. Let $\lambda_n(x) = n$ for $1/n \leqq x \leqq 1/(n-1)$, $\lambda_n(x) = 0$ for all other values of x. Then $\int_0^1 \lambda_n\, dx = 1/(n-1)$, and it is easy to verify that the integrals $\int_A \lambda_n\, dx$ are absolutely continuous uniformly with respect to n. However, l.u.b. $\lambda_n(x) \geqq 1/x$, which is not integrable. A necessary and sufficient condition that a family of integrals be absolutely continuous uniformly will be given in the next chapter.

Another useful criterion for term-by-term integration of sequences is contained in the following theorem:

THEOREM 12. *Let the sequence* (λ_n) *of integrable functions be nondecreasing with respect to* n, *and let the limit of the sequence be denoted by* μ. *Then* μ *is integrable if and only if the sequence of integrals* $\left(\int_I \lambda_n \, dx\right)$ *is bounded, and in this case*

$$\lim_n \int_A \lambda_n \, dx = \int_A \mu \, dx \tag{3:9}$$

uniformly for sets A *in* $\mathfrak{A}$.

Proof.—If μ is integrable, we have $\lambda_1(x) \leqq \lambda_n(x) \leqq \mu(x)$, so that

$$\int_I \lambda_1 \, dx \leqq \int_I \lambda_n \, dx \leqq \int_I \mu \, dx,$$

and also (3:9) holds, by Theorems 8, 11, and 7. To prove the converse, we note that the bounded and nondecreasing sequence of integrals $\int_I \lambda_n \, dx$ must satisfy the Cauchy condition for convergence, so for an arbitrary positive ϵ, there exists an integer N such that $\int_I (\lambda_n - \lambda_N) \, dx < \epsilon$ for $n > N$, and hence

$$\int_A (\lambda_n - \lambda_N) \, dx < \epsilon \quad \text{for } n > N, A \subset I. \tag{3:10}$$

By the absolute continuity of the individual integrals $\int_A \lambda_n \, dx$, there exists a positive number δ such that

$$\int_A \lambda_n \, dx < \epsilon \quad \text{for } m(A) < \delta, n \leqq N. \tag{3:11}$$

By combining (3:10) and (3:11), we obtain $\int_A \lambda_n \, dx < 2\epsilon$ for $m(A) < \delta$, and all n, so the integrals are absolutely continuous uniformly with respect to n, and we may apply Theorem 7.

We remark that under the hypotheses of Theorem 12 it is sometimes convenient to write $\int_I \mu \, dx = +\infty$ when the sequence $\int_I \lambda_n \, dx$ is unbounded. In this case we do *not* say that μ is integrable, but rather that its integral is defined and has the value $+\infty$.

A useful theorem, known as Fatou's lemma, may readily be derived from the preceding results.

THEOREM 13. *Let* λ_0 *and* λ_n *be integrable, and set* $\psi(x) = \liminf \lambda_n(x)$, $\theta(x) = \limsup \lambda_n(x)$. *If* $\lambda_0(x) \leqq \lambda_n(x)$ *almost everywhere, and* $\liminf \int_I \lambda_n\,dx < +\infty$, *then* ψ *is integrable, and*

$$\int_I \psi\,dx \leqq \liminf \int_I \lambda_n\,dx. \tag{3:12}$$

If $\lambda_0(x) \geqq \lambda_n(x)$ *almost everywhere, and* $\limsup \int_I \lambda_n\,dx > -\infty$, *then* θ *is integrable, and*

$$\int_I \theta\,dx \geqq \limsup \int_I \lambda_n\,dx.$$

Proof.—Let $\mu_{np}(x) = \text{g.l.b.}\lambda_m(x)$ for $n \leqq m \leqq p$, $\nu_n(x) = \lim\limits_p \mu_{np}(x)$. Then each μ_{np} is integrable, by Theorem 8, and each ν_n is integrable, by Theorem 12. Since $\int_I \nu_n\,dx \leqq \int_I \lambda_m\,dx$ for $m > n$, $\int_I \nu_n\,dx$ is a bounded sequence, so (3:12) follows from another application of Theorem 12. The final statement of the theorem is obtained from (3:12) by changing the signs throughout.

†THEOREM 14. *Let* ψ *be a bounded Riemann-integrable function. Then* ψ *is also integrable in the sense of Lebesgue and the two integrals of* ψ *have the same value.*

Proof.—We shall use the criterion of Chap. VI, Theorem 7, that ψ is Riemann-integrable only if it is continuous almost everywhere on I. Take a sequence (P_n) of partitions of I, with norm tending to zero, and let

$$S(P_n) = \sum_{P_n} \psi(x_h)m(i_h)$$

be the value of a Riemann sum associated with P_n. Let

$$\alpha_n = \sum_{P_n} \psi(x_h)\phi_{i_h},$$

where ϕ_{i_h} is the characteristic function of the interval i_h. Then

$S(P_n) = \int_I \alpha_n \, dx$, and since $\lim_n \alpha_n(x) = \psi(x)$ at every point x where ψ is continuous, the desired result follows from Theorem **3**.

*The arguments of Chap. VI, Sec. 1, are extensible without much change to the case of functions $f(x)$ of k variables, defined and bounded on the fundamental interval I, provided the partitions of I are restricted to those obtained by partitioning each axis. Then the argument used in proving the last theorem applies at once in this case, and is extensible also to the case when the partitions P of I are partitions into a finite number of measurable[1] sets E_h, and the norm $N(P)$ is the maximum diameter of a set E_h of the partition. This shows that the same result is obtained in defining the multiple Riemann integral when only the restricted type of partitions is admitted, as when a more general type is used.

†From Theorems 14 and 4 it follows that, if a bounded sequence of Riemann-integrable functions converges to a Riemann-integrable function, the corresponding sequence of integrals converges to the integral of the limit. This result was first proved by Osgood[2] without use of the Lebesgue integral.

4. Measurable Sets and Functions.—A set E is said to be **measurable** in case its characteristic function ϕ_E is a measurable function and, by definition,

$$m(E) = \int_I \phi_E \, dx. \tag{4:1}$$

We shall let $\mathfrak{E}$ denote the class of all measurable sets E.

A class $\mathfrak{K}$ of subsets of the interval I is said to be **additive** in case it contains (a) the sum of every denumerable family of sets in $\mathfrak{K}$; (b) the complement of every set in $\mathfrak{K}$; (c) the null set. Such a class $\mathfrak{K}$ is sometimes called **completely additive,** in contrast to the **finitely additive** classes in whose definition (a) is replaced by (a') the sum of every finite family of sets in $\mathfrak{K}$. Every additive class is evidently also closed with respect to the operations of taking differences and denumerable products. The property of being additive is extensionally attainable in the class $\mathfrak{Q}$ of all subsets of I, by Lemma 9 in Sec. 3. The extension of the class

[1] The notion of measurable set is defined in Sec. 4.

[2] "Non-uniform Convergence and the Integration of Series Term by Term," *American Journal of Mathematics*, Vol. 19 (1897), pp. 155–190. **In** this memoir all the functions are supposed to be continuous.

of subintervals of I to be additive is called the class of **Borel-measurable sets.** Every open set is Borel-measurable, and so is every closed set.

THEOREM 15. *The class* $\mathfrak{C}$ *of measurable sets is additive. If the sets of the sequence* (E_n) *are disjoint and measurable, we have* $m\left(\sum E_n\right) = \sum m(E_n)$.

The proof is based on Theorems 5 and 4. From the final statement of the theorem it follows that the definition of measure given in formula (4:1) is consistent with the definition previously given for sets in $\mathfrak{C}$. It is clear also that sets of measure zero may be disregarded in considering the measurability of a set E.

THEOREM 16. *For an arbitrary sequence* (E_n) *of measurable sets, we have*

$$m(\liminf E_n) \leqq \liminf m(E_n) \leqq \limsup m(E_n) \leqq m(\limsup E_n).$$

Proof.—Let $R = \liminf E_n$, $S = \limsup E_n$. Then

$$\phi_R = \liminf \phi_{E_n}, \qquad \phi_S = \limsup \phi_{E_n},$$

where ϕ denotes the characteristic function. Hence the theorem follows from Theorem 13.

THEOREM 17. *For every measurable set E and every positive* ϵ *there exists a set C in* $\mathfrak{C}$ *and a set A in* $\mathfrak{A}$ *such that* $m(C) < \epsilon$ *and*

$$A - C \subset E \subset A + C. \tag{4:2}$$

Proof.—Let (α_n) be a sequence of step functions converging to the characteristic function ϕ_E almost everywhere. Then by Theorem 2, $\lim_n \alpha_n = \phi_E$ almost uniformly, so that there exists a set C in $\mathfrak{C}$ and an integer k such that $m(C) < \epsilon$ and $|\alpha_k(x) - \phi_E(x)| < \frac{1}{3}$ on the complement of C. If we now let A denote the set of points where $\alpha_k(x) > \frac{2}{3}$, we find that (4:2) is verified.

COROLLARY. *If E is measurable, then*

$$m(E) = \text{g.l.b. } m(G) \textit{ for all open sets } G \supset E = \text{l.u.b. } m(F) \textit{ for all closed sets } F \subset E.$$

Conversely, when g.l.b. $m(G) =$ l.u.b. $m(F)$, *then E is measurable.*

Proof.—Since $m(A - C) + m(C) = m(A + C)$, we have $m(A - C) > m(E) - \epsilon$, $m(A + C) < m(E) + \epsilon$. By (2:1), the set C may be supposed open. Also there is a closed set A_1 and an open set A_2 such that $A_1 \subset A \subset A_2, m(A_1 - C) > m(E) - \epsilon$, $m(A_2 + C) < m(E) + \epsilon$.

From the above it follows that, when $m(E) = 0$, E must be a set of measure zero as defined in Sec. 2. To prove the last part of the corollary, let (G_n) be a nonincreasing sequence of open sets such that $\lim m(G_n) = \text{g.l.b. } m(G)$, and let (F_n) be a nondecreasing sequence of closed sets such that $\lim m(F_n) = \text{l.u.b. } m(F)$. Then by Theorem 16, $m\left(\prod G_n\right) = \lim m(G_n)$, $m\left(\sum F_n\right) = \lim m(F_n)$. But $\prod G_n \supset E \supset \sum F_n$, and so $m\left(\prod G_n - \sum F_n\right) = m\left(\prod G_n - E\right) = 0$. Thus E is measurable since it differs from $\prod G_n$ by a set of measure **zero**.

*The corollary suggests another notion that is occasionally useful—that of **exterior measure.** For an arbitrary set E we define the exterior measure $m_e(E)$ by the formula

$$m_e(E) = \text{g.l.b. } m(G) \text{ for all open sets } G \supset E.$$

We note that for a measurable set the exterior measure coincides with the measure. It follows that an arbitrary set E is included in a product G_δ of a sequence of open sets such that $m_e(E) = m(G_\delta)$. By use of this fact we can obtain the following partial extension of Theorem 16:

*THEOREM 18. *For an arbitrary sequence of sets E_n, we have*

$$m_e(\liminf E_n) \leqq \liminf m_e(E_n).$$

If λ is integrable and E is a measurable set, it follows from Theorem 8 that $\lambda\phi_E$ is also integrable. Thus the definition

$$\int_E \lambda\,dx = \int_I \lambda\phi_E\,dx \tag{4:3}$$

is valid, and we may regard the integral as a **function of measurable sets.** The next two theorems show that it is an *additive function* which is also *absolutely continuous.*

THEOREM 19. *Let λ be integrable and let the sets of the sequence (E_n) be measurable and disjoint. Let $E = \sum E_n$. Then*

$$\int_E \lambda\,dx = \sum_n \int_{E_n} \lambda\,dx. \tag{4:4}$$

Proof.—We have

$$\lambda\phi_E = \lim_n \sum_{k=1}^{n} \lambda\phi_{E_k}, \qquad \left|\sum_{k=1}^{n} \lambda\phi_{E_k}\right| \leqq |\lambda|,$$

so that the formula (4:4) follows from Theorems 11, 7, and 8.

We have already noted, following Theorem 6, that when λ is an integrable function, $\int_A \lambda\, dx$ is absolutely continuous as a function of sets A in $\mathfrak{A}$. This property extends readily to $\int_E \lambda\, dx$ as a function of measurable sets E, as follows from the next theorem.

THEOREM 20. *Suppose that λ is integrable and that $\left|\int_A \lambda\, dx\right| \leqq \epsilon$ whenever $m(A) < \delta$. Then*

$$\left|\int_E \lambda\, dx\right| \leqq \epsilon, \qquad \int_E |\lambda|\, dx \leqq 2\epsilon,$$

for every measurable set E with $m(E) < \delta$.

Proof.—From Theorem 17 it follows that there is a sequence (A_n) such that $\lim_n \phi_{A_n} = \phi_E$ almost everywhere, and $\lim_n m(A_n) = m(E)$. Then $\lim_n \lambda\phi_{A_n} = \lambda\phi_E$ almost everywhere, and by Theorems 11 and 7,

$$\lim_n \int_{A_n} \lambda\, dx = \int_E \lambda\, dx.$$

Also

$$\int_E |\lambda|\, dx = \int_{E_1} \lambda\, dx - \int_{E_2} \lambda\, dx,$$

where $\lambda(x) \geqq 0$ on E_1 and $\lambda(x) \leqq 0$ on E_2.

LEMMA 12. *The following conditions on a function ψ are all equivalent:*

(*a*) *For every finite number c the set $E[\psi > c]$ is measurable;*
(*b*) *For every finite number c the set $E[\psi \geqq c]$ is measurable;*
(*c*) *For every finite number c the set $E[\psi < c]$ is measurable;*
(*d*) *The set $E[\psi = +\infty]$ is measurable, and for every pair of finite numbers c and d the set $E[c \leqq \psi < d]$ is measurable.*

Proof.—The proof is based on Theorem 15. To show that (*a*) implies (*b*), we note that

$$E[\psi \geqq c] = \prod_n E[\psi > c - 1/n].$$

Since $E[\psi \geqq c]$ and $E[\psi < c]$ are complementary sets, (b) implies (c). To show that (d) implies (b), we note that

$$E[\psi \geqq c] = E[\psi = +\infty] + \sum_{n=0}^{\infty} E[c + n \leqq \psi < c + n + 1].$$

It is clear that other equivalent conditions are obtainable from (b) and (d) by reversing the direction of the inequalities and changing $+\infty$ to $-\infty$ in (d).

The class of all functions ψ satisfying the conditions of Lemma 12 will be denoted by $\mathfrak{N}$. In Theorem 21 below it is shown that the class $\mathfrak{N}$ is identical with the class $\mathfrak{M}$ of all measurable functions. The proof depends on the following closure property of the class $\mathfrak{N}$.

LEMMA 13. *Let (ψ_n) be a sequence of functions in $\mathfrak{N}$. Then the following functions:*

$$\text{l.u.b. } \psi_n, \qquad \text{g.l.b. } \psi_n, \qquad \limsup \psi_n, \qquad \liminf \psi_n,$$

are all in $\mathfrak{N}$.

Proof.—Let $\psi = \text{l.u.b. } \psi_n$. Then $E[\psi > c] = \sum E[\psi_n > c]$. Thus ψ is in $\mathfrak{N}$ by Theorem 15. The remainder of the lemma is proved in a similar way.

THEOREM 21. *The class $\mathfrak{N}$ is identical with the class $\mathfrak{M}$ of measurable functions.*

Proof.—It is clear that every step function α is in the class $\mathfrak{N}$, and a function equal almost everywhere to a function in the class $\mathfrak{N}$ is likewise in the class $\mathfrak{N}$. Hence $\mathfrak{M} \subset \mathfrak{N}$ by Lemma 13. Now let ψ be an arbitrary function in $\mathfrak{N}$, and let ϕ_{nk} denote the characteristic function of the set $E[k/n \leqq \psi < (k + 1)/n]$, ϕ_{n+} the characteristic function of the set $E[\psi \geqq n]$, and ϕ_{n-} the characteristic function of the set $E[\psi < -n]$. Each of these functions is in $\mathfrak{M}$, by the definition of the class $\mathfrak{N}$ and of measurable sets. The function

$$\mu_n = \sum_{k=-n^2}^{n^2-1} \frac{k}{n} \phi_{nk} + n\phi_{n+} - n\phi_{n-}$$

is a linear combination of functions in $\mathfrak{M}$ and so is in $\mathfrak{M}$, and thus $\psi = \lim_n \mu_n$ is also in $\mathfrak{M}$ by the corollary of Theorem 4.

The class $\mathfrak{B}$ of all functions satisfying the conditions of Lemma 12 when the term "measurable" is replaced by "Borel-measurable" is called the class of **Borel-measurable functions.** It is evidently always a subclass of the class $\mathfrak{M}$. It coincides with the sum of the classes of Baire described in Chap. VII, Sec. 5.[1] For a proof that there exist nonmeasurable functions, as well as functions in the class $\mathfrak{M} - \mathfrak{B}$, see McShane [2], pages 237–241.[2]

THEOREM 22. *Let the measurable function* μ *be finite almost everywhere and let* ϵ *be an arbitrary positive number. Then there exists an open set* C *in* $\mathfrak{C}$ *such that* $m(C) < \epsilon$ *and the section of* μ *defined on the complement of* C *is continuous. Hence there exists a function* ψ *continuous on the interval* I *and identical with* μ *on the complement of* C.

Proof.—Let α be a step function, and consider an interval i (degenerate or nondegenerate) on which α is constant. If i does not consist of only one point, let B denote the boundary of i, and choose a closed subinterval i_0 of i such that $i - i_0$ is contained in the neighborhood $N(B; \epsilon)$. When i reduces to a single point, take $i_0 = i$. Set $\gamma_\epsilon(x) = \alpha(x)$ on each such i_0, and extend γ_ϵ to be continuous. Let A_ϵ denote the sum of the closed subintervals i_0. Then if $\lim_n \epsilon_n = 0$, $\lim_n (I - A_{\epsilon_n}) = \Lambda$, and so $\lim_n m(I - A_{\epsilon_n}) = 0$, by Lemma 8. Hence the theorem holds for step functions. Now let (α_n) be a sequence of step functions such that $\lim \alpha_n = \mu$ almost everywhere. Then by Theorem 2 there exists a set C_1 in $\mathfrak{C}$ such that $m(C_1) < \epsilon/2$ and $\lim \alpha_n = \mu$ uniformly on $I - C_1$. The set C_1 may clearly be required to be open. By the first part of the proof, for each n there is an open set $\bar{A}_n$ such that $m(\bar{A}_n) < \epsilon/2^{n+1}$, and the section of α_n on $I - \bar{A}_n$ is continuous. Let $C = C_1 + \sum \bar{A}_n$. Then $m(C) < \epsilon$, the section on each α_n on $I - C$ is continuous, and $\lim \alpha_n = \mu$ uniformly on $I - C$. Hence the section of μ on $I - C$ is continuous. The final statement in the theorem follows from Theorem 21 of Chap. VII.

[1] See Lebesgue, "Sur les fonctions représentables analytiquement," *Journal de mathématiques* (Series 6), Vol. 1 (1905), pp. 139–216, especially pp. 156–165.

[2] McShane's text states only that the function he exhibits is not in a Baire class with finite index, but a minor modification of the proof shows that it is not in any Baire class.

Two theories of integration are said to be **consistent** if they yield the same class of integrable functions with the same value for the integral of each. It is not difficult to show that, if two theories have the same measure for intervals and, in each, formula (4:1) holds for intervals, the integral is a linear operator, and Theorems 4, 5, 12, 15, 22 and Corollary of 17 hold, then the two theories are consistent. For then the measure of open sets is the same in both, and sets of measure zero are the same for both. By Theorem 22 the class of measurable functions finite almost everywhere is the same for both. The integrals of step functions and of continuous functions are the same for both, and hence the integrals of bounded measurable functions are the same for both, by Theorem 4. By Theorem 12 we proceed to the same result for the class of all integrable functions.

In particular, our theory is consistent with that originally developed by Lebesgue. Also, a consistent theory is obtained by starting from the class of continuous functions in place of the class of step functions.

†**5. Differentiation of Functions of One Variable.**—In the remainder of this chapter we restrict attention to functions of one variable and to the case when the measure of an interval is its length. The proof given for Lebesgue's theorem on the existence of a derivative (Theorem 27) is due to Riesz [9]. An especially simple proof is given of the fundamental theorem of integral calculus for Lebesgue integrals (Theorem 29).

*For more general theorems on the differentiability of functions of one variable, the reader is referred to Hobson [3], Vol. I, pages 391–404, and references there. Extensions of some of the results of this section to functions of several variables may be found in the standard treatises on Lebesgue integrals. See, for example, Saks [1], Chap. 4, and Hobson [3], Vol. I, pages 607–616.

Let $f(x)$ be a single-real-valued function defined on the interval $I = [a, b]$, and let P be a partition of I by points x_j, where $a = x_0 < x_1 < \cdots < x_{n-1} < x_n = b$. Let

$$(5:1) \qquad V_P(x) = \sum_a^x |f(x_{j+1}) - f(x_j)|,$$

where the sum is taken over those intervals of the partition P which are contained in the closed interval $[a, x]$. Let $V_P'(x)$

denote the sum of those terms in (5:1) for which the increment $[f(x_{j+1}) - f(x_j)]$ is positive, and let $V''_P(x)$ denote the sum of those terms in (5:1) for which the increment is negative. Let $t(x)$, $p(x)$, $n(x)$, denote the least upper bounds of $V_P(x)$, $V'_P(x)$, $V''_P(x)$, respectively, for all partitions P. The functions $t(x)$, $p(x)$, $n(x)$, are called the **total variation, positive variation,** and **negative variation,** respectively, of $f(x)$ on the interval $[a, x]$. When $t(b)$ is finite, the function $f(x)$ is said to be of **bounded variation** (or of **limited variation**) on $[a, b]$.

THEOREM 23. *The class of all functions of bounded variation on* $[a, b]$ *is closed with respect to the operations* I *to* V *of Sec.* 3.

THEOREM 24. *A function* $f(x)$ *is of bounded variation on* $[a, b]$ *if and only if it is expressible as the difference of two nondecreasing bounded functions. A function of bounded variation has one-sided limits at each point and has at most a denumerable infinity of discontinuities. The discontinuities of* $f(x)$ *are the same as those of* $t(x)$.

Proof.—It is clear that $p(x)$ and $n(x)$ are nondecreasing and that, when $f(x)$ is of bounded variation,

$$\begin{aligned} f(x) &= f(a) + p(x) - n(x), \\ t(x) &= p(x) + n(x), \end{aligned} \tag{5:2}$$

since a sequence of partitions P_k may be chosen such that we have simultaneously for the corresponding sums,

$$\lim_k V'_{P_k}(x) = p(x), \qquad \lim_k V''_{P_k}(x) = n(x), \qquad \lim_k V_{P_k}(x) = t(x).$$

A nondecreasing bounded function is plainly of bounded variation, and the class of all functions of bounded variation is linear, by Theorem 23. The existence of the one-sided limits of $f(x)$ follows from Theorem 2 of Chap. IV. For a finite number of discontinuities c_j of the nondecreasing function $p(x)$, we have

$$\sum [p(c_j + 0) - p(c_j - 0)] \leqq p(b) - p(a).$$

Consequently, for each k only a finite number of "jumps" $[p(c_j + 0) - p(c_j - 0)]$ can be greater than $1/k$, and thus it is seen that the set of points of discontinuity must be either denumerable, finite, or null. To show that when $f(x)$ is continuous on the right at a point x_0, $t(x)$ is so also, select a partition P

such that $t(b) - V_P(b) < \epsilon$. We may require the points x_0 and x to be partition points, with $x > x_0$. Then $0 \leqq t(x) - t(x_0) - |V_P(x) - V_P(x_0)| < \epsilon$, and when x is sufficiently near x_0, $V_P(x) - V_P(x_0) = |f(x) - f(x_0)| < \epsilon$, so that $t(x) - t(x_0) < 2\epsilon$.

Let A denote the sum of the finite number of nonoverlapping subintervals (a_j, b_j) of $[a, b]$, and let

$$f[A] = \sum_j [f(b_j) - f(a_j)].$$

The function $f(x)$ is said to be **absolutely continuous** on $[a, b]$ in case

$$\lim_{m(A)=0} f[A] = 0.$$

It is important to note that for an absolutely continuous function f we have also

$$\lim_{m(A)=0} \sum_j |f(b_j) - f(a_j)| = 0.$$

THEOREM 25. *The class of all functions absolutely continuous on* $[a, b]$ *is closed with respect to the operations* I *to* V *of Sec.* 3.

THEOREM 26. *If* $f(x)$ *is absolutely continuous on* $[a, b]$, *then* $f(x)$ *is of bounded variation on* $[a, b]$.

It is easy to construct examples of functions that are absolutely continuous, and hence of bounded variation, on a finite interval $[a, b]$. The simplest of these is $f(x) = x$. From Theorem 25 it follows that all polynomials in x are absolutely continuous. If $|f(d) - f(c)| \leqq |g(d) - g(c)|$ for every subinterval (c, d), and $g(x)$ is absolutely continuous or of bounded variation, then $f(x)$ has the corresponding property. In the special case where $g(x) = Kx$, $f(x)$ satisfies a Lipschitz condition. By the Theorem of the Mean for derivatives, if $f(x)$ has a derivative everywhere which is bounded, then $f(x)$ satisfies a Lipschitz condition. Hence the function $f(x) = x^2 \sin(1/x)$, with $f(0) = 0$, is absolutely continuous. But the function $f_1(x) = x \sin(1/x)$, with $f_1(0) = 0$, is not of bounded variation on the interval $[0, 1]$, as may be shown by using the points $x = 2/(2n + 1)\pi$ as partition points. An example is given following Theorem 29 of a function that is nondecreasing and continuous but not absolutely continuous.

The next lemma is due to Riesz [9].

LEMMA 14. *Let the function* $g(x)$ *be bounded on* $[a, b]$, *and set*

$$G(x) = \limsup_{x'=x} g(x').$$

Let E' *(resp.* E''*) denote the set of all points* x *of the open interval* (a, b) *such that there exists a point* $x_1 > x$ *(resp.* $x_1 < x$*) such that* $g(x_1) > G(x)$. *If* E' *(resp.* E''*) is not null, it is an open set and, if* $\sum (a_k, b_k)$ *is the representation of* E' *(resp.* E''*) as a sum of disjoint open intervals, then* $g(x) \leqq G(b_k)$ *(resp.* $g(x) \leqq G(a_k)$*) on the interval* (a_k, b_k), *for every* k.

Proof.—It is easy to verify by an indirect proof that the function $G(x)$ is always upper semicontinuous, and from this property it follows at once that the set E' is open. Then the representation of E' as a sum of disjoint open intervals is unique, as was indicated in Lemma 5. If x is a point of the open interval (a_k, b_k), let x_2 denote the least upper bound of the set of points x_0 of the closed interval $[x, b_k]$ for which $g(x) \leqq G(x_0)$. Then on account of the upper semicontinuity of G,

$$g(x) \leqq G(x_2), \tag{5:3}$$

and, if $x_2 = b_k$, this is the desired result. But, if $x_2 < b_k$, by the definition of the set E' there exists a point $x_1 > x_2$ such that

$$g(x_1) > G(x_2). \tag{5:4}$$

Then $G(x_1) > g(x)$, and $x_1 > b_k$ by definition of x_2. Since b_k is not in the set E',

$$g(x_1) \leqq G(b_k), \tag{5:5}$$

and by combining (5:3), (5:4), and (5:5) we have the desired result. The alternative reading is obtained by applying the part already proved to $g(-x)$.

The four **principal derivates** or **derived numbers** of a function $f(x)$ were defined in Chap. V, Sec. 1.

LEMMA 15. *The following relations between derivates hold for an arbitrary function* f:

$$D^+(-f) = -D_+f, \qquad D^-(-f) = -D_-f; \tag{5:6}$$

if $y = -x$, $g(x) = -f(y)$, *then*

$$D^+g(x) = D^-f(y), \qquad D_+g(x) = D_-f(y). \tag{5:7}$$

Proof.—The relations (5:6) follow from the relation l.u.b. $[-f(x)] = -\text{g.l.b. } f(x)$. The relations (5:7) follow from the formula

$$\frac{g(x+h)-g(x)}{h} = \frac{f(y-h)-f(y)}{-h}.$$

THEOREM 27. *If $f(x)$ is of bounded variation on $[a, b]$ then $f(x)$ has a finite derivative almost everywhere on $[a, b]$.*

Proof.—By Theorem 24 it is sufficient to consider the case when $f(x)$ is nondecreasing, so that each derivate Df is everywhere nonnegative. Let E_0 denote the set including the discontinuities of $f(x)$ and the end points a and b, so that E_0 is denumerable and hence of measure zero. Let

$$S_R \equiv E[D^+f > R], \qquad T_r \equiv E[D_-f < r].$$

We shall show first that $S_R - E_0$ is contained in a set E_1, where $m(E_1)$ approaches zero with $1/R$, so that D^+f is finite almost everywhere. Then we shall show that, whenever $0 < r < R$, $S_RT_r - E_0$ is contained in the product of a nonincreasing sequence of sets E_n whose measure tends to zero, so that $m(S_RT_r) = 0$.

Let $g_1(x) = f(x) - Rx$, and let $G_1(x)$ and $E_1 = E' = \sum (a_j, b_j)$ correspond to $g_1(x)$ as in Lemma 14. Then, since $G_1(x) = g_1(x)$ except possibly on E_0 and since for each point x in S_R there exists a point $x_1 > x$ such that $f(x_1) - f(x) > R(x_1 - x)$, it follows that

$$S_R - E_0 \subset E_1. \tag{5:8}$$

Now since $f(x)$ is nondecreasing, by Lemma 14 the set E_1 has the property that $g_1(a_j + 0) \leqq g_1(b_j + 0)$, or

$$R(b_j - a_j) \leqq f(b_j + 0) - f(a_j + 0). \tag{5:9}$$

From this it follows that

$$Rm(E_1) \leqq f(b) - f(a).$$

Since by (5:8), $E[D^+f = \infty] \subset E_0 + E_1$ for every R, it follows that D^+f is finite almost everywhere.

Now let $g_2(x) = f(x) - rx$, and apply the alternative reading of Lemma 14 to g_2 on each interval (a_j, b_j), obtaining a set $E_j'' =$

$\sum_k (a_{jk}, b_{jk})$ such that $g_2(x) \leqq G(a_{jk})$ on the interval (a_{jk}, b_{jk}). We find then

$$r(b_{jk} - a_{jk}) \geqq f(b_{jk} - 0) - f(a_{jk} + 0), \tag{5:10}$$

and

$$S_R T_r - E_0 \subset E_2 = \sum_{jk} (a_{jk}, b_{jk}). \tag{5:11}$$

Now apply the process by which (5:8) and (5:9) were obtained to each interval (a_{jk}, b_{jk}), noting that in this process $f(b_{jk} + 0)$ may be replaced by $f(b_{jk} - 0)$. We thus obtain

$$S_R T_r - E_0 \subset E_3 = \sum_{jkl} (a_{jkl}, b_{jkl}), \tag{5:12}$$

$$R(b_{jkl} - a_{jkl}) \leqq f(b_{jkl} + 0) - f(a_{jkl} + 0), \tag{5:13}$$

where in (5:13), $f(b_{jkl} + 0)$ is to be replaced by $f(b_{jkl} - 0)$ whenever $b_{jkl} = b_{jk}$.

By alternating applications of the two processes we obtain a nonincreasing sequence of open sets E_n such that

$$\begin{aligned} S_R T_r - E_0 &\subset E_n, \\ Rm(E_3) &\leqq \sum_{jkl} [f(b_{jkl} + 0) - f(a_{jkl} + 0)] \\ &\leqq \sum_{jk} [f(b_{jk} - 0) - f(a_{jk} + 0)] \\ &\leqq rm(E_2) \leqq rm(E_1), \end{aligned} \tag{5:14}$$

and in general

$$m(E_{2n+1}) \leqq (r/R)^n m(E_1). \tag{5:15}$$

If we now assume that $0 < r < R$, we find from (5:14) and (5:15) that $m(S_R T_r) = 0$. Since

$$E[D^+f > D_-f] = \sum S_R T_r,$$

where the sum is taken over rational values of r and R for which $0 < r < R$, it follows that

$$D^+f \leqq D_-f \tag{5:16}$$

almost everywhere. From (5:7) and (5:16) it follows that

$$D^-f \leqq D_+f \tag{5:17}$$

almost everywhere. By combining (5:16) and (5:17) with the obvious inequalities $D_-f \leqq D^-f$, $D_+f \leqq D^+f$, we obtain the desired result that the four derivates are equal and finite almost everywhere.

†6. The Fundamental Theorem of Integral Calculus.—In Theorems 28 and 29 below we find extensions of Theorem 10 of Chap. VI which are made possible by the concepts of Lebesgue. We shall need the following simple preliminary result:

LEMMA 16. *If λ is an integrable function such that $\int_a^x \lambda\, dx = 0$ on $[a, b]$, then $\lambda = 0$ almost everywhere on $[a, b]$.*

Proof.—Let (α_n) be a sequence of step functions converging to λ almost everywhere, and satisfying the conditions of Theorem 6. Then for every k there exists an integer n_k such that

$$\left|\int_A \alpha_{n_k}\, dx\right| < \frac{1}{2^{2k+1}}$$

for an arbitrary set A in $\mathfrak{A}$. Hence $|\alpha_{n_k}(x)| < (\frac{1}{2})^k$ except on a set A_k with $m(A_k) < (\frac{1}{2})^k$, so that $\lim_k \alpha_{n_k} = 0$ except on a set E contained in each of the sets $C_p = \sum_{k=p}^{\infty} A_k$. Since $m(C_p) < (\frac{1}{2})^{p-1}$, it follows that $m(E) = 0$, and hence $\lambda = 0$ almost everywhere.

THEOREM 28. *If $f(x)$ is absolutely continuous on $[a, b]$ then its derivative $f'(x)$ is integrable on $[a, b]$, and*

$$\int_a^x f'\, dx = f(x) - f(a).$$

NOTE: The validity of this and following theorems involving derivatives is not affected by the fact that the derivative $f'(x)$ may fail to exist on a set of measure zero.

Proof.—For $x > b$ set $f(x) = f(b)$ and for $x < a$ set $f(x) = f(a)$. The function

$$\lambda(x, h) = \frac{f(x + h) - f(x)}{h}$$

is integrable for $h \neq 0$, since $f(x)$ is continuous. For an arbitrary set $A = \sum (a_j, b_j)$ we have

$$\begin{aligned}\int_A \lambda(x, h)\, dx &= \frac{1}{h} \sum \left[\int_{a_j+h}^{b_j+h} f(x)\, dx - \int_{a_j}^{b_j} f(x)\, dx \right] \\ &= \frac{1}{h} \sum \left[\int_{b_j}^{b_j+h} f(x)\, dx - \int_{a_j}^{a_j+h} f(x)\, dx \right] \\ &= \frac{1}{h} \int_0^h \sum\ [f(b_j + x) - f(a_j + x)]\, dx.\end{aligned}$$

Since the intervals $(a_j + x, b_j + x)$ are nonoverlapping and the function f is absolutely continuous, it follows that the integrals $\int_A \lambda(x, h)\, dx$ are absolutely continuous uniformly in h. Also $\lim_{h=0} \lambda(x, h) = f'(x)$ almost everywhere, so that by Theorem 7, $f'(x)$ is integrable and

$$\begin{aligned}\int_a^b f'(x)\, dx &= \lim_{n=\infty} \int_a^b \lambda(x, 1/n)\, dx \\ &= \lim_{h=0} \frac{1}{h} \left[\int_{a+h}^{b+h} f(x)\, dx - \int_a^b f(x)\, dx) \right] \\ &= \lim_{h=0} \frac{1}{h} \left[\int_b^{b+h} f(x)\, dx - \int_a^{a+h} f(x)\, dx \right] \\ &= f(b) - f(a).\end{aligned}$$

THEOREM 29. *If λ is a function integrable on* $[a, b]$, *there exists a function f such that* (i) *f is absolutely continuous on* $[a, b]$; (ii) *the derivative $f'(x) = \lambda(x)$ almost everywhere on* $[a, b]$. *For every function f satisfying conditions* (i) *and* (ii) *we have*

$$\int_a^b \lambda\, dx = f(b) - f(a).$$

Proof.—If we set $f(x) = \int_a^x \lambda\, dx$, then f is absolutely continuous by a remark following the proof of Theorem 6. By Theorem 28, $\int_a^x (f' - \lambda)\, dx = 0$, so that $f' = \lambda$ almost everywhere by Lemma 16. The last statement in the theorem also follows from Theorem 28.

It is now clear that, for functions of one variable, the Lebesgue integral is characterized descriptively by the conditions (i) and (ii) of Theorem 29. This descriptive approach to the integral follows the ideas of Newton, while the constructive approach of Sec. 3 is related to the ideas of Leibnitz, Cauchy, and Riemann. Certain relaxations of the conditions (i) and (ii) are possible, leading to the integrals of Denjoy. (See Saks [1], Chaps. 7, 8.) However, the condition (i) cannot be omitted entirely without losing the uniqueness of the integral. In fact a nondecreasing continuous function can be constructed whose derivative is zero almost everywhere but which is not a constant.(1) Let the fundamental interval be [0, 1] and let x be represented in the ternary system, while $f(x)$ is represented in the binary system. If the digit 1 first appears in a certain place in the representation of x, let the corresponding digit of $f(x)$ be 1 while all the following digits are 0. For all other places, let a 0 in the representation of x correspond to a 0 in the representation of $f(x)$, and a 2 in the representation of x correspond to a 1 in the representation of $f(x)$. It is easily seen that $f(x)$ is continuous and nondecreasing, that its derivative is zero on the complement of the Cantor set F of Chap. III, and that the measure of F is zero.

The need for some part of the condition (i) is also emphasized by the existence of infinite families of functions such that all the functions of a family have the same derivative, but no two of them have a constant difference. See the remark following Theorem 4 in Chap. V.

The next theorem includes a formula for the total variation of an absolutely continuous function of one variable.

THEOREM 30. *If $f(x)$ is of bounded variation, its derivative $f'(x)$ is Lebesgue-integrable, and its total variation $t(x)$ satisfies the inequality*

$$t(b) \geqq \int_a^b |f'(x)|\, dx. \tag{6:1}$$

The equality sign holds if and only if f is absolutely continuous.

Proof.—Following the notations of Sec. 5, we have $f(x) = f(a) + p(x) - n(x)$, $t(x) = p(x) + n(x)$, and so $f' = p' - n'$, $t' = p' + n'$, $|f'| \leqq t'$ almost everywhere. Let

$$\psi(x, h) = \frac{t(x + h) - t(x)}{h},$$

where it is understood that the definition of $t(x)$ is extended

[1] See Bliss [10], p. 45.

by constant values outside the interval $[a, b]$, and let $\psi(x, h, n) = \psi(x, h) \wedge n$. Then $\lim_{h=0} \psi(x, h, n) = t'(x) \wedge n$ almost everywhere. Also $\psi(x, h, n)$ is integrable with respect to x, and bounded with respect to x and h, and

$$\int_a^b \psi(x, h, n)\, dx \leqq \frac{1}{h} \int_a^b [t(x + h) - t(x)]\, dx$$
$$= \frac{1}{h}\left[\int_b^{b+h} t(x)\, dx - \int_a^{a+h} t(x)\, dx\right],$$

and hence

$$\int_a^b [t'(x) \wedge n]\, dx \leqq t(b) - t(a + 0).$$

Hence by Theorem 12, $t'(x)$ is integrable, and

$$\int_a^b t'(x)\, dx \leqq t(b) - t(a + 0).$$

It is clear that we may replace $t(b)$ by $t(b - 0)$. When $t(b) = \int_a^b t'(x)\, dx$, we have also $t(x) = \int_a^x t'(x)\, dx$, and hence $t(x)$ is absolutely continuous, and so are $p(x)$, $n(x)$, and $f(x)$.

To prove that, when f is absolutely continuous, the equality sign holds in (6:1), we note that there exist two nonnegative integrable functions λ_1 and λ_2 such that $f' = \lambda_1 - \lambda_2$, $|f'| = \lambda_1 + \lambda_2$. Then the functions $g_1(x) = \int_a^x \lambda_1\, dx$ and $g_2(x) = \int_a^x \lambda_2\, dx$ are nondecreasing, and by Theorem 28, $f(x) = f(a) + g_1(x) - g_2(x)$. Hence in this case

$$t(b) \leqq g_1(b) + g_2(b) = \int_a^b |f'|\, dx.$$

*The notion of the **metric density** of a set at a point is occasionally useful. The result below on the metric density of a measurable set in one-dimensional space is included here since it is an immediate corollary of Theorem 29. More general definitions and theorems, applicable in spaces of more dimensions, are given in Saks [1], pages 128*ff*., and in Hobson [3], Vol. 1, pages 190*ff*.

*If E is a measurable set and x_0 is an arbitrary point in one-dimensional space, and

$$(6{:}2) \qquad \lim_{m(i)=0} \frac{m(iE)}{m(i)}$$

exists, where the interval i is required to contain the point x_0, then the value of (6:2) is called the **metric density** of E at x_0.

*THEOREM 31. *A measurable set E has metric density* 1 *almost everywhere on E, and metric density* 0 *almost everywhere on cE.*

Proof.—Since $m(iE) = \int_i \phi_E \, dx$, where ϕ_E is the characteristic function of E, and since

$$\frac{f(\beta) - f(\alpha)}{\beta - \alpha} = \frac{1}{\beta - \alpha} \left[(x_0 - \alpha) \frac{f(x_0) - f(\alpha)}{x_0 - \alpha} + (\beta - x_0) \frac{f(\beta) - f(x_0)}{\beta - x_0} \right],$$

it is clear that the limit (6:2) exists and equals the derivative of

$$(6{:}3) \qquad \int_a^x \phi_E \, dx$$

at all the points x_0 where (6:3) has a derivative and at no others. So the theorem follows from Theorem 29.

***7. Rectifiable Curves.**—A set of k continuous functions

$$(7{:}1) \qquad y_i = y_i(u), \qquad i = 1, \cdots, k; a \leqq u \leqq b,$$

constitutes a **representation** or **parametrization** of a **continuous path curve** C in k-dimensional space. The variable u is called the "parameter of the representation," and the path C is said to be traversed in the direction of increasing u. Such a representation may have "intervals of constancy" $[u', u'']$ on which all the functions y_i are constant.

An **admissible change of parameter** is determined by a function

$$u = \theta(v), \qquad c \leqq v \leqq d,$$

such that (1) θ is nondecreasing; (2) $\theta(c) = a$, $\theta(d) = b$; (3) every discontinuity $[\theta(v - 0), \theta(v + 0)]$ is contained in an interval of constancy $[u', u'']$. Such a change of parameter may eliminate some intervals of constancy and introduce others. It is easily seen that, if $u = \theta(v)$ is an admissible change of parameter for the representation $y_i(u)$, then the inverse function $v = \theta^{-1}(u)$, (properly defined) is an admissible change of parameter for the representation $y_i(\theta(v))$. Two representations are said to be **equivalent** if it is possible to pass from one to the other by an admissible change of parameter. This equivalence relation is transitive. Thus we may define a **continuous path curve** C as a maximal class of equivalent representations in the form (7:1).

A partition P of the interval $a \leqq u \leqq b$ determines an inscribed polygon $\pi(P)$ formed by joining the points corresponding to successive parameter values. The length $L(\pi(P))$ of such a polygon is defined in the usual elementary way. The **length** $L(C)$ of the curve C is defined to be the least upper bound of $L(\pi(P))$ for all partitions P. When $L(C)$ is finite, the curve C is said to be **rectifiable.** The length of a curve is obviously independent of the choice of the representation.

THEOREM 32. *A curve C is rectifiable if and only if the functions $y_i(u)$ representing it are of bounded variation.*

This follows from the inequalities

$$\sum_P |\Delta y_i| \leqq L(\pi(P)) \leqq \sum_i \sum_P |\Delta y_i|,$$

which hold for each coordinate y_i. Here $\sum_P |\Delta y_i|$ means $\sum_n |y_i(u_n) - y_i(u_{n-1})|$, where u_n ranges over the partition points of P.

THEOREM 33. *For every continuous curve C,*

$$L(C) = \lim_{N(P)=0} L(\pi(P)).$$

Proof.—Let P_0 be a partition of $[a, b]$ by points $u_1, \ldots, u_q$, and suppose that $L(\pi(P_0)) = L_0$. Suppose that $|y_i(u) - y_i(u_j)| < \epsilon$ whenever $|u - u_j| < \delta$. Let P be a partition with norm $N(P) < \delta$, and let the partition P^* be formed by using the partition points of both P_0 and P. Then

$$L_0 \leqq L(\pi(P^*)) \leqq L(\pi(P)) + 2kq\epsilon.$$

Since the curve C is continuous, the desired conclusion may readily be obtained from this inequality, whether $L(C)$ is finite or infinite.

It is easily verified that a curve C is rectifiable if and only if every subarc is rectifiable, and that the length of the whole is the sum of the lengths of the parts. When C is rectifiable, the length $s(u)$ of the piece corresponding to the parameter interval

$[a, u]$ is a nondecreasing continuous function. Its inverse function $u = \theta(s)$ satisfies the conditions for an admissible change of parameter. Hence every rectifiable curve may be represented with the arc length s as parameter. With this representation the functions $y_i(s)$ satisfy a Lipschitz condition, and hence are absolutely continuous.

THEOREM 34. *For an arbitrary representation* (7:1) *of a rectifiable curve* C, *we have*

$$\left(\frac{ds}{du}\right)^2 = \sum_i \left(\frac{dy_i}{du}\right)^2 \quad \textit{almost everywhere,} \tag{7:2}$$

$$L(C) \geqq \int_a^b \left\{\sum_i \left(\frac{dy_i}{du}\right)^2\right\}^{1/2} du. \tag{7:3}$$

The equality sign holds in (7:3) *if and only if the functions* $y_i(u)$ *are absolutely continuous.*

Proof.—Since

$$\Delta s \geqq \left\{\sum_i (\Delta y_i)^2\right\}^{1/2}, \tag{7:4}$$

it follows that

$$\frac{ds}{du} \geqq \left\{\sum_i \left(\frac{dy_i}{du}\right)^2\right\}^{1/2}, \tag{7:5}$$

whenever all the derivatives involved exist. Let E denote the set of all points u at which the strict inequality holds in (7:5), and let E_q denote the set of all points u in E such that

$$\frac{\Delta s}{\Delta u} \geqq \left\{\sum_i \left(\frac{\Delta y_i}{\Delta u}\right)^2\right\}^{1/2} + \frac{1}{q}, \tag{7:6}$$

whenever the interval Δu contains u and has length less than $1/q$. Then $E = \sum E_q$, and (7:2) will follow if we show that $m(E_q) = 0$ for each q. Let $\epsilon > 0$, and let P be a partition with $N(P) < 1/q$ and

$$L(\pi(P)) > L(C) - \epsilon. \tag{7:7}$$

If we multiply (7:6) by Δu and sum over the intervals of P containing points of E_q and add to this the sum of (7:4) over the remaining intervals of P, we find that

$$L(C) \geqq L(\pi(P)) + \frac{m(E_q)}{q}. \tag{7:8}$$

From (7:7) and (7:8) we obtain $m(E_q) < \epsilon q$, and hence $m(E_q) = 0$.

It follows readily from its definition that the function $s(u)$ is absolutely continuous if and only if all the functions $y_i(u)$ have that property. Thus the remainder of the theorem follows at once from Theorem 30.

REFERENCES

1. Saks, *Theory of the Integral* (translated by L. C. Young), 1937, Chaps. 1 to 4.
2. McShane, *Integration*, 1944, Chaps. 1 to 6.
3. Hobson, *Theory of Functions of a Real Variable*, Vol. 1, Chaps. 3, 5, 7; Vol. 2, Chaps. 4, 5.
4. Pierpont, *Theory of Functions of Real Variables*, Vol. 2, Chaps. 11, 12.
5. Caratheodory, *Vorlesungen über reelle Funktionen*, Chaps. 5, 7 to 10.
6. la Vallée Poussin, *Intégrales de Lebesgue, Fonctions d'ensemble, Classes de Baire*, 1916.
7. Lebesgue, *Leçons sur l'intégration*, 2d Ed., 1928, Chaps. 1 to 9.
8. Riesz, "Sur l'intégrale de Lebesgue," *Acta Mathematica*, Vol. 42 (1920), pp. 191–205.
9. Riesz, "Sur l'existence de la derivée des fonctions d'une variable réelle et sur quelques problèmes qui s'y rattachent," *Acta Litterarum ac Scientiarum*, Szeged, Vol. 5 (1932), pp. 208–221.
10. Bliss, "Integrals of Lebesgue," *Bulletin of the American Mathematical Society*, Vol. 24 (1917), pp. 1–47.
11. Hildebrandt, "On Integrals Related to and Extensions of the Lebesgue Integrals," *Bulletin of the American Mathematical Society*, Vol. 24 (1917), pp. 113–144, 177–202.
12. Hahn and Rosenthal, *Set Functions*, 1948.

Saks [1] approaches the theory of Lebesgue integrals for real-valued functions from an abstract point of view. A very useful bibliography appears at the end. Lebesgue [7] gives some account of the ideas leading up to the development of the theory. The article by Bliss [10] gives a brief presentation of the central ideas of this theory in very readable form.

CHAPTER XI

THE LEBESGUE INTEGRAL *(Continued)*[1]

1. Differentiation with Respect to a Parameter

†THEOREM 1. *Let* $\lambda(x, t)$ *be defined and integrable with respect to* x *on the fundamental interval* I *for each* t *in a neighborhood of* t_0, *and let the partial derivative* $\lambda_t(x, t_0)$ *exist almost everywhere on* I. *Let the integrals*

$$\int_A \frac{\lambda(x, t_0 + h) - \lambda(x, t_0)}{h}\, dx$$

be absolutely continuous uniformly with respect to h. *Then the function*

$$g(t) = \int_I \lambda(x, t)\, dx$$

has a derivative at t_0, *and*

$$g'(t_0) = \int_I \lambda_t(x, t_0)\, dx.$$

This theorem follows at once from Theorem 7 of Chap. X, and holds for an interval I in any finite number of dimensions. It holds also for a general measure function with an added hypothesis similar to the one following Theorem 7. We recall that a sufficient condition for uniform absolute continuity is given by Theorem 11 of Chap. X. In particular this condition is always satisfied when the difference quotients $[\lambda(x, t_0 + h) - \lambda(x, t_0)]/h$ are uniformly bounded.

2. Fubini's Theorem on Reduction of Multiple to Repeated Integrals.—In order to prove Fubini's theorem (Theorem 2) on the reduction of a multiple integral to repeated integrals, we shall need some preliminary definitions and theorems. The first

[1] We shall continue to indicate with a † those theorems which are not known to hold in unrestricted form for a general measure function.

of these is related to Lemma 16 of Chap. X, and in the one-dimensional case is a corollary of it.

LEMMA 1. *Let* λ *be a nonnegative integrable function such that* $\int_I \lambda\, dx = 0$. *Then* $\lambda = 0$ *almost everywhere.*

Proof.—Let $E_k \equiv E[\lambda \geqq 1/k]$. Then $\int_I \lambda\, dx \geqq m(E_k)/k$, so that $m(E_k) = 0$. Since $E_0 \equiv E[\lambda > 0] = \sum E_k$, it follows that $m(E_0) = 0$.

Let $\mathfrak{M}^+$ denote the class of all functions which are limits of bounded nondecreasing sequences of step functions, and let $\mathfrak{M}^{+-}$ denote the class of all functions that are limits of bounded nonincreasing sequences of functions chosen from $\mathfrak{M}^+$. Similarly let $\mathfrak{M}^-$ denote the class of all functions that are limits of bounded nonincreasing sequences of step functions, and let $\mathfrak{M}^{-+}$ denote the class of all functions that are limits of bounded nondecreasing sequences of functions chosen from $\mathfrak{M}^-$. Here the term "limit" is used to mean convergence at each point of the interval I, not merely convergence almost everywhere. It is easy to verify that each of the four classes of functions just defined is closed with respect to the operations I, IV, and V of Chap. X, Sec. 3.

LEMMA 2. *Suppose* λ *is bounded and measurable, and* $\epsilon > 0$. *Then there exist a function* μ^+ *from the class* $\mathfrak{M}^+$ *and a function* μ^- *from* $\mathfrak{M}^-$ *such that* $\mu^- \leqq \lambda \leqq \mu^+$ *and*

$$\int_I \mu^+\, dx - \epsilon \leqq \int_I \lambda\, dx \leqq \int_I \mu^-\, dx + \epsilon.$$

Proof.—Let (α_n) be a bounded sequence of step functions converging to λ almost everywhere. Then by Theorems 2 and 4 of Chap. X, there exists a set $C = \sum i_h$ and an integer j such that $m(C) < \epsilon/4K$, $|\alpha_j - \lambda| < \epsilon/4m(I)$ on $I - C$, and

$$\left|\int_I \alpha_j\, dx - \int_I \lambda\, dx\right| < \frac{\epsilon}{4},$$

where K is a bound for $|\lambda|$ and $|\alpha_j|$. Let

$$\bar{\alpha}_n = \alpha_j + \frac{\epsilon}{4m(I)} + 2K \sum_{h=1}^{n} \phi_{i_h},$$

$$\mu^+ = \lim_n \bar{\alpha}_n,$$

where ϕ_{i_h} is the characteristic function of the interval i_h. Then

$$\int_I \mu^+ \, dx = \int_I \alpha_j \, dx + \frac{\epsilon}{4} + 2Km(C)$$
$$< \int_I \lambda \, dx + \epsilon.$$

The function μ^- is obtained by taking the negative of the function from the class $\mathfrak{M}^+$ corresponding to $(-\lambda)$.

LEMMA 3. *Let λ be bounded and measurable. Then there exist a function μ^{-+} from the class $\mathfrak{M}^{-+}$ and a function μ^{+-} from $\mathfrak{M}^{+-}$ such that $\mu^{-+} \leqq \lambda \leqq \mu^{+-}$ and*

$$\int_I \mu^{-+} \, dx = \int_I \lambda \, dx = \int_I \mu^{+-} \, dx.$$

Conversely, if there exist functions μ^{-+} from $\mathfrak{M}^{-+}$ and μ^{+-} from $\mathfrak{M}^{+-}$ such that $\mu^{-+} \leqq \lambda \leqq \mu^{+-}$ and

$$\int_I \mu^{-+} \, dx = \int_I \mu^{+-} \, dx$$

then λ is bounded and measurable.

Proof.—By Lemma 2 there exist sequences (μ_n^+) and (μ_n^-) such that $\mu_n^- \leqq \lambda \leqq \mu_n^+$ and

$$\int_I \mu_n^+ \, dx - \frac{1}{n} \leqq \int_I \lambda \, dx \leqq \int_I \mu_n^- \, dx + \frac{1}{n}.$$

If μ^+ is an arbitrary function of the class $\mathfrak{M}^+$ such that $\lambda \leqq \mu^+$, we may replace μ_n^+ by the logical product $\mu^+ \wedge \mu_n^+$. Hence we may suppose that the sequence (μ_n^+) is nonincreasing. Similarly we may suppose that the sequence (μ_n^-) is nondecreasing. From this, the desired conclusion is obvious. For the converse, we note that by Lemma 1, $\mu^{-+} = \mu^{+-}$ almost everywhere, and hence $\mu^{-+} = \lambda$ almost everywhere.

Now let us suppose that the interval I is the Cartesian product $I_y \times I_z$ of an interval I_y of a y-space and an interval I_z of a z-space. Suppose also that a measure function m_y is defined for subintervals i_y of I_y, and a measure function m_z is defined for subintervals i_z of I_z. For $i = i_y \times i_z$ we set $m(i) = m_y(i_y)m_z(i_z)$. Then it is clear that for a step function $\alpha(x) = \alpha(y, z)$, $\int_{I_z} \alpha \, dz$

is a step function defined on I_y, and

$$\int_I \alpha\, dx = \int_{I_y} \int_{I_z} \alpha\, dz\, dy.$$

For convenience we shall say that an integrable function $\lambda(x) = \lambda(y, z)$ *has the property* P in case:

P₁. $\lambda(y, z)$ is integrable on I_z for every y in I_y;

P₂. $\int_{I_z} \lambda(y, z)\, dz$ is integrable on I_y;

P₃. $\int_I \lambda\, dx = \int_{I_y} \int_{I_z} \lambda\, dz\, dy.$

In case P_1 holds only for almost all y in I_y and P_2 and P_3 hold, we shall say that λ *has the property* P*.

THEOREM 2. **Fubini's theorem.** *Every integrable function has the property* P*.

As part of the proof we shall use the following proposition:

LEMMA 4. *Let* $\lim_n \lambda_n = \lambda$ *everywhere on the interval* I, *where the functions* λ_n *and* λ *are integrable and the sequence* (λ_n) *is uniformly bounded. If each* λ_n *has the property* P, *the limit* λ *also has the property* P.

Proof.—By use of Theorem 4 of Chap. X, the preservation of the component properties P_1 to P_3 can be verified in succession.

Proof of Theorem 2.—We have already noticed that every step function α has the property P. Consequently all the functions in the classes $\mathfrak{M}^{+-}$ and $\mathfrak{M}^{-+}$ have the property P by Lemma 4. Now let λ be bounded and measurable. Then by Lemma 3 there exist functions μ^{-+} from $\mathfrak{M}^{-+}$ and μ^{+-} from $\mathfrak{M}^{+-}$ such that

$$\mu^{-+} \leqq \lambda \leqq \mu^{+-},$$

$$\int_{I_y} \int_{I_z} \mu^{-+}\, dz\, dy = \int_I \lambda\, dx = \int_{I_y} \int_{I_z} \mu^{+-}\, dz\, dy. \tag{2:1}$$

Thus

$$\int_{I_y} \int_{I_z} (\mu^{+-} - \mu^{-+})\, dz\, dy = 0,$$

and hence by Lemma 1,

$$\int_{I_z} [\mu^{+-}(y, z) - \mu^{-+}(y, z)]\, dz = 0 \tag{2:2}$$

almost everywhere in the interval I_y. Let S denote the set of points of I_y at which (2:2) holds. Then by another application of Lemma 1 and use of (2:1) we find that for each y in the set S,

$$\mu^{-+}(y, z) = \lambda(y, z) = \mu^{+-}(y, z)$$

almost everywhere on I_z. Thus $\lambda(y, z)$ is integrable on I_z and

$$\int_{I_z} \lambda(y, z)\, dz = \int_{I_z} \mu^{+-}(y, z)\, dz$$

for each y in S. Hence

$$\int_{I_z} \lambda(y, z)\, dz$$

is integrable on I_y, and

$$\int_{I_y} \int_{I_z} \lambda\, dz\, dy = \int_{I_y} \int_{I_z} \mu^{+-}\, dz\, dy = \int_I \mu^{+-}\, dx = \int_I \lambda\, dx,$$

so that λ has the property P*.

Since every integrable function is representable as the difference of two nonnegative integrable functions, it is sufficient in completing the proof to suppose that λ is nonnegative. Then $\lambda_n = \lambda \wedge n$ is bounded and measurable and so has the property P*, and the sequence (λ_n) is nondecreasing. The sum of the exceptional sets where

$$\psi_n(y) = \int_{I_z} \lambda_n(y, z)\, dz$$

may fail to have a meaning is a set E of measure zero in the interval I_y, and so may be neglected. Now

$$\int_{I_y} \psi_n(y)\, dy = \int_I \lambda_n\, dx$$

and the right-hand side tends to $\int_I \lambda\, dx$ as n tends to infinity, by Theorem 12 of Chap. X. Thus, again by Theorem 12, $\psi(y) = \lim_n \psi_n(y)$ is integrable on I_y and so is finite almost everywhere, and

$$\int_{I_y} \psi\, dy = \int_I \lambda\, dx.$$

By a third application of Theorem 12 we have

$$\psi(y) = \int_{I_z} \lambda(y, z)\, dz$$

almost everywhere on I_y, and so the function λ has the property P*.

THEOREM 3. *Let E be a measurable subset of the interval I, and let E^y denote the set of all points z such that (y, z) is in E. Then for almost all points y in I_y, the set E^y is measurable in I_z, and*

$$m(E) = \int_{I_y} m_z(E^y)\,dy. \tag{2:3}$$

This follows as a corollary of Theorem 2 by taking λ as the characteristic function of the set E.

It is interesting to note that the existence of the integral on the right in (2:3) does not imply the measurability of the set E. In fact, Sierpinski has given an example of a nonmeasurable set in the plane which intersects an arbitrary straight line in at most two points.[1] However, the following partial converse of Theorem 2 is valid.

THEOREM 4. *If $\lambda(y, z)$ is measurable on I, and integrable on I_z for almost all y in I_y, and if $\int_{I_z} |\lambda(y, z)|\,dz$ is integrable on I_y, then λ is integrable on I.*

The proof is similar to the last paragraph of the proof of Theorem 2.

†3. Integration by Parts

THEOREM 5. *Let $f(x)$ be absolutely continuous and $\lambda(x)$ be integrable on $[a, b]$. Let $g(x) - g(a) = \int_a^x \lambda\,dx$. Then $\int_a^b f(x)\lambda(x)\,dx = f(b)g(b) - f(a)g(a) - \int_a^b g(x)f'(x)\,dx$.*

Proof.—The product $f(x)g(x)$ is absolutely continuous, by Theorem 25 of Chap. X, and $(fg)' = fg' + f'g$ wherever both derivatives f' and g' exist and are finite. Moreover, the product fg', which equals $f\lambda$ almost everywhere by Theorem 29 of Chap. X, is integrable by Theorem 8 of Chap. X, since f is continuous, and so $f'g$ is also integrable. Then the conclusion follows at once from Theorem 28 of Chap. X.

The preceding theorem could also be obtained by applying Fubini's theorem to the integral

$$\int_D f'(y)\lambda(x)\,dx\,dy,$$

[1] "Sur un problème concernant les ensembles measurables superficiellement," *Fundamenta Mathematicae*, Vol. I (1920), pp. 112–115.

where D is the triangle $E[a \leqq y \leqq x \leqq b]$. It must first be proved that the product $f'(y)\lambda(x)$ is integrable over D.

†**4. Change of Variables.**—At first we consider functions of one variable. Theorem 6 is a special case which is frequently useful. It is also a steppingstone to the more general Theorem 7.

THEOREM 6. *Let $\lambda(x)$ be bounded and measurable on $a \leqq x \leqq b$, and let the function $\xi(t)$ be absolutely continuous on $c \leqq t \leqq d$, and have all its values on the interval $[a, b]$. Then the function $\lambda(\xi(t))\xi'(t)$ is integrable on $[c, d]$, and*

$$\int_{\xi(c)}^{\xi(d)} \lambda(x)\, dx = \int_c^d \lambda(\xi(t))\xi'(t)\, dt.$$

Proof.—Let $M = \text{l.u.b. } |\lambda(x)|$, $F(x) = \int_a^x \lambda\, dx$, $G(t) = F(\xi(t))$. Then the function G is absolutely continuous on $[c, d]$. For, if $[c_h, d_h]$ are nonoverlapping intervals in $[c, d]$ such that $\sum |\xi(d_h) - \xi(c_h)| < \epsilon$, we have

$$\sum |G(d_h) - G(c_h)| \leqq M \sum |\xi(d_h) - \xi(c_h)| \leqq M\epsilon,$$

so that the absolute continuity of G follows from that of ξ.[1]

Now let us consider the special case when λ is continuous. Then the derivative $F'(x)$ exists and equals $\lambda(x)$ everywhere, and hence $G'(t)$ exists and equals $\lambda(\xi(t))\xi'(t)$ wherever $\xi'(t)$ exists and is finite. From this we find

$$\begin{aligned}\int_{\xi(c)}^{\xi(d)} \lambda\, dx &= F(\xi(d)) - F(\xi(c)) = G(d) - G(c) \\ &= \int_c^d \lambda(\xi(t))\xi'(t)\, dt,\end{aligned}$$

by Theorem 28 of Chap. X.

Next let us suppose that the conclusion holds for each function λ_n of a sequence such that $|\lambda_n(x)| \leqq K$, and that $\lambda_n(x)$ converges to $\lambda(x)$ everywhere on $[a, b]$. Then $\lim_n \lambda_n(\xi(t))\xi'(t) = \lambda(\xi(t))\xi'(t)$ almost everywhere on $[c, d]$, and the sequence is dominated by the integrable function $K|\xi'(t)|$. Thus by Theorems 11 and 7 of Chap. X, the conclusion holds also for the function $\lambda(x)$.

Now it is easily seen that every step function is the limit of a

[1] It is interesting to note that this conclusion could not be drawn if λ were only assumed to be integrable. See Caratheodory [4], p. 554.

bounded sequence of continuous functions. Thus the conclusion holds when $\lambda(x)$ is a step function, and hence also when λ is a function of the class $\mathfrak{M}^{-+}$ or $\mathfrak{M}^{+-}$ of Sec. 2. By Lemmas 3 and 1, for an arbitrary bounded measurable function $\lambda(x)$ there exist functions μ^{-+} in $\mathfrak{M}^{-+}$ and μ^{+-} in $\mathfrak{M}^{+-}$ which are equal almost everywhere, such that

$$\mu^{-+}(x) \leqq \lambda(x) \leqq \mu^{+-}(x) \text{ on } [a, b], \tag{4:1}$$

$$\int_{\xi(c)}^{\xi(\tau)} \lambda \, dx = \int_{\xi(c)}^{\xi(\tau)} \mu^{-+} \, dx = \int_{\xi(c)}^{\xi(\tau)} \mu^{+-} \, dx. \tag{4:2}$$

But by what has already been proved,

$$\int_{\xi(c)}^{\xi(\tau)} \mu^{-+} \, dx = \int_c^\tau \mu^{-+}\xi' \, dt, \tag{4:3}$$

with a similar equation for μ^{+-}, so that

$$\int_c^\tau \mu^{-+}\xi' \, dt = \int_c^\tau \mu^{+-}\xi' \, dt.$$

Hence $\mu^{-+}\xi' = \mu^{+-}\xi'$ almost everywhere on $[c, d]$, by Lemma 16 of Chap. X. By (4:1) $\lambda\xi'$ lies between $\mu^{-+}\xi'$ and $\mu^{+-}\xi'$ at every point on $[c, d]$ where ξ' exists and is finite, so that $\lambda\xi' = \mu^{-+}\xi'$ almost everywhere on $[c, d]$. This with (4:2) and (4:3) gives the desired formula.

COROLLARY. *If the function $x = \xi(t)$ is absolutely continuous on the interval $c \leqq t \leqq d$, and transforms a set T of that interval into a set X of measure zero in the interval $a \leqq x \leqq b$, then the derivative $\xi'(t) = 0$ almost everywhere on T.*

Proof.—Let $\phi(x)$ be the characteristic function of the set X. Then

$$0 = \int_{\xi(c)}^{\xi(\tau)} \phi \, dx = \int_c^\tau \phi(\xi(t))\xi'(t) \, dt.$$

Hence, by Lemma 16 of Chap. X, $\phi\xi' = 0$ almost everywhere on $c \leqq t \leqq d$. But $\phi = 1$ for t in T, and hence $\xi' = 0$ almost everywhere on T.

THEOREM 7. *Let $\lambda(x)$ be integrable on $a \leqq x \leqq b$, and let $\xi(t)$ be absolutely continuous on $c \leqq t \leqq d$, and have all its values on the interval $[a, b]$. Let λ_n denote the function $(\lambda \wedge n) \vee (-n)$. Then*

1. $\displaystyle\int_{\xi(c)}^{\xi(d)} \lambda(x) \, dx = \lim_n \int_c^d \lambda_n(\xi(t))\xi'(t) \, dt;$

2. *Whenever* $\lambda(\xi(t))\xi'(t)$ *is integrable,*

$$\int_{\xi(c)}^{\xi(d)} \lambda(x)\, dx = \int_c^d \lambda(\xi(t))\xi'(t)\, dt;$$

3. $\lambda(\xi(t))\xi'(t)$ *is always integrable when* $\xi(t)$ *is monotonic.*

Proof.—By Theorem 6,

$$\int_{\xi(c)}^{\xi(d)} \lambda_n\, dx = \int_c^d \lambda_n \xi'\, dt,$$

and by Theorems 11 and 7 of Chap. X,

$$\lim_n \int_{\xi(c)}^{\xi(d)} \lambda_n\, dx = \int_{\xi(c)}^{\xi(d)} \lambda\, dx.$$

This proves the first conclusion. Next we have $|\lambda_n\xi'| \leqq |\lambda\xi'|$ wherever ξ' is defined; hence, if $\lambda\xi'$ is integrable on $[c, d]$, we have

$$\lim_n \int_c^d \lambda_n \xi'\, dt = \int_c^d \lambda\xi'\, dt.$$

To prove the third conclusion, we may suppose that $\xi(t)$ is nondecreasing and, since every integrable function is the difference of two nonnegative integrable functions, that $\lambda(x) \geqq 0$. Then the sequence $(\lambda_n\xi')$ is nondecreasing, and hence $\lambda\xi'$ is integrable by Theorem 12 of Chap. X.

We note that if $F(x) = \int_a^x \lambda\, dx$, then $F(\xi(t))$ is absolutely continuous whenever $\lambda(\xi(t))\xi'(t)$ is integrable.[1] Hence $\lambda(\xi(t))\xi'(t)$ is not integrable in the following example (McShane [2], page 214):

$$\lambda(x) = x^{-2/3}, \qquad \xi(t) = t^3 \cos^3 (\pi/t), \qquad F(x) = 3x^{1/3},$$
$$F(\xi(t)) = 3t \cos (\pi/t).$$

The transformation of multiple integrals is a difficult subject, and we shall not attempt to include the very general results obtained by W. H. Young and by Radó and Reichelderfer.[2]

[1] The converse also holds. See Caratheodory [4] pp. 562, 563.

[2] See Radó and Reichelderfer, "A Theory of Absolutely Continuous Transformations in the Plane," *Transactions of the American Mathematical Society*, Vol. 49 (1941), pp. 258–307; also Helsel and Radó, "The Transformation of Double Integrals," *Transactions of the American Mathematical Society*, Vol. 54 (1943), pp. 83–102; and references in those memoirs.

However, the results developed below are sufficient for many purposes in analysis.

Consider a transformation

$$T\colon x = f(u) \tag{4:4}$$

of a set Q into a set $R = T(Q)$. For definiteness we assume that Q and R are bounded open sets in k-dimensional space and that T establishes a one-one bicontinuous correspondence between Q and R. Upon occasion the variables may be divided notationally into sets, and attention restricted to special transformations of the form

$$T\colon \begin{array}{ll} x_i = f_i(u_1, \cdots, u_\rho; v_1, \cdots, v_\sigma) & i = 1, \cdots, \rho; \\ y_j = v_j & j = 1, \cdots, \sigma; \rho + \sigma = k. \end{array} \tag{4:5}$$

We shall also wish to consider a real-valued nonnegative function $J(u)$ (or $J(u,v)$) which is integrable on Q.

LEMMA 5. *Suppose that for every interval $i \subset R$,*

$$m(i) = \int_{T^{-1}(i)} J\, du, \tag{4:6}$$

and that Z is a subset of R of measure zero. Then $J = 0$ almost everywhere on $T^{-1}(Z)$.

Proof.—It is easily seen that $T^{-1}(i)$ is measurable. Let (C_n) be a nonincreasing sequence of open sets, with $\lim_n m(C_n) = 0$, $Z \subset C_n \subset R$, and let $Q_0 = \lim T^{-1}(C_n)$. Then since each C_n is a sum of intervals,

$$\int_{Q_0} J\, du = \lim_n \int_{T^{-1}(C_n)} J\, du = \lim_n m(C_n) = 0.$$

Hence $J = 0$ almost everywhere on Q_0 which contains $T^{-1}(Z)$.

LEMMA 6. *Suppose that* (4:6) *holds for every interval $i \subset R$, and that $\lambda(x)$ is integrable on R. Then $\lambda[f(u)]J(u)$ is integrable on Q, and*

$$\int_R \lambda\, dx = \int_Q \lambda J\, du. \tag{4:7}$$

Proof.—Suppose first that λ is bounded. Let A be a finite sum of intervals contained in R, and let (α_n) be a bounded sequence of step functions converging to λ almost everywhere in A. Then by Lemma 5, $\lim_n \alpha_n[f(u)]J(u) = \lambda[f(u)]J(u)$ almost everywhere on $T^{-1}(A)$. Also $|\alpha_n J| \leqq MJ$, where M is a bound for $|\alpha_n(x)|$. Immediately from (4:6) we have

$$\int_A \alpha_n \, dx = \int_{T^{-1}(A)} \alpha_n J \, du.$$

Hence

$$\int_A \lambda \, dx = \int_{T^{-1}(A)} \lambda J \, du.$$

The open set $R = \lim A_n$, where (A_n) is a nondecreasing sequence of finite sums of intervals. If λ is unbounded, we may assume $\lambda \geqq 0$, and set $\lambda_n = \lambda$ where $\lambda \leqq n$, $\lambda_n = n$ where $\lambda > n$. Then

$$\int_R \lambda \, dx = \lim_n \int_{A_n} \lambda_n \, dx = \lim_n \int_{T^{-1}(A_n)} \lambda_n J \, du = \int_Q \lambda J \, du.$$

LEMMA 7. *Suppose that the transformation T is in the form (4:5), and that for each interval i_x in the x-subspace and each y for which $(i_x, y) \subset R$, we have*

$$m_x(i_x) = \int_{S^v} J(u, y) \, du,$$

where $(S^v, v) = T^{-1}(i_x, y)$, and m_x is p-dimensional measure. Then for every interval $i \subset R$,

$$m(i) = \int_{T^{-1}(i)} J(u, v) \, du \, dv.$$

Proof.—If i is the Cartesian product of i_x and i_y, $T^{-1}(i)$ is the set of all (u, v) for which v is in i_y and u is in S^v. Then by Fubini's theorem,

$$\int_{T^{-1}(i)} J(u, v) \, du \, dv = \int_{i_y} \int_{S^v} J(u, y) \, du \, dy$$
$$= \int_{i_y} m_x(i_x) \, dy = m(i).$$

LEMMA 8. *Suppose that T is defined by functions of class C', that J is the Jacobian of the transformation, and that $J > 0$ on Q. Then for every interval $i \subset R$,*

$$m(i) = \int_{T^{-1}(i)} J \, du. \tag{4:6}$$

Proof.—The proof proceeds by induction on the number k of dimensions. The conclusion obviously holds for $k = 1$.

Suppose that it holds for k and that the transformation T is represented in the form

$$x = f(u, v_1, \cdots, v_k), \qquad y_j = g_j(u, v_1, \cdots, v_k) \qquad j = 1, \cdots, k.$$

If i is an interval contained in R, it is covered by a finite number of subintervals such that, on the inverse image of each, some partial derivative of f is not zero. Thus it is sufficient to verify (4:6) on subintervals i on the inverse image of which some one partial derivative of f is not zero. Hence we shall suppose $f_u > 0$ on $T^{-1}(i_0)$. (In case $f_u < 0$, we may reverse the positive direction on the u-axis and on one v_j-axis.) Consider the auxiliary transformation

$$T_1\colon w = f(u, v), \qquad z_j = v_j.$$

Then T_1 is of class C' and $J_1 = f_u > 0$ on a neighborhood Q_0 of $T^{-1}(i_0)$. Hence T_1^{-1} is single-valued and of class C' on $T_1(Q_0)$, and so the second auxiliary transformation

$$T_2 = TT_1^{-1}\colon \quad x = w, \qquad y_j = h_j(w, z),$$

is of class C' and establishes a one-one correspondence between $T_1(Q_0)$ and a neighborhood R_0 of the interval i_0. Its Jacobian $J_2 = \det(\partial h_j/\partial z_l)$ is positive and continuous, and $J = J_2J_1$. Then by the induction hypothesis, if (x, i_y) is in R_0,

$$m_y(i_y) = \int_{S^x} J_2(x, z)\, dz,$$

where $(w, S^w) = T_2^{-1}(x, i_y)$, and so by Lemma 7, if $i \subset i_0$,

$$m(i) = \int_{T_2^{-1}(i)} J_2(w, z)\, dz\, dw.$$

By Lemmas 7 and 6, applied to the transformation T_1, we have

$$m(i) = \int_{T_2^{-1}(i)} J_2\, dz\, dw = \int_{T^{-1}(i)} J_2J_1\, dv\, du = \int_{T^{-1}(i)} J\, dv\, du.$$

By combining Lemmas 8 and 6 we obtain the following result:

THEOREM 8. *Suppose the transformation T establishes a one-one bicontinuous correspondence between the bounded open sets Q and R, that T is defined by functions of class C', and that the*

Jacobian J of T is positive on Q. Then for every function λ integrable on R,

$$\int_R \lambda\, dx = \int_Q \lambda J\, du.$$

It is clear that in special cases we may be able to apply Lemmas 7 and 6 when the transformation is not of class C'. As will be indicated in Sec. 5, the result extends at once to unbounded domains. The Jacobian J may be permitted to vanish at certain exceptional points, and the restriction that the transformation be one-to-one may also be lightened slightly. These possibilities are sufficiently indicated by the familiar example of transformation to polar coordinates:

$$\text{T:}\quad \begin{array}{ll} x = u\cos v, & 0 \leqq u \leqq 1, \\ y = u \sin v, & -\pi \leqq v \leqq \pi. \end{array}$$

In this case the boundary of the rectangle Q in the uv-plane transforms into a closed set of measure zero and, when these sets are discarded, the hypotheses of the theorem are satisfied on the remainder.

***5. Integrals over Unbounded Domains.**—It was remarked in Chap. X that the Cauchy improper integral of elementary calculus is not included as a special case of the Lebesgue integral, since the absolute value of an integrable function is also integrable. We shall make the same restriction in considering integrals over unbounded sets.

Let X denote the interval $(-\infty, \infty)$, and let $I_q = [-q, q]$. In the case of space of more than one dimension, corresponding inequalities would be assumed for each coordinate, with the same value of q. A function μ is said to be **measurable** on X in case μ is measurable on each interval I_q. A function λ is said to be **integrable** on X in case λ is integrable on each I_q and the integrals $\int_{I_q} |\lambda|\, dx$ are bounded. Then we define

$$\int_X \lambda\, dx = \lim_{q=\infty} \int_{I_q} \lambda\, dx,$$

since the limit surely exists and is finite. The definition of measurable sets is extended to unbounded sets in the same way. The measure of an unbounded set may be finite or infinite. When a family of functions $\lambda_n(x)$ is given, we shall say that the integrals $\int_X |\lambda_n|\, dx$ **converge uniformly** when

$$\lim_q \int_{I_q} |\lambda_n|\, dx = \int_X |\lambda_n|\, dx$$

uniformly. The definitions of functions of bounded variation and of absolutely continuous functions extend without change to the case of functions $f(x)$ defined on unbounded domains.

The following theorems of the preceding sections are still valid when the domain of integration is the whole space X in place of a finite interval I: Theorems 8 to 13, 15, 18 to 20, 22 to 24, and 30, and the Corollary of Theorem 17, in Chap. X; Theorems 2, 4, and 8 in Chap. XI. In Theorem 11 of Chap. X we obtain the additional conclusion that the *integrals* $\int_X |\lambda_n|\, dx$ *converge uniformly*. In Chap. X, Theorem 7 is still valid with the additional hypothesis that *the integrals* $\int_X |\lambda_n|\, dx$ *converge uniformly;* Theorem 25 is still valid with the additional hypothesis, in the case of a product, that *the factors are bounded;* and Theorems 28 and 29 are still valid with the additional restriction that *the function* $f(x)$ *is of bounded variation.* In Chap. XI, Theorem 1 is still valid with an additional hypothesis corresponding to that just mentioned for Theorem 7; Theorem 3 is valid except that the formula (2:3) may fail to have a meaning; Theorem 5 is still valid under the additional assumption that $f(x)$ is of bounded variation; and the conclusions (2) and (3) of Theorem 7 are still valid when $\lambda(x)$ *is integrable on* $(-\infty, \infty)$ *and either* (*a*) $\xi(t)$ *is absolutely continuous on every finite interval, or* (*b*) $\xi(t)$ *is absolutely continuous on every interval* $[c + \epsilon, d - \epsilon]$ *and* $\xi(c) = -\infty$, $\xi(d) = \infty$. In Chap. X, Theorems 16 and 17 are still valid for subsets of a fixed set E *of finite measure,* which may be unbounded. The left-hand inequality in Theorem 16 holds without this restriction, as follows from Theorem 12. Theorem 26 does not extend, since the function $f(x) = x$ is absolutely continuous but is not of bounded variation on the whole x-axis. However, a function $f(x)$ is absolutely continuous if it is of bounded variation and is absolutely continuous on each I_q.

The proofs of these extensions will be indicated for Theorems 7, 9, and 17. For Theorem 7, we have

$\lim_q \int_{I_q} |\lambda_n| \, dx = \int_X |\lambda_n| \, dx$ uniformly with respect to n,

$\lim_n \int_{I_q} |\lambda_n| \, dx = \int_{I_q} |\mu| \, dx$ for each q.

Hence by Theorem 2 of Chap. VII,

$$\lim_n \int_X |\lambda_n| \, dx = \lim_q \int_{I_q} |\mu| \, dx = \int_X |\mu| \, dx.$$

The hypotheses required by Theorem 2 still apply when the absolute value signs are dropped, so $\lim_n \int_X \lambda_n \, dx = \int_X \mu \, dx$. Also $\lim_n \int_X |\lambda_n - \mu| \, dx = 0$, and since $\left| \int_E (\lambda_n - \mu) \, dx \right| \leqq \int_X |\lambda_n - \mu| \, dx$, the convergence is uniform for measurable sets E.

For Theorem 9, let (α_{nq}) be a double sequence of step functions such that $\lim_n \alpha_{nq} = \lambda$ almost everywhere on I_q, $\alpha_{nq} = 0$ outside I_q, and $\lim_n \int_{I_q} |\alpha_{nq} - \lambda| \, dx = 0$. From this double sequence we may select a simple sequence $(\bar{\alpha}_q)$ such that $\bar{\alpha}_q = 0$ outside I_q, $\int_{I_q} |\bar{\alpha}_q - \lambda| \, dx < 1/2^q$, and $|\bar{\alpha}_q - \lambda| < 1/2^q$ on $I_q - C_q$, where $m(C_q) < 1/2^q$. Then it is easily verified that $\lim \bar{\alpha}_q = \lambda$ almost everywhere and $\lim \int_X |\bar{\alpha}_q - \lambda| \, dx = 0$.

For Theorem 17, since $m(E) < \infty$, there is an interval I_q such that $m(E - I_q) < \epsilon/2$. There is a set C_1 in $\mathfrak{C}$ containing $E - I_q$, with $m(C_1) < \epsilon/2$, since this is so for the part of $E - I_q$ contained in each I_p. There is also a set C_2 in $\mathfrak{C}$ and a set A in $\mathfrak{A}$ such that $m(C_2) < \epsilon/2$, and $A - C_2 \subset EI_q \subset A + C_2$. Then we may take $C = C_1 + C_2$.

†The extension of the notion of measure to unbounded sets makes it possible to regard the integral of a nonnegative integrable function of k variables as the $(k + 1)$-dimensional measure of the set of ordinates.

†THEOREM 9. *Suppose that $\mu(x)$ is a nonnegative measurable function defined on the space X. Let $E(\mu)$ denote the set of all points (x, y) with $0 \leqq y < \mu(x)$. Then $E(\mu)$ is measurable and, if μ is integrable, $m(E(\mu)) = \int_X \mu \, dx$.*

Proof.—Let G be a bounded measurable set in X, and let ϕ_G be its characteristic function. Then there is a sequence of step functions $\alpha_n(x)$, each of which takes only the values zero and one, such that

$$\lim_n \alpha_n(x) = \phi_G(x) \text{ almost everywhere.}$$

Then

$$\lim_n \phi_{E(\alpha_n)} = \phi_{E(\phi_G)} \text{ almost everywhere.}$$

Also $m(E(\alpha_n)) = \int \alpha_n(x)\,dx$, and hence $E(\phi_G)$ is measurable and $m(E(\phi_G)) = \int \phi_G\,dx = m(G)$. From this we see that the conclusions of the theorem hold when μ is a function that takes a positive constant value on each of a finite number of bounded measurable sets and is zero elsewhere. Since every μ satisfying the hypothesis is the limit of a nondecreasing sequence of such functions, the desired result follows.

***†6. Invariance of Lebesgue Integrals and Lebesgue Measure of Sets under Motion.**—It is easily seen that in the case of the Lebesgue measure, the measurability of a set and its measure are invariant under a translation of axes. Every rotation of axes can be obtained from a succession of rotations in each of which all axes but two remain fixed. Let i be an open interval in the coordinate system X'' obtained from the coordinate system X' by rotating only two axes. Then i is a sum of intervals in X', by Lemma 5 of Chap. X. Since every interval in X'' is a product of a sequence of open intervals in X'', it follows readily that every set which is Borel-measurable in X'' is Borel-measurable in X', and conversely. Moreover, the measure in the system X' of an interval i in X'' can be calculated by means of Theorem 3 and an evaluation of three elementary integrals and is thus found to equal the product of the edges of i. Hence every open set has the same measure in the two systems, and so has every closed set. Thus by the Corollary of Theorem 17 of Chap. X, every set that is measurable in one system is measurable in the other and has the same measure. By starting from functions that are step functions in one system it is easily seen that a function that is integrable in one system is also integrable in the other and has the same integral. This result extends at once to integrals over unbounded sets.

7. Mean Value Theorems.—The first theorem is a generalization of Theorem 18 at the end of Chap. VI.

THEOREM 10. **First Theorem of the Mean.** *Let $\lambda(x)$ be integrable, and $\lambda(x) \geqq 0$ (or $\lambda(x) \leqq 0$) almost everywhere on the measurable set E, and let $\mu(x)$ be measurable and essentially bounded on E. Suppose*

(7:1) $$L \leqq \mu(x) \leqq U \text{ almost everywhere on } E.$$

Then

(i) $$\int_E \lambda\mu\, dx = M \int_E \lambda\, dx,$$

where $L \leqq M \leqq U$;

(ii) *In case E is a one-dimensional interval (a, b) (where a or b or both may be infinite) and $\mu(x)$ is equal to the derivative of a continuous function at every point of (a, b), then $M = \mu(x_0)$, where $a < x_0 < b$.*

Proof.—Part (i) follows immediately from Theorem 8 of Chap. X. To obtain part (ii), we note first that, if $\lambda = 0$ almost everywhere on (a, b), then M may be chosen arbitrarily and so may the point x_0. Since the sum of a sequence of sets of measure zero is also of measure zero, it is easily seen that the least upper bound of the numbers L effective in (7:1) is also effective, and likewise for the greatest lower bound of the numbers U. For the remainder of the proof we suppose that L is the greatest possible and U the least possible. If $\lambda(x) > 0$ on a subset E_1 of (a, b) with $m(E_1) > 0$ and if $\mu(x) > L$ on a subset E_2 of E_1 with $m(E_2) > 0$, then $M > L$ by Lemma 1 in Sec. 2. Likewise, if $\mu(x) < U$ on a subset E_3 of E_1 with $m(E_3) > 0$, then $M < U$. Thus, if $M = L$, we have $\mu(x) = M$ at almost every point of E_1 and, if $M = U$, we have $\mu(x) = M$ at almost every point of E_1, and E_1 is a subset of the open interval (a, b). But if $L < M < U$, there is a point x_0 with $a < x_0 < b$ where $\mu(x_0) = M$, by Theorem 5 of Chap. V.

*†THEOREM 11. **Second Theorem of the Mean.** *Let $\lambda(x)$ be integrable and $\mu(x)$ be bounded and nondecreasing on the interval (a, b) where a or b or both may be infinite. Let $L \leqq \mu(a + 0)$, $U \geqq \mu(b - 0)$. Then there is a point x_0 with $a \leqq x_0 \leqq b$, such that*

$$\int_a^b \lambda\mu\, dx = L \int_a^{x_0} \lambda\, dx + U \int_{x_0}^b \lambda\, dx.$$

Proof.—We shall suppose that the interval (a, b) is bounded, since the conclusion extends at once to the unbounded case by a simple argument. In case the conclusion is valid for a particular set μ, L, and U, it is also true for the set $\mu + c$, $L + c$, $U + c$, where c is any constant. Hence it is sufficient to consider the case when $U = 0$. We first take up the case when the graph of the function $\mu(x)$ is a polygon, with $\mu(a) = L$, $\mu(b) = U = 0$. Then $\mu(x)$ is absolutely continuous. If we set $g(x) = \int_a^x \lambda\, dx$, we may apply the formula for integration by parts (Theorem 5) to obtain

$$\int_a^b \lambda\mu\, dx = -\int_a^b g\mu'\, dx.$$

By the First Theorem of the Mean, the right-hand side is equal to

$$-g(x_0)\int_a^b \mu'\, dx = g(x_0)\mu(a) = L\int_a^{x_0} \lambda\, dx.$$

In the general case when $\mu(x)$ is any bounded nondecreasing function, let the interval (a, b) be divided into $n + 1$ equal parts by points $x_1, x_2, \ldots, x_n$, and let the graph of $\mu_n(x)$ be the simple polygon with vertices (a, L), $(x_1, \mu(x_1))$, . . . , $(x_n, \mu(x_n))$, $(b, 0)$. Then $\lim \mu_n(x) = \mu(x)$ almost everywhere, since it is easily verified that the only possible exceptional points are the discontinuities of $\mu(x)$, which form a denumerable set. Since the sequence (μ_n) is uniformly bounded, we have

$$\lim_n \int_a^b \lambda\mu_n\, dx = \int_a^b \lambda\mu\, dx,$$

by Theorems 11 and 7 of Chap. X. But, by the part of the theorem already proved,

$$\int_a^b \lambda\mu_n\, dx = L\int_a^{x_{0n}} \lambda\, dx.$$

Since $\int_a^x \lambda\, dx$ is a continuous function of the upper limit we have

$$\int_a^b \lambda\mu\, dx = L\int_a^{x_0} \lambda\, dx$$

for each point of accumulation x_0 of the sequence (x_{0n}).

8. The Inequalities of Schwarz, Hölder, and Minkowski.—We have used the symbol $\mathfrak{L}$ to denote the class of all integrable functions. The symbol $\mathfrak{L}_p$ is frequently used to denote the class of all measurable functions λ for which $|\lambda|^p$ is integrable, where

p is a positive number. These symbols are used with reference to a fixed measurable set E as the domain of integration. For convenience the symbol E is omitted in the formulas that follow. The proofs are made by means of the following elementary inequality:[1]

LEMMA 9. *If U and V are nonnegative, and $0 < \epsilon < 1$, then*

$$U^{\epsilon}V^{1-\epsilon} \leqq \epsilon U + (1 - \epsilon)V,$$

and equality holds only for $U = V$.

Proof.—Let $f(t) = t^{\epsilon} - \epsilon t + \epsilon - 1$. Then $f(1) = f'(1) = 0$, $f'(t) > 0$ for $0 < t < 1$, $f'(t) < 0$ for $t > 1$, and so $f(t) < 0$ for all $t \geqq 0$ except $t = 1$. Now the lemma obviously holds when $V = 0$. If $V \neq 0$, we may set $t = U/V$, and so we have

$$f\left(\frac{U}{V}\right) = \left(\frac{U}{V}\right)^{\epsilon} - \epsilon\frac{U}{V} + \epsilon - 1 \leqq 0.$$

Upon multiplying by V and transposing, we obtain the inequality that was to be proved.

THEOREM 12. **Hölder's inequality.** *Suppose that $p > 0$, $q > 0$, and $p + q = pq$. Let λ be a function in $\mathfrak{L}_p$, and let μ be in $\mathfrak{L}_q$. Then $\lambda\mu$ is in $\mathfrak{L}$, and*

$$\left|\int \lambda\mu\, dx\right| \leqq \left(\int|\lambda|^p\, dx\right)^{1/p}\left(\int|\mu|^q\, dx\right)^{1/q}.$$

Proof.—In case either λ or μ is zero almost everywhere, the conclusion is obvious. In all other cases we may set

$$\lambda_1(x) = \frac{\lambda(x)}{\left(\int|\lambda|^p\, dx\right)^{1/p}}, \qquad \mu_1(x) = \frac{\mu(x)}{\left(\int|\mu|^q\, dx\right)^{1/q}}.$$

Then

$$\int|\lambda_1|^p\, dx = \int|\mu_1|^q\, dx = 1. \tag{8:1}$$

In the lemma, take $\epsilon = 1/p$, $U = |\lambda_1|^p$, $V = |\mu_1|^q$. Then $1 - \epsilon = 1/q$, and

$$|\lambda_1\mu_1| \leqq \frac{|\lambda_1|^p}{p} + \frac{|\mu_1|^q}{q}. \tag{8:2}$$

Now the product $\lambda_1\mu_1$ is measurable, by Theorem 5 of Chap. X, and so is integrable, by Theorem 10 of the same chapter, and

[1] See F. Riesz, "Su alcune disuguaglianze," *Bolletino dell'Unione Matematica Italiana*, 1928, p. 77.

from (8:2) and (8:1) it follows that

$$\left|\int \lambda_1\mu_1\, dx\right| \leqq \frac{1}{p} + \frac{1}{q} = 1.$$

The inequality of the theorem follows at once.

We note that equality holds if and only if $|\lambda|^p$ bears a constant ratio to $|\mu|^q$ almost everywhere and the product $\lambda\mu$ has the same sign almost everywhere on the set where it is not zero.

The inequality of Schwarz is the special case of Hölder's inequality for which $p = q = 2$.

THEOREM 13. **Minkowski's inequality.** *Let λ and μ be functions in $\mathfrak{L}_p$, where $p \geqq 1$. Then $\lambda + \mu$ is in $\mathfrak{L}_p$, and*

$$(\int|\lambda + \mu|^p\, dx)^{1/p} \leqq (\int|\lambda|^p\, dx)^{1/p} + (\int|\mu|^p\, dx)^{1/p}.$$

Proof.—The case $p = 1$ follows from Theorem 8 of Chap. X. In the remainder of the proof we may suppose $p > 1$, and $\lambda \geqq 0$, $\mu \geqq 0$, since $|\lambda + \mu| \leqq |\lambda| + |\mu|$. By the theorem just referred to, the function $\lambda^p \vee \mu^p$ is integrable, and since

$$(\lambda + \mu)^p \leqq 2^p(\lambda \vee \mu)^p = 2^p(\lambda^p \vee \mu^p),$$

the function $\lambda + \mu$ is in $\mathfrak{L}_p$. Thus $(\lambda + \mu)^{p-1}$ is in $\mathfrak{L}_q$, where $q = p/(p - 1)$, and so by Theorem 12, the functions $\lambda(\lambda + \mu)^{p-1}$ and $\mu(\lambda + \mu)^{p-1}$ are in $\mathfrak{L}$, and

$$\begin{aligned}\int(\lambda + \mu)^p\, dx &= \int\lambda(\lambda + \mu)^{p-1}\, dx + \int\mu(\lambda + \mu)^{p-1}\, dx\\ &\leqq [(\int\lambda^p\, dx)^{1/p} + (\int\mu^p\, dx)^{1/p}](\int(\lambda + \mu)^p\, dx)^{(p-1)/p}.\end{aligned}$$

Division by the factor outside the square bracket yields the desired result.

Minkowski's inequality is also called the **triangle inequality.** When $p = 1$, a necessary and sufficient condition for equality to hold is that $\lambda\mu \geqq 0$ almost everywhere. When $p > 1$, the condition is that λ bears a constant nonnegative ratio to μ almost everywhere.

COROLLARY. *If the n functions λ_j are in $\mathfrak{L}_p$, and*

$$\int|\lambda_j|^p\, dx < \epsilon \qquad (j = 1, \cdots, n)$$

then

$$\int\left|\sum_{j=1}^{n} \lambda_j\right|^p dx < n^p\epsilon.$$

***9. A Criterion for Uniform Absolute Continuity.**[1]—The following necessary and sufficient condition is useful in applications:

THEOREM 14. *Let $\mathfrak{M}_0$ be a class of functions μ, measurable on the set E^* of finite measure. Then a necessary and sufficient condition that the functions μ are integrable on E^* and the integrals $\int \mu\, dx$ are absolutely continuous uniformly and bounded uniformly on $\mathfrak{M}_0$ is that there exist a constant H and a function $\Phi(t)$ such that*

1. $\Phi(t) \geqq 0$ *for* $0 \leqq t < \infty$;
2. $\lim\limits_{t=\infty} \dfrac{\Phi(t)}{t} = \infty$;
3. *For every μ in $\mathfrak{M}_0$, $\Phi(|\mu(x)|)$ is integrable on E^* and* $\int_{E^*} \Phi(|\mu(x)|)\, dx < H$.

Proof.—To prove the sufficiency, let E be a measurable subset of E^*, and let $\epsilon > 0$. By (2), there is a value t_1 such that $\Phi(t) \geqq 2Ht/\epsilon$ for $t \geqq t_1$. Let $E_1 = E[|\mu| < t_1]$, $E_2 = E[|\mu| \geqq t_1]$. On E_2, $|\mu(x)| \leqq \epsilon\Phi(|\mu(x)|)/2H$, so that μ is integrable and

$$\int_E |\mu|\, dx \leqq t_1 m(E_1) + \frac{\epsilon}{2H} \int_{E^*} \Phi(|\mu|)\, dx < t_1 m(E_1) + \frac{\epsilon}{2}$$

In proving the necessity of the condition we shall show that the function Φ may be taken to be continuous and nondecreasing. Let K be chosen so that $\int_{E^*} |\mu|\, dx < K$. Let $E_{n\mu} = E^*[n \leqq |\mu| < n + 1]$. Then $\sum\limits_{n=0}^{\infty} nm(E_{n\mu}) < K$, and hence for each integer q,

$$\sum_{n=q}^{\infty} m(E_{n\mu}) < \frac{K}{q}. \tag{9:1}$$

By hypothesis there is a sequence of positive numbers δ_j such that

$$\int_E |\mu|\, dx < \frac{1}{3^j} \tag{9:2}$$

whenever $m(E) < \delta_j$. Let (q_j) be an increasing sequence of integers such that $q_j\delta_j > K$. Then by (9:1) and (9:2)

[1] See C. J. de la Vallée Poussin, "Sur l'intégrale de Lebesgue," *Transactions of American Mathematical Society*, Vol. 16 (1915), pp. 451, 452.

$$\sum_{n=q_j}^{q_{j+1}-1} \int_{E_{n\mu}} |\mu|\, dx < \frac{1}{3^j}. \tag{9:3}$$

Now set

$$\begin{aligned}\Phi(t) &= q_1 \text{ for } 0 \leqq t < q_1,\\ &= \left(\frac{3}{2}\right)^{j-1}\left[1 + \frac{t - q_j}{2(q_{j+1} - q_j)}\right] t \text{ for } q_j \leqq t < q_{j+1}.\end{aligned}$$

Then with the help of (9:3) we find that

$$\begin{aligned}\int_{E^*} \Phi(|\mu|)\, dx &= \sum_{n=0}^{q_1-1} \int_{E_{n\mu}} \Phi(|\mu|)\, dx + \sum_{j=1}^{\infty} \sum_{n=q_j}^{q_{j+1}-1} \int_{E_{n\mu}} \Phi(|\mu|)\, dx\\ &\leqq q_1 m(E^*) + \sum_{j=1}^{\infty} \frac{1}{2^j} = q_1 m(E^*) + 1.\end{aligned}$$

10. Modes of Convergence.—In this section we shall discuss the properties of and the relations between several modes of convergence. Let $\psi(x, y)$ be a function which is real-valued for x in a set E and for y in a set T, let b be a point of accumulation of T, and let $g(x)$ be real-valued on E. We shall consider the limit

$$\lim_{y=b} \psi(x, y) = g(x) \tag{10:1}$$

in the following modes:

A. Uniformly on E;
B. On E, or everywhere on E (ordinary convergence);
C. Almost uniformly on E;
D. Almost everywhere on E;
E. In measure on E;
F. In the mean of order p on E.

Uniform convergence has been discussed in Chap. VII, and ordinary convergence in Chaps. IV and VII. Modes C and D were introduced in Chap. X for the case when x ranges over the interval I and y ranges over the positive integers, but the definitions are unchanged in form for the more general case of (10:1). **Convergence in measure** is a notion introduced by F. Riesz and is sometimes called **approximate convergence.** If we set

$$E_{y\epsilon} = E[|\psi(x, y) - g(x)| > \epsilon],$$

then $\lim\limits_{y=b} \psi(x, y) = g(x)$ **in measure** on E in case

$$\lim_{y=b} m_e(E_{y\epsilon}) = 0 \quad \text{for every } \epsilon > 0.$$

Here we may agree that the points x where $\psi(x, y)$ and $g(x)$ are infinite of the same sign are not included in $E_{y\epsilon}$, but that other points where either $\psi(x, y)$ or $g(x)$ is infinite shall be so included.

Finally, we say that $\lim\limits_{y=b} \psi(x, y) = g(x)$ **in the mean of order** p **on** E in case

$$\lim_{y=b} \int_E |\psi(x, y) - g(x)|^p \, dx = 0.$$

Here it is understood that E is measurable and $|\psi(x, y) - g(x)|^p$ is integrable on E. We note that by Theorem 13 this will be so whenever $p \geqq 1$ and both $\psi(x, y)$ and $g(x)$ are in the space $\mathfrak{L}_p$ on E.[1] When the term "convergence in the mean" is used without qualification, it is sometimes understood to mean "convergence in the mean of order two" or "convergence in the mean of order one."

We can properly use the term *convergence* only when the limit $g(x)$ is everywhere finite in modes A and B, and almost everywhere finite in the remaining modes. But the use of the symbol (10:1) is subject to those restrictions only in modes A and C. We note, however, that even for modes E and F, we have $g(x)$ finite almost everywhere when $\psi(x, y)$ is finite almost everywhere for every value of y. The definitions for modes C and E are sometimes phrased so as to remove such restrictions, as well as the need for the hypothesis that $g(x)$ is finite almost everywhere in Theorems 17 to 19 below.[2] But we are interested principally in the case when $g(x)$ is integrable.

THEOREM 15. *If* $\lim\limits_{y=b} \psi(x, y) = g_1(x)$ *and* $\lim\limits_{y=b} \psi(x, y) = g_2(x)$ *in mode* C, D, E, *or* F, *then* $g_1(x) = g_2(x)$ *almost everywhere.*

Proof.—For mode E, let $E_\epsilon = E[|g_1 - g_2| > 2\epsilon]$, $E_{1y\epsilon} = E[|\psi - g_1| > \epsilon]$, $E_{2y\epsilon} = E[|\psi - g_2| > \epsilon]$. Then $E_\epsilon \subset E_{1y\epsilon} + E_{2y\epsilon}$ for every y. Hence $m_e(E_\epsilon) \leqq m_e(E_{1y\epsilon}) + m_e(E_{2y\epsilon})$, and from this

[1] For a discussion of convergence in the mean of positive order less than one, see G. C. Evans, *The Logarithmic Potential*, 1927, pp. 139–144.

[2] See McShane [2], pp. 163, 164.

the desired conclusion is readily obtained. For mode F, we apply Theorem 13 in Sec. 8 and Lemma 1 in Sec. 2.

Theorem 16. *If* $\lim_{y=b} \psi(x, y) = g(x)$ *in any one of the six modes, then for every sequence* (y_n) *in* T *with* $\lim_{n=\infty} y_n = b$, *we have* $\lim_{n=\infty} \psi(x, y_n) = g(x)$ *in the same mode. Conversely, if for every sequence* (y_n) *in* T *with* $\lim_{n=\infty} y_n = b$, $\lim_{n=\infty} \psi(x, y_n)$ *exists in mode* A, B, E, *or* F, *then* $\lim_{y=b} \psi(x, y)$ *exists in the same mode. The converse does not hold for modes* C *and* D.

Proof.—If we set

$$\beta(y) = \text{l.u.b. } |\psi(x, y) - g(x)| \text{ for } x \text{ on } E,$$

then $\lim_{y=b} \psi(x, y) = g(x)$ uniformly on E is equivalent to $\lim_{y=b} \beta(y) = 0$. Then it is clear that the first part of the theorem follows from Theorem 13 of Chap. IV. For the converse, we note first that from two sequences (y_{1n}) and (y_{2n}) we may form a new sequence (y_n) by taking terms alternately from the given sequences. Then by the first part of the theorem, a limit function for the sequence (y_n) will be one also for (y_{1n}) and (y_{2n}). By Theorem 15, a limit function for (y_{1n}) will be one for (y_{2n}). Hence we may apply Theorem 13 of Chap. IV.

The following example shows that the converse is not true for modes C and D. Let E be the interval $0 \leqq x \leqq 1$, and let T be the interval $0 \leqq y \leqq 1$. Let

$$\begin{aligned} \psi(x, y) &= 1 \quad \text{for} \quad y = \frac{1}{p+1} + \frac{x}{p(p+1)}, \; p = 1, 2, \ldots, \\ &= 0 \quad \text{for all other points } (x, y). \end{aligned}$$

Then $\limsup_{y=0} \psi(x, y) = 1$, $\liminf_{y=0} \psi(x, y) = 0$, but for each y, $\psi(x, y) = 0$ almost everywhere.

The following relations between the various modes of convergence are easily verified: A implies B and C; B implies D; C implies D and E. That C implies D was proved in Theorem 1 of Chap. X for the case of sequences, and the same proof is valid in the general case. Mode D implies C under special conditions, as is shown in the next theorem, which is a generalization of Theorem 2 of Chap. X.

THEOREM 17. **Egoroff's theorem.** *Suppose that each function $\mu_n(x)$ is measurable on the measurable set E of finite measure, that $g(x)$ is finite almost everywhere on E, and that* $\lim_n \mu_n(x) = g(x)$ *almost everywhere on E. Then* $\lim_n \mu_n(x) = g(x)$ *almost uniformly on E.*

Proof.—Let $E_{n\epsilon} = E[|\mu_n(x) - g(x)| > \epsilon]$, where we shall include in $E_{n\epsilon}$ all the points where $g(x)$ is infinite. Let

$$S_{p\epsilon} = \sum_{n \geqq p} E_{n\epsilon}, \qquad \prod_{p=1}^{\infty} S_{p\epsilon} = S_\epsilon.$$

Then $m(S_\epsilon) = 0$, and hence $\lim_{p=\infty} m(S_{p\epsilon}) = 0$ by Theorem 16 of Chap. X. If we set $\epsilon_k = 1/k$, then for each k there is an integer p_k such that $m(S_{p_k\epsilon_k}) < 1/2^k$. We have $m(E_q) < 1/2^{q-1}$, where

$$E_q = \sum_{k=q}^{\infty} S_{p_k\epsilon_k},$$

and thus by the Corollary of Theorem 17 of Chap. X, there exists a set C_q in $\mathfrak{C}$, including E_q, with $m(C_q) < 1/2^{q-1}$. Then, if x is not in C_q, we have $|\mu_n(x) - g(x)| \leqq 1/k$ for $n \geqq p_k$, or $\lim_n \mu_n(x) = g(x)$ uniformly on $E - C_q$.

THEOREM 18. *Suppose that E is a measurable set of finite measure, that $\psi(x, y)$ is measurable on E for each y in T, that $g(x)$ is finite almost everywhere, and that $\lim_{y=b} \psi(x, y) = g(x)$ almost everywhere on E. Then* $\lim_{y=b} \psi(x, y) = g(x)$ *in measure on E.*

Proof.—By Theorem 16 it is sufficient to prove the result for sequences, but for this case it follows from Theorem 17 and a previously noted relation.

THEOREM 19. *Suppose that $g(x)$ is finite almost everywhere and that $\lim_{y=b} \psi(x, y) = g(x)$ in measure on E. Then there exists a sequence (y_k) of distinct points in the range T of y, such that* $\lim_{k=\infty} y_k = b$, *and* $\lim_{k=\infty} \psi(x, y_k) = g(x)$ *almost uniformly on E.*

Proof.—By Theorem 16, it is sufficient to consider the case of a sequence $(\psi_n(x))$. Let $E_{n\epsilon} = E[|\psi_n(x) - g(x)| > \epsilon]$, where it is understood for convenience in the following that the points where $g(x)$ is infinite are included in $E_{n\epsilon}$, and let $\epsilon_k = 1/k$. Since $\lim_n m_e(E_{n\epsilon}) = 0$ for every $\epsilon > 0$, for each k we may choose $n_k > n_{k-1}$ such that $m_e(E_{n_k\epsilon_k}) < 1/2^k$. By definition of exterior measure, there exists an open set $G_k \supset E_{n_k\epsilon_k}$ such that $m(G_k) < 1/2^k$. If we set $E_p = \sum_{k=p}^{\infty} G_k$, then $m(E_p) < 1/2^{p-1}$ and, on $E - E_p$, $|\psi_{n_k}(x) - g(x)| \leqq 1/k$ for $k \geqq p$, so that the sequence (ψ_{n_k}) is the required one.

It is easy to construct a sequence of functions $\psi_n(x)$ converging in measure to zero, but such that the sequence converges in the ordinary sense at no value of x. For each positive integer k, let the fundamental interval I be divided in any manner into k measurable subsets $E_{k1}, \ldots, E_{kk}$ of equal measure. Arrange the sets E_{kj} in any manner as a simple sequence S_n, and let ψ_n be the characteristic function of S_n. Then $\lim m(S_n) = 0$, but $\limsup \psi_n(x) = 1$, $\liminf \psi_n(x) = 0$ for every x.

THEOREM 20. *If E is measurable, $\psi(x, y)$ is measurable on E for each value of y, and $\lim_{y=b} \psi(x, y) = g(x)$ in any one of the modes* A *to* E, *then $g(x)$ is measurable on E. In the case of mode* E, *we assume also that $g(x)$ is finite almost everywhere.*

Proof.—This follows readily from the preceding theorems and the Corollary of Theorem 4, Chap. X.

†THEOREM 21. *Suppose that the set E is measurable, and that the function $\psi(x, y)$ is in the class $\mathfrak{L}_p$ on E for each y in T, where $p \geqq 1$. Suppose that the integrals $\int |\psi(x, y)|^p \, dx$ are absolutely continuous uniformly with respect to y, and converge uniformly with respect to y in case E has infinite measure. Suppose finally that*

$$\lim_{y=b} \psi(x, y) = g(x) \tag{10:1}$$

in any one of the five modes A, B, C, D, *or* E. *Then $g(x)$ is in $\mathfrak{L}_p$ and* (10:1) *holds in mode* F.

Proof.—It is sufficient to prove the result for the case of sequences $(\psi_n(x))$, by Theorem 16. For the modes A, C, and E it follows from the definitions and the fact that the functions $\psi_n(x)$ must be finite almost everywhere that the limit $g(x)$ must be finite almost everywhere. Thus in any case there is a subsequence, for which we use the same notation $(\psi_n(x))$, such that $\lim \psi_n(x) = g(x)$ in mode D, and $\lim |\psi_n|^p = |g|^p$ in mode D. By

Theorem 20, $g(x)$ is measurable. Then by Theorem 7 of Chap. X, $g(x)$ is in $\mathfrak{L}_p$, and by Theorem 13 of Sec. 8, the functions $(\psi_n - g)$ are in $\mathfrak{L}_p$. From the inequality $|\psi_n - g|^p \leqq 2^p[|\psi_n|^p + |g|^p]$ it follows that the integrals $\int|\psi_n - g|^p\,dx$ are absolutely continuous uniformly and converge uniformly. Hence

$$\lim_n \int_E |\psi_n - g|^p\,dx = 0 \tag{10:2}$$

by Theorem 7 of Chap. X. If a subsequence was chosen, it follows easily that (10:2) holds on the original sequence.

*For the case of a general measure function, with convergence in mode B or D, it is necessary to add an assumption ensuring that $g(x)$ is finite almost everywhere. See the remark following Theorem 6 in Chap. X.

When the functions ψ and g in the preceding discussion depend also on a parameter σ, it is sometimes desirable to know that the integrals converge uniformly with respect to σ. For the case of convergence in mode D we have the following result:

THEOREM 22. *Suppose that E is measurable and that $\psi(x, y, \sigma)$ is in $\mathfrak{L}_p$ on E for each y and σ, where $p \geqq 1$. Suppose that the integrals $\int|\psi(x, y, \sigma)|^p\,dx$ are absolutely continuous uniformly with respect to y and σ, and converge uniformly with respect to y and σ in case E has infinite measure. Suppose finally that $\lim_{y=b} \psi(x, y, \sigma) = g(x, \sigma)$ uniformly with respect to σ, except for x in a fixed subset E_0 of E of measure zero. Then the integrals $\int|g(x, \sigma)|^p\,dx$ are absolutely continuous uniformly with respect to σ and converge uniformly with respect to σ, and*

$$\lim_{y=b} \int_E |\psi(x, y, \sigma) - g(x, \sigma)|^p\,dx = 0$$

uniformly with respect to σ.

Proof.—Since

$$[\int|g(x, \sigma)|^p\,dx]^{1/p} \leqq [\int|g(x, \sigma) - \psi(x, y, \sigma)|^p\,dx]^{1/p} + [\int|\psi(x, y, \sigma)|^p\,dx]^{1/p}$$

by Theorem 13, the first part of the conclusion follows from Theorem 21. If the last part is false, there exist a positive number ϵ and sequences (y_n) and (σ_n) such that $\lim_n y_n = b$, and

$\int_E |\psi(x, y_n, \sigma_n) - g(x, \sigma_n)|^p\, dx > \epsilon$. If we set $\psi_n(x) = \psi(x, y_n, \sigma_n) - g(x, \sigma_n)$, we have $\lim\limits_{n} \psi_n(x) = 0$ except on E_0, and the remaining hypothesis of Theorem 21 for the functions ψ_n is verified with the help of the Corollary of Theorem 13, so that we are led to a contradiction.

THEOREM 23. *If*

$$\lim_{y=b} \psi(x, y) = g(x) \tag{10:1}$$

in the mean of order p on E, then (10:1) *holds also in measure on E.*

Proof.—If we let

$$E_{y\epsilon} = E[|\psi(x, y) - g(x)| > \epsilon],$$

then $E_{y\epsilon}$ is measurable and

$$\int_E |\psi(x, y) - g(x)|^p\, dx > \epsilon^p m(E_{y\epsilon}).$$

The conclusion follows at once from this inequality.

The next theorem in combination with the preceding forms a partial converse of Theorem 21. Its proof is immediate.

THEOREM 24. *If* $\lim\limits_{n=\infty} \psi_n(x) = g(x)$ *in the mean of order p on E, then the integrals* $\int |\psi_n - g|^p\, dx$ *are absolutely continuous uniformly and converge uniformly with respect to n. When* $g(x)$ *is in* $\mathfrak{L}_p$, *the integrals* $\int |\psi_n|^p\, dx$ *also have these properties.*

THEOREM 25. *Let* $0 < s < q$, *and let* (10:1) *hold in the mean of order q on E, where E is a set of finite measure. Then* (10:1) *holds also in the mean of order s on E.*

Proof.—By Theorem 16, it is sufficient to consider the case of a sequence $(\psi_n(x))$. Let $\mu_n(x) = |\psi_n(x) - g(x)|$. Then $\lim\limits_{n=\infty} \mu_n(x) = 0$ in measure on E, by Theorem 23. Also $\mu_n^s \leqq 1 + \mu_n^q$, so that μ_n^s is integrable, and

$$\int_{E_0} \mu_n^s\, dx \leqq m(E_0) + \int_{E_0} \mu_n^q\, dx$$

for every measurable subset E_0 of E. With the help of Theorem 24 it follows that the integrals $\int \mu_n^s\, dx$ are absolutely continuous uniformly with respect to n, and then $\lim\limits_{n=\infty} \int_E \mu_n^s\, dx = 0$ by Theorem 21 for $p = 1$.

The Cauchy condition for convergence in mode A was given in Theorem 1 of Chap. VII, and for mode B in Theorem 10 of Chap. IV. The corresponding condition for modes C, D, E, and F is stated in the following theorem:

THEOREM 26. *Suppose that* $\psi(x, y)$ *is finite almost everywhere on* E *for each* y *in* T. *Then a necessary and sufficient condition that there exists a function* $g(x)$, *finite almost everywhere on* E, *such that* $\lim_{y=b} \psi(x, y) = g(x)$ *in mode* C, D, E, *or* F, *is that*

$$\lim_{\substack{y_1=b\\y_2=b}} |\psi(x, y_1) - \psi(x, y_2)| = 0 \tag{10:3}$$

in the corresponding mode. For mode F *we suppose that* $p \geqq 1$ *and that* $\psi(x, y)$ *is in* $\mathfrak{L}_p$ *for each* y *in* T, *and then* $g(x)$ *is necessarily also in* $\mathfrak{L}_p$.

Proof.—For mode C, the proof is based on Theorem 1 of Chap. VII, and the necessity of the condition is then obvious. Also if

$$\lim_{\substack{y_1=b\\y_2=b}} |\psi(x, y_1) - \psi(x, y_2)| = 0$$

uniformly on $E - C_n$, then the limit $g(x)$ is determined and finite except on C_n. We may suppose $m(C_n) < 1/2^n$, and so $g(x)$ is determined except on the set $Z = \prod C_n$, and $m(Z) = 0$.

For mode D, the condition follows from Theorem 10 of Chap. IV.

To prove the necessity of the condition for mode E, we note that

$$E[|\psi(x, y_1) - \psi(x, y_2)| > 2\epsilon] \subset E[|\psi(x, y_1) - g(x)| > \epsilon] + E[|\psi(x, y_2) - g(x)| > \epsilon],$$

so that, if the exterior measure of each of the last two sets is less than ρ, the exterior measure of the first is less than 2ρ. In proving the sufficiency of the condition for mode E, we may first prove by familiar methods that

$$\lim_{\substack{n=\infty\\k=\infty}} |\psi(x, y_n) - \psi(x, y_k)| = 0$$

in mode E for every sequence (y_n) with $\lim_{n=\infty} y_n = b$. Hence by

Theorem 16 we may restrict attention to the case of a sequence $(\psi_n(x))$. For each j, there is an integer n_j such that the set $E[|\psi_n - \psi_k| > 1/2^j]$ has exterior measure less than $1/2^j$ whenever $n \geqq n_j$, $k \geqq n_j$. We may also suppose $n_j > n_{j-1}$. For each j there is an open set $G_j \supset E[|\psi_{n_{j+1}} - \psi_{n_j}| > 1/2^j]$ such that $m(G_j) < 1/2^j$. Let $C_k = \sum_{j=k}^{\infty} G_j$. Then for $l > j \geqq k$, $|\psi_{n_j}(x) - \psi_{n_l}(x)| \leqq 1/2^{j-1}$ except on C_k, so that by the Cauchy condition for mode C, there exists a function $g(x)$ such that $\lim_{j=\infty} \psi_{n_j}(x) = g(x)$ almost uniformly on E. Moreover, $|\psi_{n_j}(x) - g(x)| \leqq 1/2^{j-1}$ except on C_j, so that for $n \geqq n_j$,

$$|\psi_n(x) - g(x)| \leqq |\psi_n(x) - \psi_{n_j}(x)| + |\psi_{n_j}(x) - g(x)| \leqq \frac{1}{2^{j-2}}$$

except on a set whose exterior measure is less than $1/2^{j-2}$.

For mode F, the necessity of the condition follows readily from the Corollary of Theorem 13. To prove the sufficiency, we note that by Theorem 23, (10:3) holds in mode E, and hence by the part of the theorem already proved, there is a function $g(x)$ such that $\lim_{y=b} \psi(x, y) = g(x)$ in measure. Then by Theorem 19 of the present chapter and Theorem 1 of Chap. X, there is a sequence (y_n) with $\lim_{n=\infty} y_n = b$, such that $\lim_{n=\infty} \psi(x, y_n) = g(x)$ almost everywhere. Let $\psi_n(x) = \psi(x, y_n)$. Then for each value of k,

$$\lim_{n=\infty} |\psi_n - \psi_k|^p = |g - \psi_k|^p \text{ almost everywhere.}$$

We next proceed to show that for each value of k, the integrals $\int |\psi_n - \psi_k|^p \, dx$ are absolutely continuous uniformly and converge uniformly with respect to n. For every $\epsilon > 0$, there is an integer k_0 such that if $n > k_0$, then

$$\int_E |\psi_n - \psi_{k_0}|^p \, dx < \epsilon. \tag{10:4}$$

Also there exists a number $\delta > 0$ such that if $n \leqq k_0$ and $m(E_0) < \delta$, then

$$\int_{E_0} |\psi_n - \psi_k|^p \, dx < \epsilon, \tag{10:5}$$

since there are only a finite number of integrals in this set when k is fixed. By applying the Corollary of Theorem 13 to (10:5) with $n = k_0$ and (10:4) with E replaced by E_0 we find that, for $n > k_0$ and $m(E_0) < \delta$,

$$\int_{E_0} |\psi_n - \psi_k|^p \, dx < 2^p \epsilon.$$

The uniform convergence of the integrals is proved in a similar way. Then by Theorem 7 of Chap. X,

$$\lim_{n=\infty} \int_E |\psi_n - \psi_k|^p \, dx = \int_E |g - \psi_k|^p \, dx,$$

and by Theorem 3 of Chap. VII,

$$\lim_{k=\infty} \int_E |g - \psi_k|^p \, dx = 0.$$

Since by Theorem 13,

$$\left[\int_E |\psi(x, y) - g(x)|^p \, dx\right]^{1/p} \leqq \left[\int_E |\psi(x, y) - \psi_k(x)|^p \, dx\right]^{1/p} + \left[\int_E |\psi_k(x) - g(x)|^p \, dx\right]^{1/p},$$

we are led to the desired result.

The next theorem outlines sufficient conditions that the limit operator in the various modes be distributive with respect to the operations I to V of Chap. X, Sec. 3.

THEOREM 27. *Suppose that $g_1(x)$ and $g_2(x)$ are finite almost everywhere on E, and that*

$$\lim_{y=b} \psi_1(x, y) = g_1(x), \qquad \lim_{y=b} \psi_2(x, y) = g_2(x),$$

on E in any one of the six modes A *to* F. *Then*

I. $\lim_{y=b} (\psi_1 + \psi_2) = g_1 + g_2$,

II. $\lim_{y=b} a\psi_1 = ag_1$, *for every finite constant a,*

IV. $\lim_{y=b} (\psi_1 \vee \psi_2) = g_1 \vee g_2$,

V. $\lim_{y=b} (\psi_1 \wedge \psi_2) = g_1 \wedge g_2$,

in the same mode, provided that g_1 and g_2 are everywhere finite in case of mode A, *that g_1 and g_2 are nowhere infinite of opposite sign in case of mode* B. *and that we set $0 \cdot \infty = 0$. We have also*

III. $\lim_{y=b} \psi_1\psi_2 = g_1g_2,$

in modes A *to* E *provided that* g_1 *and* g_2 *are bounded in case of mode* A, *that the form* $0 \cdot \infty$ *does not occur in case of mode* B, *and that the set* E *has finite measure in case of modes* C *and* E, *and further that* g_1 *and* g_2 *are measurable in case of mode* E. *In case* $p + q = pq$, $p > 0$, $q > 0$, ψ_1 and g_1 *are in* $\mathfrak{L}_p$, ψ_2 *and* g_2 *are in* $\mathfrak{L}_q$, $\lim \psi_1 = g_1$ *in the mean of order* p *and* $\lim \psi_2 = g_2$ *in the mean of order* q, *then* III *holds in the mean of order* 1.

Proof.—We shall indicate the proof for III in mode E. The proofs in the other cases are readily constructed. Let $\rho > 0$. Then there is an integer n such that

$$m(E[|g_1| > n]) < \rho,\ m(E[|g_2| > n]) < \rho,$$

by Theorem 16 of Chap. X. Then if $0 < \epsilon < 1$, there is a neighborhood $N(b;\ \delta)$ such that for y in $N(b;\ \delta)$,

$$m_e(E[|\psi_1(x, y) - g_1(x)| > \epsilon]) < \rho,$$

with a corresponding relation for ψ_2 and g_2. From these relations it follows that for y in $N(b;\ \delta)$,

$$|\psi_1(x, y)\ \psi_2(x, y) - g_1(x)g_2(x)| \leqq (2n + 1)\epsilon$$

except on a set whose exterior measure is less than 5ρ.

In Chap. VII, Sec. 4, the space $\mathfrak{C}$, composed of all continuous functions $f(x)$ defined on a fixed bounded closed set E, was discussed and was seen to be a complete normed linear space, with $\|f\| = \text{l.u.b.}\ |f(x)|$ on E. The results of the preceding paragraphs indicate that we may use each of the modes of convergence A to F to define points of accumulation in a space consisting of a suitable class of functions. For $p \geqq 1$, we may set

$$\|\lambda\| = [\textstyle\int |\lambda(x)|^p\, dx]^{1/p}$$

for each λ in $\mathfrak{L}_p$. We meet here with the difficulty that $\|\lambda\| = 0$ does not imply $\lambda(x) \equiv 0$. However, if we agree that two functions are **equivalent** when they are equal almost everywhere, we find with the help of Theorems 13 and 26 that the space of all equivalence classes composed of functions λ in $\mathfrak{L}_p$ is a complete normed linear space. It is convenient to denote this space by the same symbol $\mathfrak{L}_p$, and to denote the equivalence class to which a function λ belongs by the same symbol λ.

The modes of convergence B, C, D, and E do not correspond to normed linear spaces. We may define a norm $\|\psi\|$, such that $\lim_n \psi_n = \psi$ in measure if and only if $\lim_n \|\psi_n - \psi\| = 0$, as follows:

$$\|\psi\| = \text{g.l.b. of all } \epsilon \text{ such that } m_e(E[|\psi(x)| > \epsilon]) < \epsilon.$$

But this norm does not have the property that $\|a\psi\| = |a| \cdot \|\psi\|$. Since it does have the property that $\|\psi_1 + \psi_2\| \leqq \|\psi_1\| + \|\psi_2\|$, we see that the space of equivalence classes of functions is a metric space with the distance between ψ_1 and ψ_2 defined to be $\|\psi_1 - \psi_2\|$.[1]

*We conclude this section with the following theorem, which may be regarded as showing that the operation of translation in the space $\mathfrak{L}_p$ is continuous:

*†THEOREM 28. *If $\lambda(x)$ is in $\mathfrak{L}_p$ where $p \geqq 1$, then*

$$\lim_{t=0} \int_X |\lambda(x+t) - \lambda(x)|^p \, dx = 0.$$

Proof.—By Theorem 13 it is sufficient to consider the case when $\lambda \geqq 0$. By Theorem 9 of Chap. X, there is a sequence (α_n) of step functions such that $\lim_n \int_X |\alpha_n - \lambda^p| \, dx = 0$. It is clear that we may require that $\alpha_n \geqq 0$, and then we may set $\beta_n^p = \alpha_n$. Since $|\beta_n - \lambda|^p \leqq |\beta_n^p - \lambda^p|$, we have

$$\lim_n \int_X |\beta_n - \lambda|^p \, dx = 0.$$

For fixed n, $\lim_{t=0} |\beta_n(x+t) - \beta_n(x)| = 0$ almost everywhere and, since β_n is bounded and equal to zero outside a sufficiently large interval, we have

$$\lim_{t=0} \int_X |\beta_n(x+t) - \beta_n(x)|^p \, dx = 0.$$

By another application of Theorem 13 we are led to the desired result.

We note that Theorem 28 holds true for functions of several variables, but not for a general measure function.

***11. Orthonormal Systems in the Space $\mathfrak{L}_2$.**—Let E be a fixed measurable set of positive measure, and let (λ_n) be a sequence of

[1] See Fréchet, *Les espaces abstraits*, pp. 91, 92, where a slightly different distance is defined.

functions in $\mathfrak{L}_2$ on the set E. The **linear extension** $(\lambda_n)_L$ of (λ_n) consists of all finite linear combinations of functions chosen from the sequence. The **linear closed extension** $(\lambda_n)_{LC}$ consists of all functions that are limits in the mean of order two of sequences chosen from $(\lambda_n)_L$. As usual we do not distinguish between functions that are equal almost everywhere on E.

The system (λ_n) is said to be **orthonormal** on E in case $\int \lambda_m \lambda_n \, dx = \delta_{mn}$, where $\delta_{nn} = 1$, $\delta_{mn} = 0$ for $m \neq n$. All integrals are understood to be taken over the set E. A familiar example of an orthonormal system is the set of trigonometric functions,

$$(11{:}1) \quad \lambda_0(x) = \frac{1}{\sqrt{2\pi}}, \qquad \lambda_{2n}(x) = \frac{\cos nx}{\sqrt{\pi}}, \qquad \lambda_{2n-1}(x) = \frac{\sin nx}{\sqrt{\pi}},$$

when the set E is an interval of length 2π.

THEOREM 29. *For every sequence (ψ_n) in $\mathfrak{L}_2$, there is an orthonormal sequence (λ_n) (which may be finite) which has the same linear extension.*

Proof.—Let $\|\psi\| = [\int \psi^2 \, dx]^{1/2}$, and let μ_0 denote the first ψ_n with $\|\psi_n\| \neq 0$. Let $\lambda_0 = \mu_0/\|\mu_0\|$. If $\lambda_0, \cdots, \lambda_q$ have been determined, let ψ_k be the next unused function of the sequence (ψ_n). Let

$$\mu_k = \psi_k - \sum_{j=0}^{q} \rho_j \lambda_j, \qquad \rho_j = \int \psi_k \lambda_j \, dx.$$

Then $\int \mu_k \lambda_j \, dx = 0$ for $j = 0, \cdots, q$. If $\|\mu_k\| \neq 0$, set $\lambda_{q+1} = \mu_k/\|\mu_k\|$. If $\|\mu_k\| = 0$, discard ψ_k and try ψ_{k+1}.

A sequence (λ_n) is said to be **complete in** $\mathfrak{L}_2$ in case the only functions ψ in $\mathfrak{L}_2$ for which

$$(11{:}2) \qquad \int \lambda_n \psi \, dx = 0 \quad (n = 0, 1, 2, \cdots),$$

are equal to zero almost everywhere. A sequence (λ_n) is said to be **closed in** $\mathfrak{L}_2$ in case the linear closed extension of (λ_n) is the whole of $\mathfrak{L}_2$.

THEOREM 30. *The sequence* (11:1) *is complete in* $\mathfrak{L}_2$.

Proof.—We shall show that (11:1) is complete in the class $\mathfrak{L}$ on the interval $I = [0, 2\pi]$. This is a larger class than $\mathfrak{L}_2$, since the interval I is finite. If ψ is in $\mathfrak{L}$ and satisfies (11:2) with the functions (11:1), let $f(x) = \int_0^x \psi \, dx$. Then $f(0) = f(2\pi) = 0$

and, by integrating by parts in (11:2), we find

$$\int_0^{2\pi} \lambda_n f\, dx = 0 \qquad (n = 1, 2, \cdots).$$

If $\int_0^{2\pi} f\, dx = 2\pi c$, then $\int_0^{2\pi} (f - c)\, dx = 0$. Thus (11:2) holds with ψ replaced by $g = f - c$. If $g(x) \not\equiv 0$, suppose for definiteness that $g(x_0) = 2\epsilon > 0$, where $0 < x_0 < 2\pi$. Since g is continuous, there is an interval $I_0 = [x_0 - \delta, x_0 + \delta] \subset I$ such that $g(x) > \epsilon$ on I_0. Let

$$t(x) = 1 + \cos(x - x_0) - \cos \delta.$$

Then $t(x) > 1$ on the interior of I_0, but $|t(x)| < 1$ on the interior of $I - I_0$. Now by (11:2) with g in place of ψ,

$$0 = \int_0^{2\pi} gt^n\, dx = \int_{I_0} gt^n\, dx + \int_{I - I_0} gt^n\, dx. \tag{11:3}$$

But the first integral on the right in (11:3) approaches infinity, and the second integral approaches zero, which leads to a contradiction. Hence $g(x) \equiv 0$, and so $\psi(x) = 0$ almost everywhere.

THEOREM 31. **Bessel's inequality.** *Let*

$$a_n = \int \psi \lambda_n\, dx \qquad (n = 0, 1, 2, \cdots), \tag{11:4}$$

where (λ_n) *is an orthonormal system and* ψ *is an arbitrary function in* $\mathfrak{L}_2$. *Then*

$$\sum_{n=0}^{\infty} a_n^2 \leqq \int \psi^2\, dx = \|\psi\|^2.$$

Proof.—We have

$$0 \leqq \int \left(\psi - \sum_{n=0}^{q} a_n \lambda_n\right)^2 dx = \|\psi\|^2 - \sum_{n=0}^{q} a_n^2. \tag{11:5}$$

THEOREM 32. *If* (λ_n) *is an orthonormal system, then for fixed* ψ *and* q, *the expression*

$$\int \left(\psi - \sum_{n=0}^{q} a_n \lambda_n\right)^2 dx$$

is a minimum when the coefficients a_n *are given by* (11:4) *for* $n = 0, 1, \cdots, q$.

THEOREM 33. *Let* (λ_n) *be an orthonormal system and let the series* $\sum a_n^2$ *converge. Then there is a function* ψ *in* $\mathfrak{L}_2$ *such that*

$$\lim_{q=\infty} \sum_{n=0}^{q} a_n\lambda_n = \psi$$

in the mean of order 2.

Proof.—Since

$$\int \left(\sum_{n=p}^{q} a_n\lambda_n\right)^2 dx = \sum_{n=p}^{q} a_n^2,$$

the desired result follows from the Cauchy condition for the convergence of the series $\sum a_n^2$ and the Cauchy condition for convergence in the mean (Theorem 26).

THEOREM 34. *If* (λ_n) *is an orthonormal system and*

$$\lim_{q=\infty} \sum_{n=0}^{q} a_n\lambda_n = \psi \tag{11:6}$$

in the mean of order 2, *then the coefficients* a_n *are given by* (11:4) *and*

$$\sum_{n=0}^{\infty} a_n^2 = \|\psi\|^2. \tag{11:7}$$

Proof.—From the Schwarz inequality (Theorem 12) we find that

$$\lim_{q=\infty} \int \psi' \left(\sum_{n=0}^{q} a_n\lambda_n - \psi\right) dx = 0 \tag{11:8}$$

for every function ψ' in $\mathfrak{L}_2$. Then the first part of the theorem is obtained by taking $\psi' = \lambda_n$. The equation (11:7) follows at once from (11:6) and the right-hand equality in (11:5).

THEOREM 35. **The Riesz-Fischer theorem.** *If* (λ_n) *is an orthonormal system and the series* $\sum a_n^2$ *converges, there is a function* ψ *in* $\mathfrak{L}_2$ *satisfying the equation* (11:4). *The function* ψ *is uniquely determined (apart from sets of measure zero) if and only if the system* (λ_n) *is complete.*

THEOREM 36. **Parseval's theorem.** *If* (λ_n) *is a complete orthonormal system,* ψ *and* ψ' *are functions in* $\mathfrak{L}_2$*, and*

$$a_n = \int \psi\lambda_n \, dx, \qquad a_n' = \int \psi'\lambda_n \, dx,$$

then

$$\sum_{n=0}^{\infty} a_n^2 = \|\psi\|^2, \qquad \sum_{n=0}^{\infty} a_n a_n' = \int \psi\psi' \, dx.$$

Parseval's theorem follows at once from Theorems 31, 33 to 35, and equation (11:8).

THEOREM 37. *A necessary and sufficient condition that a sequence* (λ_n) *be closed in* $\mathfrak{L}_2$ *is that it be complete in* $\mathfrak{L}_2$.

Proof.—By Theorem 29 we may suppose the system (λ_n) is orthonormal. Then the necessity of the condition follows from Theorems 32 and 34, and the sufficiency from Theorems 31, 33, and 35.

It is obvious that a sequence (λ_n) is closed in $\mathfrak{L}_2$ in case it is known that its linear closed extension contains a set everywhere dense in $\mathfrak{L}_2$, as for example the set of all step functions or the set of all continuous functions. However, there exist orthonormal systems (λ_n) of continuous functions which are *not* complete in $\mathfrak{L}_2$ but are such that the only continuous function ψ satisfying (11:2) is identically zero. An example may be constructed as follows. Let (π_n) be an orthonormal system of continuous functions which is complete in $\mathfrak{L}_2$. Let ϕ be a function in $\mathfrak{L}_2$ which is not equivalent to a continuous function. Not all the coefficients

$$c_n = \int \phi\pi_n \, dx$$

are zero, and we suppose for convenience of notation that $c_0 \neq 0$. Then let $\lambda_n = c_0\pi_{n+1} - c_{n+1}\pi_0$, and suppose

$$\int \psi\lambda_n \, dx = 0 \qquad (n = 0, 1, 2, \cdots). \tag{11:9}$$

From this it follows that the coefficients

$$b_n = \int \psi\pi_n \, dx$$

are proportional to the coefficients c_n of the function ϕ. Then by Theorem 35, ψ is proportional to ϕ. Conversely, (11:9) holds when ψ is proportional to ϕ. But then ψ cannot be continuous unless it vanishes identically.

***†12. Additional Theorems on Differentiation.**—The next theorem on interchange of order of limit and derivative bears little resemblance to Theorem 8 of Chap. VII.

THEOREM 38. *Suppose that the functions* $f_n(x)$ *and* $f(x)$ *are of bounded variation on* $[a, b]$, *and that* $\lim_{n=\infty} t(f_n - f) = 0$. *Then* $\lim_{n=\infty} f'_n = f'$ *in measure on* $[a, b]$.

Proof.—By Theorem 30 of Chap. X, Sec. 6,

$$t(f_n - f) \geqq \int_a^b |f'_n - f'| \, dx.$$

Then the conclusion follows from Theorem 23 of Sec. 10.

COROLLARY. *Let the functions* $g_k(x)$ *be nondecreasing on* $[a, b]$, *and let the series* $\sum [g_k(b) - g_k(a)]$ *converge. Then* $f(x) = \sum [g_k(x) - g_k(a)]$ *converges uniformly on* $[a, b]$ *and* $f'(x) = \sum g'_k(x)$ *almost everywhere on* $[a, b]$.

This follows with the help of Theorem 19 and the fact that $g'_k(x) \geqq 0$ almost everywhere. The corollary has an immediate extension to the case where the functions $g_k(x)$ are only of bounded variation, and the series $\sum t(g_k)$ converges.

Let $f(x, y)$ be an integrable function of two variables, which we may suppose to be defined throughout the xy-plane, and let

$$F(x, y) = \int_0^x \int_0^y f(\xi, \eta) \, d\eta \, d\xi. \tag{12:1}$$

Then it may be shown that

$$\lim_{\substack{h=0 \\ k=0}} \frac{F(x+h, y+k) - F(x, y+k) - F(x+h, y) + F(x, y)}{hk} = f(x, y)$$

almost everywhere, provided either (*a*) the function $|f| \log^+ |f|$ is integrable, where $\log^+ |f| = \log [|f| \vee 1]$; or (*b*) the limit is taken over sequences (h_n), (k_n) on which the ratios h_n/k_n and k_n/h_n are bounded. For the proof, see Saks [1], Chap. 4, especially pages 106, 118, 132–133, 147–149. A related but independent result is the following:

THEOREM 39. *If* $f(x, y)$ *is integrable and* $F(x, y)$ *is given by* (12:1), *then there exists the partial derivative*

$$F_x(x, y) = \int_0^y f(x, \eta) \, d\eta \tag{12:2}$$

except for x in a set G which has linear measure zero and is independent of y, and there exists the mixed partial derivative $F_{xy}(x, y) = f(x, y)$ almost everywhere.

Proof.—By Theorem 29 of Chap. X, we see that the first part of the conclusion holds when y is restricted to be rational. For the remainder of this paragraph it is convenient to suppose $f(x, y) \geqq 0$. We may then show that the exceptional set G effective for rational y's is effective for irrational y's as well. For, an irrational y lies between two rational values y_1 and y_2 having the same sign as y and then, since $f(x, y)$ preserves its sign, each partial derivate $D_xF(x, y)$ lies between

$$F_x(x, y_1) = \int_0^{y_1} f(x, \eta)\, d\eta \qquad \text{and} \qquad F_x(x, y_2) = \int_0^{y_2} f(x, \eta)\, d\eta$$

for x not in G. But $\int_0^y f(x, \eta)\, d\eta$ is a continuous function of y for x not in G, and hence there exists $F_x(x, y) = \int_0^y f(x, \eta)\, d\eta$. By another application of Theorem 29 of Chap. X, we see that there exists $F_{xy}(x, y) = f(x, y)$ unless x is in G, or y is in a set H_x whose linear measure is zero. Then by Theorem 3 it follows that the exceptional set, where F_{xy} does not exist or is not equal to f, has planar measure zero if it is measurable. Thus to complete the proof it is sufficient to show that each of the four Dini derivates D_yF_x is measurable, where the set G is neglected.

The expression

$$M(x, y; h, k) \equiv \int_x^{x+k} \int_y^{y+h} f(\xi, \eta)\, d\eta\, d\xi$$

is continuous in (x, y) for each h and k, and so is measurable. Except for x in G,

$$Q(x, y; h) \equiv \frac{1}{h} \int_y^{y+h} f(x, \eta)\, d\eta = \lim_{k=0} \frac{M(x, y; h, k)}{hk},$$

and so $Q(x, y; h)$ is measurable for $h \neq 0$. For each x not in G, Q is continuous in h, and so

$$\begin{aligned} \beta(x, y; \delta) &\equiv \underset{0<h<\delta}{\text{l.u.b.}}\ Q(x, y; h) \\ &= \underset{0<r<\delta}{\text{l.u.b.}}\ Q(x, y; r) \text{ for rational } r. \end{aligned}$$

Then by Lemma 13 and Theorem 21 of Chap. X, Sec. 4, $\beta(x, y;\delta)$ is measurable, and finally $\lim_{\delta=0} \beta(x, y; \delta)$, which is the upper righthand derivate of $F_x(x, y)$, is also measurable. The measurability of the other three derivates follows with the help of Lemma 15 of Chap. X, Sec. 5.

***†13. Integral Means.**—In Sec. 11 we considered briefly the approximation of functions in $\mathfrak{L}_2$ by linear combinations of functions from an orthonormal system. In Chap. VII, Sec. 4, we considered the approximation of continuous functions by polynomials. In this section we shall develop a few elementary properties of the approximation to functions in $\mathfrak{L}_p$ or in $C^{(n)}$ by integral means. At first we restrict attention to functions of one variable.

Let X denote the x-axis, let E be a measurable subset of X, and let $\lambda(x)$ be a measurable function which is integrable on every bounded subset of E. For convenience we define $\lambda(x) = 0$ on the complement of E. Then we may define the integral mean

$$(13{:}1) \qquad \lambda_h(x) = \frac{1}{2h} \int_{-h}^{h} \lambda(x + s)\, ds = \frac{1}{2h} \int_{x-h}^{x+h} \lambda(s)\, ds$$

for all $h > 0$ and for all values of x. It has the following properties:

M1. $\lim_{h=0} \lambda_h = \lambda$ almost everywhere, and in particular at all the points where λ is continuous.

M2. λ_h is absolutely continuous on each finite interval, and

$$(13{:}2) \qquad \lambda_h'(x) = \frac{\lambda(x + h) - \lambda(x - h)}{2h}$$

almost everywhere, and in particular at the points x such that λ is continuous at $(x + h)$ and at $(x - h)$. Hence, if λ is continuous everywhere, λ_h is of class C'.

M3. If λ is in $\mathfrak{L}_p$ $(p \geqq 1)$, so is λ_h.

M4. On every finite interval the integrals $\int \lambda_h\, dx$ are absolutely continuous uniformly for $0 < h < 1$.

M5. If λ is in $\mathfrak{L}_p$, the integrals $\int |\lambda_h|^p\, dx$ are absolutely continuous uniformly and converge uniformly for $0 < h < 1$, and $\lim_{h=0} \lambda_h = \lambda$ in the mean of order p.

M6. If λ is continuous at the points of a bounded closed set E_1, then $\lim_{h=0} \lambda_h = \lambda$ uniformly on E_1.

M7. If λ is continuous on a neighborhood of x_0 and has a derivative at x_0, then

$$\lim_{h=0} \lambda'_h(x_0) = \lambda'(x_0).$$

M8. If λ is absolutely continuous on each finite interval, $\lambda'_h = (\lambda')_h$.

M9. If λ is of class $C^{(n)}$, and its nth derivative $\lambda^{(n)}$ is absolutely continuous on every finite interval, then $\lambda_h^{(n+1)} = (\lambda^{(n+1)})_h$.

M10. If λ is of class $C^{(n)}$, then λ_h is of class $C^{(n+1)}$; if E_1 is a bounded set, $\lim_{h=0} \lambda_h^{(n)} = \lambda^{(n)}$ uniformly on E_1.

It should be noted that, since $\lambda_h(x_0)$ depends only on the values of $\lambda(x)$ for $x_0 - h < x < x_0 + h$, even the properties M8, M9, and M10 could be restated as local properties.

M1 follows from Theorem 29 of Chap. X and Theorem 9 of Chap. VI. The absolute continuity of λ_h follows from the relation

$$\lambda_h(b) - \lambda_h(a) = \frac{1}{2h}\left[\int_{a+h}^{b+h} \lambda(s)\,ds - \int_{a-h}^{b-h} \lambda(s)\,ds\right]$$

and the fact that $\int \lambda\,ds$ is absolutely continuous on every finite interval. The validity of (13:2) follows from Theorem 29 of Chap. X, and the remainder of M2 from more elementary considerations.

To prove M3 we show first that $\lambda(x + s)$ as a function of two variables is in $\mathfrak{L}_p$ on XS, where S is the interval $[-h, h]$. For any set E in X, we shall let E^* denote the set of all points (x, s) such that $x + s$ is in E. Then, if E is closed, E^* is closed relative to XS and, if E is open, E^* is open relative to XS. Thus if i is an interval, i^* is measurable and, if ϕ denotes the characteristic function,

$$m(i^*) = \int \phi_{i^*}\,dx\,ds = \int_{-h}^{h} \int_X \phi_i(x + s)\,dx\,ds = 2hm(i).$$

From this it is easy to see that, if E has measure zero, then E^* has measure zero. If $\alpha(x)$ is a step function, $\alpha(x + s)$ is measurable and, if $\lim_n \alpha_n(x) = \lambda(x)$ almost everywhere on X, $\lim_n \alpha_n(x + s) = \lambda(x + s)$ almost everywhere on XS, and thus $\lambda(x + s)$ is measurable on XS. Obviously $\int_X |\lambda(x + s)|^p \, dx$ is independent of s, and so by Theorem 4 of Sec. 2, $\lambda(x + s)$ is in $\mathfrak{L}_p$ on XS. By Fubini's theorem, $\int_{-h}^{h} |\lambda(x + s)|^p \, ds$ is integrable on X, and since by Hölder's inequality,

$$(13:3) \qquad \left|\int_{-h}^{h} \lambda(x + s) \, ds\right|^p \leqq (2h)^{p-1} \int_{-h}^{h} |\lambda(x + s)|^p \, ds,$$

λ_h is in $\mathfrak{L}_p$ on X.

To prove M4, we have, with the help of Fubini's theorem,

$$\left|\int_A \lambda_h \, dx\right| = \frac{1}{2h} \left|\int_{-h}^{h} \int_A \lambda(x + s) \, dx \, ds\right| \leqq \underset{|s|<1}{\text{l.u.b.}} \left|\int_A \lambda(x + s) \, dx\right|.$$

The first part of M5 is verified in a similar way with the help of (13:3), and then the last part follows from M1 and Theorem 21. M6 is proved easily by use of the uniform continuity of λ on E_1. M7 follows from M2. M8 follows from M2 and Theorem 28 of Chap. X. M9 follows at once from M8 by induction, and M10 follows from M9, M2, and M6.

It is easily seen that each time we repeat the process of taking integral means, we obtain an approximating function having an additional derivative, so that taking integral means is a smoothing process. For functions of two variables, we may take integral means over rectangles, squares, circles, or some other configuration. In two-dimensional potential theory, it is convenient to take integral means over circles, since a harmonic function is characterized by the property that it is everywhere *equal* to its integral mean over circles. In studying the differentiability properties of integral means, it is simpler to use squares, and we shall restrict attention to that case. Possible extensions to functions of more than two variables will be apparent. Some additional properties for functions of two variables are listed in a paper by Helsel and Radó.[1]

[1] "The Transformation of Double Integrals," *Transactions of the American Mathematical Society*, Vol. 54 (1943), especially pp. 87–95.

The increment $\Delta(\lambda; i)$ of a function $\lambda(x, y)$ of two variables over an interval $i = (a, c; b, d)$ is defined by the formula

$$(13:4) \quad \Delta(\lambda; i) = \lambda(b, d) - \lambda(a, d) - \lambda(b, c) + \lambda(a, c).$$

Here it is not essential to specify whether an interval is open or closed. A set A will be understood to be a finite sum $\sum i$ of intervals i which are nonoverlapping but not necessarily disjoint. The notation $\Delta(\lambda; A)$ will be used for the sum of $\Delta(\lambda; i)$ over the intervals i making up A. A set A has infinitely many representations as a sum of nonoverlapping intervals, but it is readily seen that they all give the same value for $\Delta(\lambda; A)$. A function $\lambda(x, y)$ is said to be **absolutely continuous** in case $\lim_{m(A)=0} \Delta(\lambda; A) = 0$. If $f(x, y)$ is an integrable function and $F(x, y)$ is defined by formula (12:1), then it follows from Theorem 7 of Chap. X that $F(x, y)$ is absolutely continuous. In other words, the definitions of absolute continuity for the set function $\int_A f(x, y)\, dy\, dx$ and the point function $F(x, y)$ correspond.

It should be noted, however, that the correspondence set up by (13:4) between point functions $\lambda(x, y)$ and interval functions is not one-to-one, since an arbitrary function of x and an arbitrary function of y may be added to λ without changing the values of $\Delta(\lambda; i)$. Thus a function $\lambda(x, y)$ may be absolutely continuous according to our definition, and yet be discontinuous. Caratheodory ([4], page 653) in defining absolute continuity for functions of two variables adds the requirement that $\lambda(x, y)$ be absolutely continuous in y for one fixed value x_0 of x, and absolutely continuous in x for one fixed value y_0 of y. Then λ is absolutely continuous in y uniformly with respect to x, and in x uniformly with respect to y, on each finite interval.

A related but different concept for functions of more than one variable is frequently useful. A function $\lambda(x, y)$ of two variables is said to be **absolutely continuous in the sense of Tonelli** in case it is continuous, and absolutely continuous as a function of x for almost every y, absolutely continuous as a function of y for almost every x, and the partial derivatives λ_x and λ_y are integrable. Like the preceding one, this definition may be applied either to a finite interval or to the whole plane.

As in the case of functions of one variable, we may suppose that the functions $\lambda(x, y)$ to be considered are defined in the whole xy-plane, which will be denoted by R, and integrable over every finite interval. The mean λ_h is defined by the formula

$$\lambda_h(x, y) = \frac{1}{4h^2}\int_{-h}^{h}\int_{-h}^{h} \lambda(x + s, y + t)\,dt\,ds,$$
$$= \frac{1}{4h^2}\int_{x-h}^{x+h}\int_{y-h}^{y+h} \lambda(s, t)\,dt\,ds.$$

It has the following properties:

M11. Same as M1.

M12. λ_h is absolutely continuous, and also absolutely continuous in the sense of Tonelli, on each finite interval, and

(13:5) $$\frac{\partial \lambda_h}{\partial x} = \frac{1}{4h^2}\int_{y-h}^{y+h} [\lambda(x + h, t) - \lambda(x - h, t)]\,dt$$

except for x in a set G of measure zero, and

(13:6) $$\frac{\partial^2 \lambda_h}{\partial y\,\partial x} = \frac{1}{4h^2}[\lambda(x + h, y + h) - \lambda(x + h, y - h) - \lambda(x - h, y + h) + \lambda(x - h, y - h)]$$

almost everywhere. If λ is continuous, then λ_h is of class C' and has a continuous mixed derivative, and formulas (13:5) and (13:6) hold everywhere.

M13. Same as M3.

M14. Same as M4.

M15. Same as M5.

M16. Same as M6.

M17. If λ is absolutely continuous in the sense of Tonelli on each finite interval, then

$$\left(\frac{\partial \lambda}{\partial x}\right)_h = \frac{\partial \lambda_h}{\partial x}, \qquad \left(\frac{\partial \lambda}{\partial y}\right)_h = \frac{\partial \lambda_h}{\partial y}.$$

M18. If λ is of class $C^{(n)}$, then λ_h is of class $C^{(n+1)}$, and on each bounded set E_1, the partial derivatives of λ_h up to and including those of order n converge uniformly to the corresponding partial derivatives of λ.

The proof of M11 is like that of M1, except that it depends on the theorem quoted just preceding Theorem 39 in Sec. 12. For M12, we obtain each type of absolute continuity by a manipulation similar to that for functions of one variable. Formulas

(13:5) and (13:6) follow from Theorem 39. The proofs of the remaining properties also parallel those for functions of one variable.

EXERCISES

1. Show that if (E_n) is a nondecreasing sequence of sets, then $m_e(\lim E_n) = \lim m_e(E_n)$.

2. Show that Theorem 16 of Chap. X holds true for unbounded sets E_n, provided they are all contained in a set E of finite measure. Give an example to show that the right-hand inequality may fail when $\sum E_n$ has infinite measure.

3. If g is an additive function defined on the class $\mathfrak{E}$ of measurable sets E, prove that g is absolutely continuous if and only if $g(E) = 0$ whenever $m(E) = 0$.

4. Construct a function $f(x)$ which is properly increasing and absolutely continuous and has $f'(x) = 0$ on a set of positive measure. Prove that the inverse of a function with these properties cannot be absolutely continuous.

5. Show that $\lambda(x, y) = (x - y)/(x + y)^3$ is not Lebesgue-integrable on $0 \leqq x \leqq 1$, $0 \leqq y \leqq 1$, by computing the repeated integrals in the two orders.

6. Exhibit a sequence of functions complete in $\mathfrak{L}_q$ but not in $\mathfrak{L}_p$, where $1 \leqq p < q \leqq \infty$.

REFERENCES

1. Saks, *Theory of the Integral*, Chaps. 3, 4.
2. McShane, *Integration*, Chaps. 2 to 5, 7, 10.
3. Hobson, *Theory of Functions of a Real Variable*, Vol. 1, Chap. 7; Vol. 2, Chaps. 5, 10.
4. Caratheodory, *Vorlesungen über reelle Functionen*, Chaps. 6, 8, 10, 11.

CHAPTER XII

THE STIELTJES INTEGRAL

1. Definitions and First Properties.—Stieltjes defined the integral known by his name for a special case in a paper published in 1894.[1] Various modifications and generalizations have been introduced since then by a number of authors. In this chapter we shall discuss the definitions that seem to be the most interesting, as well as the relations between them. The discussion will be restricted to functions of one variable. The definitions and some of the theorems are extensible to the case of functions of two or more variables, but those extensions involve a number of troublesome details.

Let ψ and f be finite real-valued functions defined on the interval $[a, b]$, let P be a partition of $[a, b]$ into subintervals $[x_{j-1}, x_j]$, and let points z_j be chosen so that $x_{j-1} \leqq z_j \leqq x_j$. Set $N(P)$ = maximum of $(x_j - x_{j-1})$, and

$$(1{:}1) \quad S(P; \psi, f) = \sum_j \psi(z_j)[f(x_j) - f(x_{j-1})] = \sum_j \psi(z_j)\, \Delta_j f.$$

When no ambiguity can arise, we may write $S(P; f)$, $S(P; \psi)$ or merely $S(P)$ in place of $S(P; \psi, f)$. Then, if

$$\lim_{N(P)=0} S(P; \psi, f)$$

exists and is finite, it is defined to be the Stieltjes integral of ψ with respect to f and is denoted by the symbol

$$(S) \int_a^b \psi(x)\, df,$$

and ψ is said to be **S-integrable with respect to f**. We note that this differs from the definition of the Riemann integral given in Chap. VI only in replacing the length of an interval of the partition P by the increment of $f(x)$ over that interval.

[1] See *Annales de la faculté des sciences de Toulouse*, Vol 8 (1894), p. J71.

The following criterion is obtained at once from Theorem 10 of Chap. IV.

THEOREM 1. *A necessary and sufficient condition for* $\psi(x)$ *to be S-integrable with respect to f on* $[a, b]$ *is that*

$$\lim_{\substack{N(P_1)=0 \\ N(P_2)=0}} [S(P_1) - S(P_2)] = 0.$$

A slight generalization of the S-integral has been considered by Pollard and others.[1] We shall call it the GS-integral. It depends on a modification of the limiting process. We shall say that a partition P_1 is **finer than** P_2—in notation, $P_1 \supset P_2$—in case all the division points for P_2 are used in P_1. The notation is suggested by the fact that each partition is determined by its points of division. We say that

$$\lim_{P,\supset} S(P) = L$$

in case

$$\epsilon > 0 :\supset: \exists P_\epsilon \ni: P \supset P_\epsilon \cdot\supset\cdot |S(P) - L| < \epsilon,$$

with the usual modification in case L is infinite. A necessary and sufficient condition for the limit L to exist and be finite is that

$$\epsilon > 0 :\supset: \exists P_\epsilon \ni: P_1 \supset P_\epsilon . P_2 \supset P_\epsilon \cdot\supset\cdot |S(P_1) - S(P_2)| < \epsilon.$$

The sufficiency of this condition may be proved by considering a monotonic sequence of partitions P_{ϵ_n} corresponding to a sequence of numbers ϵ_n with ϵ_n tending to zero.

Now referring back to the sums $S(P; \psi, f)$ defined in (1:1), we say that ψ is GS-integrable with respect to f when

$$\lim_{P,\supset} S(P; \psi, f)$$

exists and is finite. In this case the limit is denoted by the symbol

$$(GS) \int_a^b \psi \, df.$$

The letters (S) and (GS) before the integral sign may be omitted when no ambiguity can arise.

[1] See Pollard, "The Stieltjes Integral and Its Generalizations," *Quarterly Journal of Mathematics*, Vol. 49 (1920–1923) pp. 73–138; Hildebrandt [5].

It is easy to see that for either the S-integral or the GS-integral, we may replace the functional value $\psi(z_i)$ in the sum $S(P; \psi, f)$ by any number between the upper and the lower bound of ψ on the interval $[x_{i-1}, x_i]$, without changing the force of the definition.

A Riemann-integrable function is necessarily bounded, but an unbounded function ψ may be S- or GS-integrable with respect to f when f has intervals of constancy. However, in the next theorem it is shown that ψ may be replaced by a bounded function ψ_1 (depending also on f) such that

$$\int_a^x \psi\, df = \int_a^x \psi_1\, df \qquad (a \leqq x \leqq b).$$

But when integrals with respect to functions f_n of a sequence are considered, it is a real restriction to assume that ψ is bounded.

THEOREM 2. *Suppose that ψ is S- or GS-integrable with respect to f, and let $\psi_k = (\psi \wedge k) \vee (-k)$. Then, when k is sufficiently large, we have $\int_a^x \psi_k\, df = \int_a^x \psi\, df$ for every x on $[a, b]$. In the case of the S-integral, the points where $\psi_k \neq \psi$ are contained in a finite set of intervals each interior to an interval of constancy of f. In the case of the GS-integral, the points where $\psi_k \neq \psi$ are interior to a finite number of intervals of constancy of f.*

Proof for the S-integral.—There exists a positive δ such that $\left|S(P) - \int_a^b \psi\, df\right| < 1$ whenever $N(P) < \delta$. If E is the set of points at which ψ has an infinite discontinuity, then f must be constant on each interval of the open set $N(E; \delta)$. This set consists of a finite number of intervals, since each has length at least 2δ. We select k so that $\psi = \psi_k$ on the complement of $N(E; \delta/2)$. Then if $N(P) < \delta/2$, $S(P; \psi_k) = S(P; \psi)$.

Proof for the GS-integral.—There exists a partition P_1 such that when $P \supset P_1$, $\left|S(P) - \int_a^b \psi\, df\right| < 1$. Then f is constant on each interval of P_1 on which ψ is unbounded, and hence when k is sufficiently large and $P \supset P_1$, $S(P; \psi_k) = S(P; \psi)$.

THEOREM 3. *The S-integral and the GS-integral $\int_a^b \psi\, df$ are linear in f for each fixed ψ, and linear in ψ for each fixed f.*

This is obvious from the corresponding properties of limits. An operator $K(\psi, f)$ with these properties is called a **bilinear** operator. Note that the domain of K as a function of f may vary with ψ, and vice versa.

For the case of the S-integral, we have the following necessary condition for its existence:

THEOREM 4. *If ψ is S-integrable with respect to f, then ψ and f have no common discontinuities.*

Proof.—Suppose ψ and f are both discontinuous at the point c. In case f has right-hand and left-hand limits at c, and $f(c - 0) = f(c + 0) \neq f(c)$, we choose c as a partition point of a partition P with arbitrarily small norm. There is a number $\epsilon > 0$, independent of P, such that on one of the two closed intervals abutting c, the oscillation of ψ is greater than ϵ. Then, if the norm $N(P)$ is sufficiently small, we can construct two sums $S_1(P)$ and $S_2(P)$, differing only on one interval, such that

$$S_1(P) - S_2(P) > \epsilon \frac{|f(c + 0) - f(c)|}{2}.$$

In all other cases, there exist a number $\delta > 0$ and arbitrarily small intervals with c as an interior point, such that $|\Delta f| > \delta$, where Δf represents the increment over the interval in question. There also exists a number $\epsilon > 0$ such that the oscillation of ψ over every such integral is greater than ϵ. Thus for partitions P with norm $N(P)$ arbitrarily small, we can construct sums $S_1(P)$ and $S_2(P)$ such that $S_1(P) - S_2(P) > \epsilon\delta$. Hence in both cases we have a contradiction with the criterion of Theorem 1 for the existence of the integral.

In case f is a step function and ψ is continuous at the jumps of f, it is easily seen that the S-integral of ψ with respect to f exists. We shall consider the case when f has only one jump, say at the point c. Then for every partition P, $S(P) = \psi(\xi)\,[f(c + 0) - f(c - 0)]$ and, when $N(P)$ tends to zero, $S(P)$ tends to the value $\psi(c)[f(c + 0) - f(c - 0)]$.

For the GS-integral, the situation is slightly different.

THEOREM 5. *If ψ is GS-integrable with respect to f, then ψ and f have no common discontinuities on the right, nor on the left.*

Proof.—Suppose ψ and f are discontinuous on the right at c. Then there exist a number $\epsilon > 0$ and points z_1, z_2, and d arbitrarily near c, with $c \leqq z_1 < z_2 \leqq d$, such that $|f(d) - f(c)| > \epsilon$, $|\psi(z_1) - \psi(z_2)| > \epsilon$. Hence for every partition P with c and d as successive partition points, we may choose sums $S_1(P)$ and $S_2(P)$ such that $S_1(P) - S_2(P) > \epsilon^2$. From this it follows that ψ is not GS-integrable.

Now let $f(x) = 0$ for $a \leqq x \leqq c$, $f(x) = \gamma$ for $c < x \leqq b$, and let $\psi(x)$ be continuous on the right at c. Then it is easily seen that $(GS) \int_a^b \psi\, df$ exists and has the value $\gamma\psi(c)$. The extension to other cases is obvious.

THEOREM 6. *When a function ψ is S-integrable with respect to f, it is also GS-integrable, and the two integrals are equal.*

This is an immediate consequence of the definitions. Theorem 4 and the remark preceding Theorem 6 show that the converse is not true. However, we can prove the following result:

THEOREM 7. *When ψ and f are bounded and have no common discontinuity and ψ is GS-integrable with respect to f, it is also S-integrable.*

Proof.—By hypothesis, corresponding to an arbitrary $\epsilon > 0$, there is a partition P_ϵ such that for every refinement P_1 of P_ϵ we have

$$\left|S(P_1) - \int_a^b \psi\, df\right| < \epsilon. \tag{1:2}$$

Let $y_1, \cdots, y_q$ be the division points of P_ϵ, where $a < y_j < b$, and let $M \geqq |\psi(x)|$, $M \geqq |f(x)|$. Then there is a number $\delta > 0$ such that, if $|x - y_j| < \delta$, we have

$$\begin{aligned} |\psi(x) - \psi(y_j)| &< \epsilon/2Mq \text{ if } \psi \text{ is continuous at } y_j, \\ |f(x) - f(y_j)| &< \epsilon/2Mq \text{ if } \psi \text{ is discontinuous at } y_j. \end{aligned} \tag{1:3}$$

Now let P be any partition with $N(P) < \delta$ and let P_1 be the partition formed by using all the division points of P and P_ϵ. If $S(P) = \sum \psi(z_k)[f(x_k) - f(x_{k-1})]$, we may choose the functional values of ψ for $S(P_1)$ so that $S(P_1) - S(P)$ reduces to at most q terms of the form

$$[\psi(y_j) - \psi(z_k)][f(u_j) - f(v_j)],$$

where one of the values u_j, v_j is y_j and the other is either x_k or x_{k-1}, and where y_j is in the interval $[x_{k-1}, x_k]$. Then by (1:3), $|S(P_1) - S(P)| < \epsilon$, and hence by (1:2) $\left|S(P) - \int_a^b \psi\, df\right| < 2\epsilon$.

Suppose ψ is S-integrable or GS-integrable with respect to f on the interval $[a, b]$, and let $[c, d]$ be a subinterval of $[a, b]$. Then ψ is integrable in the same sense on $[c, d]$, as is easily shown by use of the Cauchy condition. On the other hand, if ψ is GS-integrable with respect to f on $[a, b]$ and on $[b, c]$, it is so on

$[a, c]$. But Theorem 4 shows that this result does not hold for the S-integral.

THEOREM 8. **Integration by parts.** *When* $(S) \int_a^b \psi\, df$ *exists,* $(S) \int_a^b f\, d\psi$ *also exists and*

$$(S) \int_a^b \psi\, df + (S) \int_a^b f\, d\psi = \psi(b)f(b) - \psi(a)f(a).$$

The same relation holds for the GS-integral.

Proof.—Let

$$S(P; f, \psi) = \sum_{j=1}^{n} f(z_j)[\psi(x_j) - \psi(x_{j-1})],$$

$$S(P_1; \psi, f) = \sum_{j=1}^{n} \psi(x_{j-1})[f(z_j) - f(x_{j-1})] + \sum_{j=1}^{n} \psi(x_j)[f(x_j) - f(z_j)],$$

where $x_0 = a$, $x_n = b$. We note that the partition P_1 is obtained from P by using all the points x_j and z_j as points of division. When $z_j = x_j$ or $z_j = x_{j-1}$, the corresponding term in the sum drops out. Obviously P_1 is finer than P, and $N(P_1) \leqq N(P)$. Also

$$S(P_1; \psi, f) + S(P; f, \psi) = \psi(b)f(b) - \psi(a)f(a).$$

By taking limits, we obtain the conclusions desired.

The next theorem motivates the restriction that is commonly made that the function f be of bounded variation. But the theorem on integration by parts shows that the Stieltjes integral may exist in important cases when f is not of bounded variation.

THEOREM 9. *If every continuous function* ψ *is GS-integrable with respect to* f, *then* f *is of bounded variation.*

Proof.—Suppose f is not of bounded variation on the interval $[a, b]$. Then by the method of successive subdivision, a point X may be determined such that for every interval $[c, d]$ to which X is interior, f is not of bounded variation on $[c, d]$. In case X is at a or at b, the requirement of interiority is waived. Hence f fails to be of bounded variation on every interval $[X, d]$, or else f fails to be of bounded variation on every interval $[c, X]$. For definiteness, we consider the latter case and suppose first that $|f(x)| \leqq M$ on a left-hand neighborhood of X. Then there exist points $c_0, c_1, \cdots, c_{p_1}$, with $a = c_0 < c_1 < \cdots < c_{p_1} < X$, $|f(c_{p_1})| \leqq M$, and

$$\sum_{j=1}^{p_1} |f(c_j) - f(c_{j-1})| + |f(X) - f(c_{p_1})| > 2M + 1.$$

Hence

$$\sum_{j=1}^{p_1} |f(c_j) - f(c_{j-1})| > 1.$$

The process may be repeated for the interval $[c_{p_1}, X]$. By a sequence of such repetitions we obtain an increasing sequence of points c_j approaching X, and an increasing sequence of integers p_k, such that

$$\sum_{j=p_k+1}^{p_{k+1}} |f(c_j) - f(c_{j-1})| > 1. \tag{1:4}$$

If we let $\eta_j = 1/k$ for $p_{k-1} < j \leqq p_k$, we have

$$\sum_{j=1}^{\infty} \eta_j |f(c_j) - f(c_{j-1})| = +\infty. \tag{1:5}$$

In case f has an infinite discontinuity on the left at X, it is easy to see that we may still obtain (1:4) and so (1:5).

Now set

$$\begin{aligned} \psi(c_j) &= \eta_j \operatorname{sgn} [f(c_j) - f(c_{j-1})], \\ \psi(x) &= \psi(c_1) \qquad \text{for} \quad a \leqq x \leqq c_1, \\ \psi(x) &= 0 \qquad\quad\ \ \text{for} \quad X \leqq x \leqq b, \end{aligned}$$

and extend ψ to be continuous on $[a, b]$, for example, by making it linear in the intervals where it is still undefined. Whenever $[c_{j-1}, c_j]$ is an interval of a partition P, we may take

$$\psi(c_j)[f(c_j) - f(c_{j-1})] = \eta_j |f(c_j) - f(c_{j-1})|$$

as the corresponding term of $S(P)$. Hence for $\rho > 0$ and an arbitrary partition P_1 we can find a finer partition P such that $S(P) > \rho$, simply by using enough of the points c_j as partition points. Then ψ is not GS-integrable with respect to f.

The accompanying figure illustrates a simple case when the *GS*-integral exists but the *S*-integral does not. It also illustrates

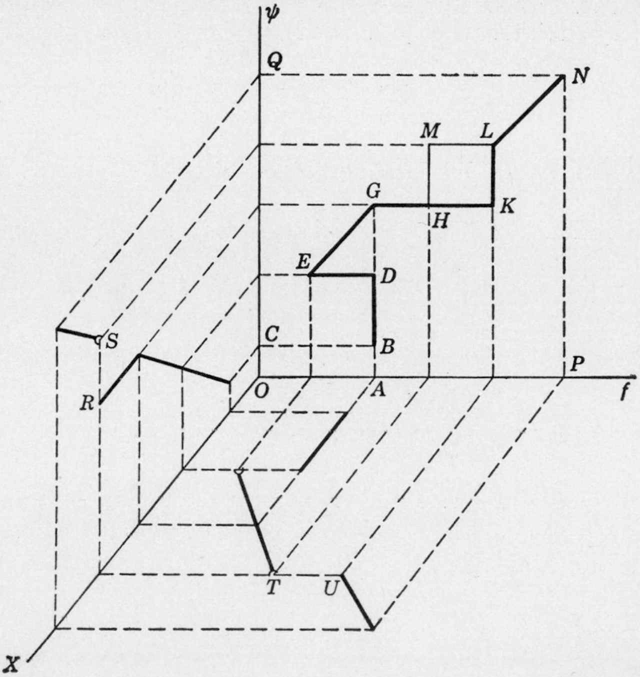

the formula for integration by parts. The area bounded by *ADEGKLNP* equals $(GS)\int \psi\, df$, and the area bounded by *CBD-EGKLNQ* equals $(GS)\int f\, d\psi$. The definition of the *S*-integral is inadequate to decide between *HKL* and *HML* as possible parts of the boundary. If the point *S* were a point on the graph of $\psi(x)$ in place of *R*, the definition of the *GS*-integral would also be inadequate to decide, but the *LS*-integral (to be discussed in Sec. 3) would decide for *HML* in the case of $\int \psi\, df$ and for *HKL* in the case of $\int f\, d\psi$. From this we see that the formula for integration by parts does not always hold for the *LS*-integral.

2. Functions of Bounded Variation.—We have seen in Chap. X, Sec. 5, that if $f(x)$ is of bounded variation on $[a, b]$ and $t(x)$, $p(x)$, $n(x)$ are, respectively, its total, positive, and negative variations, then

$$(2{:}1) \quad f(x) = f(a) + p(x) - n(x), \qquad t(x) = p(x) + n(x).$$

The decomposition (2:1) of $f(x)$ into the difference of two nondecreasing functions is a minimum decomposition, in the sense that, if $f(x) = g(x) - h(x)$ where g and h are nondecreasing, then for every subinterval of $[a, b]$ we have $\Delta p \leqq \Delta g$, $\Delta n \leqq \Delta h$. For

$$\Delta p + \Delta n = \Delta t \leqq \Delta g + \Delta h,$$
$$\Delta p - \Delta n = \Delta g - \Delta h.$$

By adding we obtain $\Delta p \leqq \Delta g$, and by subtracting we obtain $\Delta n \leqq \Delta h$.

A function f of bounded variation may also be decomposed into its continuous part and its jump function. We may suppose that f is nondecreasing, and then the two expressions

$$\sum_{a \leqq c < b} [f(c+0) - f(c)],$$
$$\sum_{a < c \leqq b} [f(c) - f(c-0)],$$

have no negative terms and at most a denumerable infinity of positive terms, so they represent finite or infinite series which will remain convergent if some of the terms are omitted. Let

$$\text{(2:2)} \quad j(x) = \sum_{a \leqq c < x} [f(c+0) - f(c)] + \sum_{a < c \leqq x} [f(c) - f(c-0)].$$

Then $j(x)$ is nondecreasing. It also has exactly the discontinuities of f. For by taking δ sufficiently small, the series $j(x + \delta) - j(x)$ may be made to exclude any finite set of terms of the series for $j(b)$ except the term $[f(x + 0) - f(x)]$, so that $j(x + 0) - j(x) = f(x + 0) - f(x)$. The same argument holds for left-hand discontinuities. Then $g(x) \equiv f(x) - j(x)$ is continuous and is also nondecreasing, as is easily verified. A jump function is characterized by the fact that it is the sum of an absolutely convergent series of step functions, each of which is discontinuous on only one side of a single point, and vanishes at $x = a$. In such a series, terms having the same discontinuity on the same side may be grouped together. We see that after such a grouping a discontinuity of the sum of the series is exactly the discontinuity of some one of the terms, so that the function defined by the series is its own jump function as defined above.

If p and n are the positive and negative variations of f, the jump functions of p and n are, respectively, the positive and negative variations of j, since each jump of p is a positive jump of f and hence of j. From this we find that, if $g = f - j$, the total variation of f is the sum of the total variations of g and j.

Still another decomposition of f is that into its absolutely continuous part and its function of singularities. The derivative $f'(x)$ is Lebesgue-integrable, by Theorem 30 of Chap. X, and $\int_a^x f'\,dx$ is absolutely continuous. The function

$$s(x) \equiv f(x) - f(a) - \int_a^x f'\,dx$$

is called the **function of singularities** of $f(x)$. It is identically zero if and only if f is absolutely continuous. The jump function of f is included in the function of singularities.

The class of functions of bounded variation is linear and, if f and g are two such functions, we have

$$t_{cd}(f + g) \leqq t_{cd}(f) + t_{cd}(g),$$

where the notation $t_{cd}(f)$ is used temporarily to denote the total variation of f over the subinterval $[c, d]$. From this we may also deduce the inequalities

$$\begin{aligned} t_{cd}(f) - t_{cd}(g) &\leqq t_{cd}(f - g), \\ t_{cd}[t_{ax}(f) - t_{ax}(g)] &\leqq t_{cd}(f - g). \end{aligned} \tag{2:3}$$

3. Further Definitions and Relations between Integrals.—The upper and lower integrals of ψ with respect to f are useful when f is a nondecreasing function. Under this restriction we may set

$$\begin{aligned} U_j &= \text{l.u.b. } \psi(x) \text{ on } [x_{j-1}, x_j], \\ L_j &= \text{g.l.b. } \psi(x) \text{ on } [x_{j-1}, x_j], \\ S^*(P; \psi, f) &= \sum_j U_j\,\Delta_j f, \\ S_*(P; \psi, f) &= \sum_j L_j\,\Delta_j f, \\ \overline{\int_a^b} \psi(x)\,df &= \text{g.l.b. } S^*(P; \psi, f), \\ \underline{\int_a^b} \psi(x)\,df &= \text{l.u.b. } S_*(P; \psi, f). \end{aligned}$$

Here it is understood that $0 \cdot \infty = 0$, so that the upper and lower integrals may still be finite even when ψ is unbounded. As elsewhere in this chapter, f is assumed to take only finite values on the closed interval $[a, b]$.

If P_1 and P_2 are arbitrary partitions of $[a, b]$ and P_3 is the partition formed by using all the points of both P_1 and P_2, we see at once that

$$(3{:}1) \qquad S_*(P_2) \leqq S_*(P_3) \leqq S^*(P_3) \leqq S^*(P_1),$$

and from this it follows at once that

$$(3{:}2) \qquad \underline{\int_a^b} \psi(x)\,df \leqq \overline{\int_a^b} \psi(x)\,df.$$

THEOREM 10. *A necessary and sufficient condition that ψ be GS-integrable with respect to a nondecreasing function f is that the upper and lower integrals of ψ with respect to f be equal and finite. The common value of the upper and lower integrals then equals the GS-integral of ψ with respect to f.*

This theorem is easily verified by use of the fact that, when additional partition points are inserted in P, the sums $S^*(P)$ do not increase, and the sums $S_*(P)$ do not decrease, so that

$$\overline{\int_a^b} \psi\,df = \lim_{P,\supset} S^*(P), \qquad \underline{\int_a^b} \psi\,df = \lim_{P,\supset} S_*(P).$$

COROLLARY. *Another necessary and sufficient condition is that for every $\epsilon > 0$, there exists a partition P such that $S^*(P; \psi, f)$ and $S_*(P; \psi, f)$ are finite and $S^*(P; \psi, f) - S_*(P; \psi, f) < \epsilon$.*

THEOREM 11. *A necessary and sufficient condition that ψ be S-integrable with respect to a nondecreasing function f is that*

$$\lim_{N(P)=0} [S^*(P; \psi, f) - S_*(P; \psi, f)] = 0.$$

Proof.—To prove the sufficiency of the condition, we note that, since $S_*(P) < +\infty$ and $S^*(P) > -\infty$, it is clear that both must be finite when $N(P)$ is sufficiently small. From (3:1) it follows that the intervals $[S_*(P_1), S^*(P_1)]$ and $[S_*(P_2), S^*(P_2)]$ always have at least one common point. If each of these intervals has length less than ϵ, then $|S(P_1) - S(P_2)| < 2\epsilon$, since $S(P_1)$ always lies in the first interval and $S(P_2)$ in the second. Thus Theorem 1 yields the sufficiency of the condition. The necessity follows from the observation that the value of $S(P)$

may be made arbitrarily close to either $S^*(P)$ or $S_*(P)$ by a proper choice of the points z_j.

Still using the restriction that f is nondecreasing, we may obtain a measure function $m_f(i)$ defined for all subintervals i of $[a, b]$, as was indicated at the beginning of Chap. X. Then the processes of that chapter yield the f measure $m_f(E)$ and the Lebesgue-Stieltjes or LS-integral. Some further properties of that integral and its relations with the S-integral and the GS-integral will be developed in this chapter.

It is easily seen that, when f is a nondecreasing jump function having only a finite number of jumps, and ψ is single-valued and finite at the discontinuities c_j of f, then the Lebesgue-Stieltjes integral of ψ with respect to f exists and has the value $\sum_{j=1}^{n} \psi(c_j)$ $[f(c_j + 0) - f(c_j - 0)]$. This agrees with the value of the GS-integral when it exists.

Various further modifications of the integral of Stieltjes have been considered by a number of authors. The reader is referred to the papers of Hildebrandt ([4], [5]) which contain bibliographies.

Many of the following theorems contain three theorems, stated simultaneously for the S-integral, the GS-integral, and the LS-integral.

THEOREM 12. *Let f and g be nondecreasing functions, with $\Delta f \geqq \Delta g$ on every subinterval. If*

$$\int_a^b \psi \, df$$

exists as an S-, GS-, or LS-integral, then

$$\int_a^b \psi \, dg \tag{3:3}$$

also exists in the same sense, and when $\psi \geqq 0$, we have

$$\int_a^b \psi \, dg \leqq \int_a^b \psi \, df. \tag{3:4}$$

Proof for the GS-integral.—It is easily seen that $S^*(P; g)$ is finite whenever $S^*(P; f)$ is, with a corresponding relation for S_*, and that

$$S^*(P; g) - S_*(P; g) \leqq S^*(P; f) - S_*(P; f) \tag{3:5}$$

for every partition P. Hence the existence of (3:3) follows from the Corollary of Theorem 10. When $\psi \geqq 0$ we have $S^*(P; g) \leqq S^*(P; f)$, and from this inequality (3:4) follows.

Proof for the S-Integral.—This case follows immediately from Theorem 11 with the help of (3:5).

Proof for the LS-integral.—Suppose first that ψ is bounded, and let (α_n) be a bounded sequence of step functions converging to ψ except on a set E with $m_f(E) = 0$. Then $m_g(E) = 0$, and hence there exists

$$\int_a^b \psi \, dg = \lim_n \int_a^b \alpha_n \, dg.$$

When $\psi \geqq 0$, we may suppose $\alpha_n \geqq 0$, and so obtain the inequality (3:4). In case ψ is unbounded, suppose $\psi \geqq 0$, and let $\psi_n = \psi \wedge n$. Then

$$\int_a^b \psi_n \, dg \leqq \int_a^b \psi_n \, df \leqq \int_a^b \psi \, df,$$

and so the desired result follows from Theorem 12 of Chap. X.

As was indicated in Theorem 3, the S-integral and the GS-integral are bilinear operators. To obtain a similar result for the LS-integral, we need the following property:

LEMMA 1. *Suppose that g and h are nondecreasing functions and that ψ is LS-integrable with respect to g, and also with respect to h. Then ψ is LS-integrable with respect to $f = g + h$, and*

$$\int_a^b \psi \, df = \int_a^b \psi \, dg + \int_a^b \psi \, dh. \tag{3:6}$$

Proof.—Suppose first that ψ is bounded. By Lemma 3 of Chap. XI there exist functions μ^{-+} and ν^{-+} from the class $\mathfrak{M}^{-+}$ and μ^{+-} and ν^{+-} from the class $\mathfrak{M}^{+-}$ such that

$$\mu^{-+} \leqq \psi \leqq \mu^{+-}, \quad \nu^{-+} \leqq \psi \leqq \nu^{+-}, \tag{3:7}$$

$$\int_a^b \mu^{-+} \, dg = \int_a^b \psi \, dg = \int_a^b \mu^{+-} \, dg, \tag{3:8}$$

$$\int_a^b \nu^{-+} \, dh = \int_a^b \psi \, dh = \int_a^b \nu^{+-} \, dh. \tag{3:9}$$

Let $\lambda^{-+} = \mu^{-+} \vee \nu^{-+}$, $\lambda^{+-} = \mu^{+-} \wedge \nu^{+-}$. Then λ^{-+} is in $\mathfrak{M}^{-+}$, λ^{+-} is in $\mathfrak{M}^{+-}$, and hence each is measurable with respect to f. Also λ^{-+} may be substituted for μ^{-+} and ν^{-+}, and λ^{+-} may be substituted for μ^{+-} and ν^{+-} in (3:7) to (3:9). Since (3:6) holds for step functions, it holds for all functions in $\mathfrak{M}^{-+}$ and $\mathfrak{M}^{+-}$. Hence by the converse part of the lemma just quoted, ψ is measurable with respect to f and (3:6) holds. In case ψ is unbounded, we may suppose $\psi \geqq 0$, and let $\psi_n = \psi \wedge n$. Then, by the result already proved for the bounded case,

$$\int_a^b \psi_n \, df = \int_a^b \psi_n \, dg + \int_a^b \psi_n \, dh.$$

Theorem 12 of Chap. X then shows that ψ is integrable with respect to f, and (3:6) continues to hold.

We extend the definition of $(LS)\int \psi \, df$ to the case when f is a function of bounded variation but not monotonic by means of a minimum decomposition $f(x) = p(x) - n(x)$, where p and n are nondecreasing. We define

$$(3:10) \qquad (LS) \int_a^b \psi \, df = (LS) \int_a^b \psi \, dp - (LS) \int_a^b \psi \, dn,$$

when both integrals on the right exist.

When $g_1(x)$ and $g_2(x)$ are nondecreasing and $f(x) = g_1(x) - g_2(x)$, then

$$\int_a^b \psi \, df = \int_a^b \psi \, dg_1 - \int_a^b \psi \, dg_2,$$

whenever the integrals on the right exist. For, we always have $\Delta g_1 \geqq \Delta p$, $\Delta g_2 \geqq \Delta n$, as was shown at the beginning of Sec. 2. Hence the integrals on the right of (3:10) exist, by Theorem 12. Then by the lemma just proved,

$$\int_a^b \psi \, dp + \int_a^b \psi \, dg_2 = \int_a^b \psi \, dn + \int_a^b \psi \, dg_1.$$

It is now easy to verify the following result:

THEOREM 13. *The LS-integral* $\int \psi \, df$ *is a bilinear operator.*

The next theorem will justify our restricting attention to nondecreasing functions f in certain later proofs.

THEOREM 14. *Let* $\psi(x)$ *be bounded and* $f(x)$ *be of bounded variation, and let* $t(x)$, $p(x)$, *and* $n(x)$ *be, respectively, the total, positive, and negative variations of* f. *Then a necessary and sufficient condition that* $\int_a^b \psi \, df$ *exist as an S-integral, GS-integral, or LS-integral is that* $\int_a^b \psi \, dt$ *exist in the same sense. A second necessary and sufficient condition is that* $\int_a^b \psi \, dp$ *and* $\int_a^b \psi \, dn$

exist in the same sense. The condition that ψ *be bounded is to be omitted in the case of the LS-integral.*

Proof.—For the case of the *LS*-integral, the statement follows directly from the definition and Theorems 13 and 12. To prove the necessity of the first condition in the case of the *GS*-integral, we note that for an arbitrary $\epsilon > 0$, there is a partition P such that we have simultaneously $\left|\int_a^b \psi\, df - S(P;\, f)\right| \leqq \epsilon$, and $t(b) - \sum_j |f(x_{j+1}) - f(x_j)| \leqq \epsilon$. From the first of these inequalities we find that $\sum_j (U_j - L_j)|f(x_{j+1}) - f(x_j)| \leqq 2\epsilon$, where U_j and L_j have the meanings indicated at the beginning of this section. If $|\psi(x)| \leqq M$ on $[a, b]$,

$$\sum_j (U_j - L_j)[t(x_{j+1}) - t(x_j) - |f(x_{j+1}) - f(x_j)|]$$
$$\leqq 2M[t(b) - \sum |f(x_{j+1}) - f(x_j)|] \leqq 2\mathrm{M}\epsilon.$$

Hence $\sum_j (U_j - L_j)[t(x_{j+1}) - t(x_j)] \leqq 2(M + 1)\epsilon$. Thus by Theorem 10, ψ is *GS*-integrable with respect to t. The necessity of the second condition follows from Theorem 12. The sufficiency of the conditions then follows from the linearity of the integral. To prove the conditions for the *S*-integral, we recall that $f(x)$ and $t(x)$ have the same discontinuities. Since ψ was assumed to be bounded, Theorems 6 and 7 are applicable to obtain the desired result.

THEOREM 15. *Suppose that* $f(x)$ *is a function of bounded variation and that* $\psi_1(x)$ *and* $\psi_2(x)$ *are bounded and S-, GS-, or LS-integrable with respect to* f. *Then the functions* $\psi_3 = \psi_1 \vee \psi_2$, $\psi_4 = \psi_1 \wedge \psi_2$ *and* $|\psi_1|$ *are integrable with respect to* f *in the same sense. The condition that* ψ_1 *and* ψ_2 *are bounded is to be omitted in the case of the LS-integral and, when* f *is monotonic, also in the case of the S- and GS-integrals.*

Proof.—By the last theorem, we may restrict attention to the case when f is nondecreasing. For the *LS*-integral, the result was obtained in Theorem 8 of Chap. X. For the *S*- and *GS*-integrals we may apply Theorem 11 and the Corollary of Theorem 10, respectively. For the oscillation of ψ_3 on a given interval is not greater than the sum of the oscillations of ψ_1 and ψ_2, and hence

$$S^*(P;\psi_3) - S_*(P;\psi_3) \leqq S^*(P;\psi_1) - S_*(P;\psi_1) + S^*(P;\psi_2) - S_*(P;\psi_2).$$

A corresponding inequality holds also for ψ_4. Since $|\psi| = \psi \vee (-\psi)$, the result for $|\psi_1|$ follows from the linearity of the integrals.

THEOREM 16. *Suppose that the functions f and h satisfy the inequality $|\Delta f| \leqq \Delta h$ on every subinterval, where h is a nondecreasing bounded function. If $\int_a^b \psi\, dh$ exists as an S-, GS-, or LS-integral, then $\int_a^b \psi\, df$ exists in the same sense, and*

$$\left|\int_a^b \psi\, df\right| \leqq \int_a^b |\psi|\, dh. \tag{3:11}$$

Proof.—If $t(x)$ is the total variation function of f, we have $\Delta t \leqq \Delta h$, so that the existence of $\int_a^b \psi\, df$ follows from Theorem 12 and the linearity of the integral.

To obtain the inequality (3:11), let $p(x)$ and $n(x)$ denote, respectively, the positive and the negative variations of f, and let $\psi_1 = \psi \vee 0$, $\psi_2 = -(\psi \wedge 0)$. Then

$$\left|\int_a^b \psi\, df\right| \leqq \int_a^b \psi_1\, dp + \int_a^b \psi_2\, dp + \int_a^b \psi_1\, dn + \int_a^b \psi_2\, dn = \int_a^b |\psi|\, dt \leqq \int_a^b |\psi|\, dh,$$

by the bilinearity of the integral and inequality (3:4).

COROLLARY. *Suppose $f(x)$ is of bounded variation, $\psi(x)$ is S-, GS-, or LS-integrable with respect to f, and $|\psi(x)| \leqq M$.* Then

$$\left|\int_a^b \psi\, df\right| \leqq Mt(b),$$

where $t(b)$ is the total variation of $f(x)$ on $[a, b]$.

THEOREM 17. *Suppose that each function $g_n(x)$ is nondecreasing and that the series $\sum g_n(a)$ and $\sum g_n(b)$ converge. Then the series $\sum g_n(x)$ converges uniformly on $[a, b]$ and defines a nondecreasing function $f(x)$. Necessary conditions for the existence of $\int_a^b \psi\, df$ as an S-, GS-, or LS-integral are*

(i) *All the integrals* $\int_a^b \psi\, dg_n$ *exist in the same sense;*

(ii) *The series* $\sum \int_a^b |\psi|\, dg_n$ *converges;*

and then we have

$$\int_a^b \psi\, df = \sum \int_a^b \psi\, dg_n. \tag{3:12}$$

For the LS-integral, these conditions are also sufficient. For the S- and GS-integrals a set of sufficient conditions is obtained by replacing (ii) *by the stronger condition that* ψ *is bounded.*

Proof.—The uniform convergence of $\sum g_n(x)$ follows from the inequality

$$g_n(x) - g_n(a) \leqq g_n(b) - g_n(a).$$

The necessity of the conditions follows from Theorems 12 and 15 and the relations

$$\int_a^b |\psi|\, df \geqq \int_a^b |\psi|\, d\left(\sum_{n=1}^{q} g_n\right) = \sum_{n=1}^{q} \int_a^b |\psi|\, dg_n. \tag{3:13}$$

In the case when ψ is bounded, the equation (3:12) follows from the Corollary of Theorem 16, with f replaced by $\left(f - \sum_1^q g_n\right)$. When ψ is unbounded, we may suppose $\psi \geqq 0$, and set $\psi_k = \psi \wedge k$. Then

$$\int_a^b \psi_k\, df = \sum_{n=1}^{\infty} \int_a^b \psi_k\, dg_n \leqq \sum_{n=1}^{\infty} \int_a^b \psi\, dg_n. \tag{3:14}$$

But by Theorem 2 for the S- and GS-integrals, and by Theorem 12 of Chap. X for the LS-integral,

$$\int_a^b \psi\, df = \lim_{k=\infty} \int_a^b \psi_k\, df,$$

so that

$$\int_a^b \psi\, df \leqq \sum_{n=1}^{\infty} \int_a^b \psi\, dg_n.$$

But this with (3:13) above yields the desired result.

Proof of Sufficiency for the S- and GS-integrals.—If $L \leqq \psi \leqq U$ and $\epsilon > 0$, we may choose an integer q such that

$$(U - L) \sum_{n=q+1}^{\infty} [g_n(b) - g_n(a)] < \epsilon,$$

and hence

$$\sum_{n=q+1}^{\infty} [S^*(P; g_n) - S_*(P; g_n)] < \epsilon$$

for every partition P. But

$$S^*(P; f) - S_*(P; f) = \sum_{n=1}^{q} [S^*(P; g_n) - S_*(P; g_n)] + \sum_{n=q+1}^{\infty} [S^*(P; g_n) - S_*(P; g_n)].$$

The desired result now follows by application of Theorem 11 for the S-integral, and of the Corollary of Theorem 10 for the GS-integral.

Proof of Sufficiency for the LS-integral.—We take first the case when ψ is bounded. Then by Lemma 3 of Chap. XI there exist functions μ_n from the class $\mathfrak{M}^{-+}$ and ν_n from the class $\mathfrak{M}^{+-}$, having the same bounds as ψ, such that

$$(3{:}15) \quad \mu_n \leqq \psi \leqq \nu_n, \qquad \int_a^b \mu_n \, dg_n = \int_a^b \psi \, dg_n = \int_a^b \nu_n \, dg_n.$$

Let $\mu(x) = \text{l.u.b. } \mu_n(x)$, $\nu(x) = \text{g.l.b. } \nu_n(x)$. Then μ and ν are Borel-measurable and

$$(3{:}16) \qquad \mu_n \leqq \mu \leqq \psi \leqq \nu \leqq \nu_n,$$

and so

$$(3{:}17) \qquad \int \mu \, dg_n = \int \psi \, dg_n = \int \nu \, dg_n.$$

By the first part of the theorem, since μ and ν are LS-integrable with respect to f,

$$\int_a^b \mu \, df = \sum_{n=1}^{\infty} \int_a^b \mu \, dg_n = \sum_{n=1}^{\infty} \int_a^b \psi \, dg_n,$$

$$\int_a^b \nu \, df = \sum_{n=1}^{\infty} \int_a^b \nu \, dg_n = \sum_{n=1}^{\infty} \int_a^b \psi \, dg_n,$$

and hence by Lemma 1 of Chap. XI, $\mu = \nu = \psi$ almost everywhere with respect to f, and so ψ is LS-integrable with respect to f. When ψ is unbounded, we may suppose $\psi \geqq 0$. Then the inequality (3:14) with Theorem 12 of Chap. X shows that ψ is LS-integrable with respect to f.

COROLLARY. *Let $f(x)$ be of bounded variation and let $j(x)$ be its jump function, defined by formula* (2:2). *Then* $\int_a^b \psi\, dj$ *exists* (i) *as an LS-integral when the series* $\sum \psi(c)[f(c+0) - f(c)]$ *and* $\sum \psi(c)[f(c) - f(c-0)]$ *are both absolutely convergent;* (ii) *as a GS-integral when ψ is bounded and ψ and f have no common discontinuities on the same side;* (iii) *as an S-integral when ψ is bounded and ψ and f have no common discontinuities. In each case*

$$\int_a^b \psi\, dj = \sum \psi(c)[f(c+0) - f(c-0)].$$

We can now obtain necessary and sufficient conditions for the existence of $\int_a^b \psi\, df$ as an S-integral or as a GS-integral, under the assumption that ψ is bounded and f is of bounded variation. Let D denote the set of discontinuities of ψ, $t(x)$ the total variation of $f(x)$, and $\tau(x)$ the total variation of $g(x) = f(x) - j(x)$, where $j(x)$ is the jump function of $f(x)$. Let m_t and m_τ denote the measures associated with the nondecreasing functions $t(x)$ and $\tau(x)$, respectively, by the processes of Chap. X.

THEOREM 18. *Suppose that ψ is bounded and f is of bounded variation. Then* $\int_a^b \psi\, df$ *exists* (i) *as an S-integral if and only if* $m_t(D) = 0$; (ii) *as a GS-integral if and only if* $m_\tau(D) = 0$ *and ψ and f have no common discontinuities on the same side.*

Proof.—By Theorems 4 and 5 and the Corollary of Theorem 17, the existence of $\int_a^b \psi\, df$ in either sense implies the existence of $\int_a^b \psi\, dj$ in the same sense, and consequently that of $\int_a^b \psi\, dg$. Also if $\tau_1(x)$ denotes the total variation of $j(x)$, $t = \tau + \tau_1$, $m_t = m_\tau + m_{\tau_1}$, and hence $m_t(D) = 0$ implies the existence of $(S) \int_a^b \psi\, dj$. Thus it is sufficient to consider the case when $f(x)$ is continuous, and then the distinction between the S-integral and the GS-integral disappears, by Theorems 6 and 7. By Theorem 14 we may further restrict $f(x)$ to be nondecreasing.

Now let (P_n) be a sequence of partitions, each obtained from the preceding by further subdivision, and set

$$\omega_n(x) = 0 \text{ if } x \text{ is a partition point of } P_n,$$
$$\omega_n(x) = \text{oscillation of } \psi \text{ on the interval of } P_n \text{ containing } x, \text{ for all other values of } x.$$

Then the sequence of step functions ω_n is nonincreasing and bounded, and hence $\lambda(x) = \lim \omega_n(x)$ is nonnegative and LS-integrable with respect to f, and $\int_a^b \lambda\, df = \lim_n \int_a^b \omega_n\, df$. But $\int_a^b \omega_n\, df = S^*(P_n) - S_*(P_n)$, and it follows with the help of the Corollary of Theorem 10 that ψ is GS-integrable with respect to f if and only if there is a sequence (P_n) such that $\lim_n \int_a^b \omega_n\, df = 0$. By Lemma 1 of Chap. XI the last statement holds if and only if $\lambda = 0$ almost everywhere with respect to f. Since the set of all the partition points of the P_n forms a denumerable set, it may be neglected, so that $\lambda = 0$ almost everywhere with respect to f if and only if $m_f(D) = 0$.

THEOREM 19. *Suppose that f is of bounded variation, and ψ is S- or GS-integrable with respect to f. Then ψ is also LS-integrable, and the integrals have the same value.*

Proof.—The bounded function ψ_k of Theorem 2 in Sec. 1 is equal to ψ almost everywhere with respect to the total variation function $t(x)$ of f, so that we may suppose ψ is bounded. As in the proof of Theorem 18 we may also restrict attention to the case when f is continuous and nondecreasing, and then the proof is the same as that given for Theorem 14 of Chap. X.

We shall close this section with some theorems relating to change of integrator. If $\theta(x)$ is LS-integrable with respect to $h(x)$, we note that $g(x) = \int_a^x \theta\, dh$ may fail to be well-defined at points of discontinuity of $h(x)$. For convenience in what follows we define $g(x)$ at every such point c so that

$$[g(c) - g(c - 0)][h(c + 0) - h(c)] = [g(c + 0) - g(c)][h(c) - h(c - 0)].$$

LEMMA 2. *Let $h(x)$ be nondecreasing, and let $\theta(x)$ be nonnegative and LS-integrable with respect to h. Let $g(x) = \int_a^x \theta\, dh$.*

Then, if $m_h(E) = 0$, *also* $m_g(E) = 0$. *If* $m_g(E) = 0$, *then* $\theta(x) = 0$ *almost everywhere with respect to* h *on* E.

Proof.—If C is a sum of intervals, we note that $m_g(C) = \int_C \theta\, dh$. Since $\int \theta\, dh$ is absolutely continuous with respect to h, for each $\epsilon > 0$ there is a $\delta > 0$ such that $m_g(C) < \epsilon$ whenever $m_h(C) < \delta$. From this the first part of the Lemma follows at once. Similarly we find that when $m_g(E) = 0$, $\int_E \theta\, dh = 0$, and so the last part follows from Lemma 1 of Chap. XI.

THEOREM 20. *Let* $f(x)$, $h(x)$, *and* $k(x)$ *be nondecreasing, and let* $\theta(x)$ *be nonnegative and LS-integrable with respect to* h. *Suppose that* ψ *is LS-integrable with respect to* f *and that* $f(x) = \int_a^x \theta\, dh + k(x)$. *Then* $\psi\theta$ *is LS-integrable with respect to* h, *and*

$$\int_a^b \psi\, df = \int_a^b \psi\theta\, dh + \int_a^b \psi\, dk.$$

Proof.—Let $g(x) = \int_a^x \theta\, dh$. By Theorem 12, ψ is integrable with respect to g and to k. If (α_n) is a sequence of step functions converging to ψ almost everywhere with respect to g, we have $\lim_n \alpha_n\theta = \psi\theta$ almost everywhere with respect to h, by Lemma 2. Since $\int_a^b \alpha\, dg = \int_a^b \alpha\theta\, dh$ for every step function α, we have $\int_a^b \psi\, dg = \int_a^b \psi\theta\, dh$ when ψ is bounded, by Theorems 11 and 7 of Chap. X. The formula is extended to the unbounded case by the usual device, using Theorem 12 of Chap. X.

COROLLARY. *If* $f(x)$ *is absolutely continuous, and* $\psi(x)$ *is LS-integrable with respect to* f, *then* $\psi(x)f'(x)$ *is L-integrable, and*

$$\int_a^b \psi\, df = \int_a^b \psi f'\, dx.$$

Here we use the term "*L*-integrable" in place of "*LS*-integrable with respect to x."

We have already noted in the Corollary of Theorem 17 that $\int \psi\, df$ reduces to an infinite series when f is a jump function.

THEOREM 21. *Let* $h(x)$ *be nondecreasing, let* $\theta(x)$ *be LS-integrable with respect to* h, *and let* $f(x) = \int_a^x \theta\, dh$. *Suppose that* $\psi(x)$ *is S-, GS-, or LS-integrable with respect to* h, *and that either* ψ *or* θ *is bounded. Then* ψ *is integrable in the same sense with respect to* f, *provided* f *is properly defined at the discontinuities of* h.

Proof.—When θ is bounded, this follows from Theorem 16. For the remaining case, we may suppose $\theta \geqq 0$ and, if necessary, we may decompose h into its continuous part and its jump function. For the S- and GS-integrals, the result follows from Theorem 18 and Lemma 2. With the help of Lemma 2 the proof for the LS-integral is like the corresponding part of the proof of Theorem 12.

An important special case of Theorem 21 occurs when $h(x) = x$ and $f(x)$ is absolutely continuous. The example $\psi(x) = \theta(x) = x^{-1/2}$ shows that we cannot allow both ψ and θ to be unbounded without some other restriction. However, it is easily seen that, whenever ψ is measurable with respect to h, it is measurable with respect to the total variation of f.

4. Convergence Theorems.—In this section we shall consider various sets of conditions justifying interchange of order of integral and limit, as well as some examples in which such an interchange is not valid. By Theorem 13 of Chap. IV, it is sufficient to consider the case of sequences of functions.

Since in many cases the variable x will not need to be written, we may conveniently use the notation $t(f)$ for the total variation function $t(x)$ of $f(x)$.

Following are the conditions from which the hypotheses of Theorems 22 to 28 will be selected:

A_1. The functions $g_k(x)$ and $f(x)$ are of bounded variation.

A_2. The functions $g_k(x)$ and $f(x)$ are of *uniformly* bounded variation.

A_3. There is a nondecreasing function $h(x)$ such that $g_k(x)$ and $f(x)$ satisfy the inequalities $|\Delta g_k| \leqq \Delta h$, $|\Delta f| \leqq \Delta h$ on every subinterval of $[a, b]$.

A_4. The functions $g_k(x)$ and $f(x)$ are absolutely continuous uniformly in k.

B_1. There is a set E dense on $[a, b]$ and including the points a and b, such that $\lim_k g_k(x) = f(x)$ on E.

B_2. $\lim_k t(g_k - f) = 0$.

B_3. $g_k = f$ for each k.

C_1. The functions $\psi_n(x)$ are S-, GS-, or LS-integrable with respect to each function $g_k(x)$.

C_2. The functions $\psi_n(x)$ are S-, GS-, or LS-integrable with respect to $h(x)$.

C_3. The integrals $\int \psi_n\, dh$ are absolutely continuous with respect to h uniformly in n, and bounded uniformly.

C_4. The functions $\psi_n(x)$ and $\theta(x)$ are bounded with respect to x and n.

C_5. The functions $\psi_n(x)$ and $\theta(x)$ are continuous on $[a, b]$.

D_1. $\lim_n \psi_n = \theta$ almost everywhere with respect to each function $t(g_k)$.

D_2. $\lim_n \psi_n = \theta$ almost everywhere with respect to h.

D_3. $\lim_n \psi_n = \theta$ uniformly on $[a, b]$.

D_4. $\psi_n = \theta$ for each n.

We are interested in the validity of the formula

$$\lim_{\substack{n=\infty \\ k=\infty}} \int_a^b \psi_n\, dg_k = \int_a^b \theta\, df, \tag{4:1}$$

where the integrals exist in a suitable one of the three senses which we are considering. When either B_3 or D_4 holds, the double sequence reduces to a simple sequence. Theorems for these cases are needed as preliminaries to the treatment of the double sequence. Theorem 22 is sometimes known as the Helly-Bray theorem.

THEOREM 22. A_2, B_1, C_5, D_4 *imply* (4:1), *where the integrals are S-integrals.*

Proof.—If P is a partition of $[a, b]$ into intervals $[x_{j-1}, x_j]$, let $\omega(P)$ denote the maximum oscillation of θ on an interval of P. Since θ is uniformly continuous, $\lim_{N(P)=0} \omega(P) = 0$. Let

$$S(P; \theta, g_k) = \sum_j \theta(z_j)[g_k(x_j) - g_k(x_{j-1})].$$

Then

$$\left|S(P; \theta, g_k) - \int_a^b \theta\, dg_k\right| = \left|\sum_j \int_{x_{j-1}}^{x_j} [\theta(z_j) - \theta(x)]\, dg_k\right| \leqq \omega(P)t(g_k), \tag{4:2}$$

by the Corollary of Theorem 16.

Hence $\lim_{N(P)=0} S(P; \theta, g_k) = \int_a^b \theta\, dg_k$ uniformly with respect to k. When the partition points of P are required to belong to the set E, we have $\lim_{k=\infty} S(P; \theta, g_k) = S(P; \theta, f)$, provided the same points

z_j are used in all the sums corresponding to a given partition P. Since the integrals are known to exist, we may restrict attention to a particular sequence of partitions and corresponding points z_j. Hence the desired conclusion follows from Theorem 2 of Chap. VII.

THEOREM 23. A_2, B_1, C_5, D_3 *imply* (4:1), *where the integrals are S-integrals.*

Proof.—By the Corollary of Theorem 16, $\lim_n \int_a^b \psi_n \, dg_k = \int_a^b \theta \, dg_k$ uniformly with respect to k. From this and Theorem 22 the desired result follows at once.

This theorem could also be proved directly from the inequality analogous to (4:2) for the sums $S(P; \psi_n, g_k)$, since the functions ψ_n are equicontinuous by Theorem 24 of Chap. VII, Sec. 4.

THEOREM 24. *The function θ is S-, GS-, or LS-integrable with respect to f, and* (4:1) *holds, if* A_1, B_3, C_1, C_4, D_3 *hold.*

Proof.—For the case of the LS-integral, this was proved in Chap. X. For the other cases, we note that every discontinuity of θ is a discontinuity of some ψ_n on the same side. Then Theorem 18 shows that θ is integrable in the proper sense, and (4:1) follows from the Corollary of Theorem 16.

THEOREM 25. *The function θ is S-, GS-, or LS-integrable with respect to f, and* (4:1) *holds, if* A_1, B_2, C_1, C_4, D_4 *hold.*

Proof.—The equality (4:1) follows from the Corollary of Theorem 16 whenever it is known that $\int \theta \, df$ exists. To prove the existence in case of the S-integral, let D denote the set of discontinuities of θ. Then by Theorem 18, the measure of D with respect to the total variation of g_k is zero. The total variation of $(f - g_k)$ over an arbitrary sum of nonoverlapping intervals is not greater than $t(f - g_k)$ over $[a, b]$, and so approaches zero with $1/k$. Since $t(f) \leqq t(f - g_k) + t(g_k)$ over every interval, the total variation of f over the set D must also be zero, so that $(S)\int \theta \, df$ must exist, by another application of Theorem 18.

To prove the existence in case of the GS-integral, let j_k and j_f denote the jump functions of g_k and of f, respectively, and let $h_k = g_k - j_k$, $h_f = f - j_f$. Then by the results of Sec. 2, $t(f - g_k) = t(h_f - h_k) + t(j_f - j_k)$, so that $\lim_{k=\infty} t(h_f - h_k) = 0$. By the proof in the last paragraph, $\int \theta \, dh_f$ exists. Every discontinuity of f is a discontinuity of some g_k on the same side, since $g_k(x) - g_k(a)$ approaches $f(x) - f(a)$ uniformly on $[a, b]$. Hence θ and f have no common discontinuity on the same side, so that $(GS)\int \theta\, df$ exists, again by Theorem 18.

When θ is bounded and Borel-measurable and f is of bounded variation, $(LS)\int \theta\, df$ always exists. When θ is not Borel-measurable but is LS-integrable with respect to each g_k, we may show that it is LS-integrable with respect to f, as follows. By Lemma 3 of Chap. XI, there are for each k, Borel-measurable functions μ_k and ν_k such that

$$(4{:}3) \qquad \mu_k \leqq \theta \leqq \nu_k,$$

$$(4{:}4) \qquad \int_a^b \mu_k\, dt(g_k) = \int_a^b \theta\, dt(g_k) = \int_a^b \nu_k\, dt(g_k).$$

Then $\mu = \text{l.u.b. } \mu_k$ and $\nu = \text{g.l.b. } \nu_k$ are Borel-measurable and also satisfy conditions analogous to (4:3) and (4:4). By (2:3), $\lim\limits_{k=\infty} t[t(f) - t(g_k)] = 0$, and so, by (4:1) for the case of Borel-measurable functions,

$$\int_a^b \mu\, dt(f) = \int_a^b \nu\, dt(f).$$

Since $\mu \leqq \nu$, we have $\mu = \nu$ almost everywhere with respect to $t(f)$ by Lemma 1 of Chap. XI. Thus $\mu = \theta$ almost everywhere with respect to $t(f)$, and thus θ is LS-integrable with respect to $t(f)$, and so also with respect to f, by Theorem 12.

THEOREM 26. *The function θ is LS-integrable with respect to f, and* (4:1) *holds, if* A_1, B_2, C_1, C_4, D_1 *hold.*

Proof.—By Theorem 4 of Chap. X, θ is LS-integrable with respect to each g_k, and $\lim\limits_n \int \psi_n\, dg_k = \int \theta\, dg_k$. The functions ψ_n and θ are LS-integrable with respect to f, by Theorem 25, and by the Corollary of Theorem 16, $\lim\limits_k \int \psi_n\, dg_k = \int \psi_n\, df$ uniformly in n, and $\lim\limits_k \int \theta\, dg_k = \int \theta\, df$. Then (4:1) follows from Theorem 2 of Chap. VII.

LEMMA 3. *Suppose that* A_3, B_1 *hold. Then* A_2 *holds, and* $\lim\limits_{k=\infty} g_k(x + 0) = f(x + 0)$, $\lim\limits_{k=\infty} g_k(x - 0) = f(x - 0)$ *for every x on* $[a, b]$.

Proof.—Since $|\Delta g_k| \leqq \Delta h$ on every subinterval, and h has a right-hand limit at each point, it follows from Theorem 1 of Chap. VII that $\lim\limits_{s=0+} g_k(x + s) = g_k(x + 0)$ uniformly with respect to k. Since the one-sided limits $g_k(x+0)$, $f(x+0)$ are known to exist, they may be evaluated by restricting $x+s$ to lie in the set E and, since $\lim_{k=\infty} g_k(x+s) = f(x+s)$ for $x+s$ in E, we may apply Theorem 2 of Chap. VII to obtain the desired conclusion.

THEOREM 27. *If* A_3, B_1, C_2, C_3, D_2 *hold, then* ψ_n *and* θ *are LS-integrable with respect to* f *and to each* g_k, *and* (4:1) *holds.*

Proof.—By Theorem 7 of Chap. X, θ is LS-integrable with respect to h, and hence ψ_n and θ are LS-integrable with respect to f and to each g_k, and

$$\left|\int_a^b (\psi_n - \theta)\, dg_k\right| \leqq \int_a^b |\psi_n - \theta|\, dh,$$
$$\left|\int_a^b (\psi_n - \theta)\, df\right| \leqq \int_a^b |\psi_n - \theta|\, dh,$$

by Theorem 16. Thus $\lim_n \int_a^b \psi_n\, dg_k = \int_a^b \theta\, dg_k$ uniformly with respect to k. We shall next show that

$$\lim_k \int_a^b \psi\, dg_k = \int_a^b \psi\, df \tag{4:5}$$

for every function ψ which is LS-integrable with respect to h, and then (4:1) will follow from Theorem 2 of Chap. VII. By definition of the integral, there is a sequence (α_n) of step functions such that C_3 and D_2 hold with ψ_n replaced by α_n and θ replaced by ψ, and hence $\lim_n \int_a^b \alpha_n\, dg_k = \int_a^b \psi\, dg_k$ uniformly with respect to k, by the first part of the proof. But from Lemma 3 it follows that $\lim_k \int_a^b \alpha_n\, dg_k = \int_a^b \alpha_n\, df$, and thus (4:5) follows from Theorem 2 of Chap. VII.

Attention is called to the special case when the functions f and g_k satisfy a uniform Lipschitz condition. Then the function $h(x)$ in A_3 may be taken to be a constant multiple of x, and the conditions C_2, C_3, D_2 may be expressed in terms of ordinary Lebesgue integrals and measure.

THEOREM 28. *If* A_4, B_1, C_2, C_4, D_2 *hold with* $h(x) = x$, *then* ψ_n *and* θ *are LS-integrable with respect to* f *and to each* g_k, *and* (4:1) *holds.*

Proof.—By C_2, C_4, D_2, and Theorem 4 of Chap. X, θ is L-integrable, and by A_4 and Theorem 21, ψ_n and θ are LS-integrable with respect to each g_k and to f. Also

$$\int_a^b \psi_n \, dg_k = \int_a^b \psi_n g_k' \, dx, \quad \int_a^b \theta \, dg_k = \int_a^b \theta g_k' \, dx,$$

by the Corollary of Theorem 20. By A_4 and Theorems 28 and 20 of Chap. X, corresponding to an arbitrary $\epsilon > 0$, there is a $\delta > 0$ such that

$$\int_E |g_k'| \, dx < \epsilon, \qquad \int_E |f'| \, dx < \epsilon,$$

whenever $m(E) < \delta$. From this it follows readily that there is a constant Q such that $t(g_k) = \int_a^b |g_k'| \, dx \leqq Q$. By D_2 and Theorem 18 of Chap. XI, $\lim_n m(E_{n\epsilon}) = 0$ for every ϵ, where $E_{n\epsilon} = E[|\psi_n - \theta| > \epsilon]$. Let M be a bound for $|\psi_n(x)|$ and $|\theta(x)|$. Then

$$\left| \int_a^b (\psi_n - \theta) \, dg_k \right| \leqq 2M \int_{E_{n\epsilon}} |g_k'| \, dx + \epsilon \int_a^b |g_k'| \, dx \leqq (2M + Q)\epsilon$$

whenever n is sufficiently large, so that $\lim_n \int_a^b \psi_n \, dg_k = \int_a^b \theta \, dg_k$ uniformly in k. The remainder of the proof parallels that for Theorem 27.

The following examples illustrate the essential role of various hypotheses in the preceding theorems:

1. Let $\psi_n(x) = 0$ for $0 \leqq x \leqq 1/n$, $3/n \leqq x \leqq 4$, $\psi_n(x) = 1$ for $x = 2/n$, and let ψ_n be linear on the two remaining intervals. Let $g_k(x) = 0$ for $0 \leqq x \leqq 2/k$, $g_k(x) = 1$ for $2/k < x \leqq 4$. Then all the hypotheses of Theorem 23 are satisfied except D_3.

2. Let $\psi_n(x) = x^{1/2} \sin(\pi/x)$ for $1/q_n \leqq x \leqq 1/n$, $\psi_n(x) = 0$ for all other values of x. Let $f(x) = x^{1/2} \cos(\pi/x)$. Then $(S) \int_0^1 \psi_n \, df$ exists, the functions ψ_n are continuous and converge uniformly to zero but, if the sequence of integers q_n increases sufficiently rapidly, the sequence $\int_0^1 \psi_n \, df$ diverges. By setting $\theta(x) = f(x)$, $g_k(x) = \psi_k(x)$, we obtain an example where all the hypotheses of Theorem 22 are satisfied except A_2.

3. Let $\theta(x) = \cos(\pi/x)$, and let $g_k(x) = x \sin(\pi/x)$ for $1/q_k \leqq x \leqq 1/k$, $g_k(x) = 0$ for all other values of x. The sequence of integers q_k may be so chosen that

$$1 < \sum_{m=k+2}^{q_k+1} \frac{1}{m} < 2.$$

Then the sequence $\int_0^1 \theta\, dg_k$ does not approach zero, but all the hypotheses of Theorem 22 are satisfied except that θ is discontinuous at one point, and all the hypotheses of Theorem 25 are satisfied except B_2.

4. Let $\theta(x) = 1/x$ for $0 < x \leqq 1$, $\theta(0) = 0$. Let $g_k(x) = x^{1/k} f(x)$, where $f(x) = x$. Then $\int_0^1 \theta\, dg_k = k + 1$, and $\int_0^1 \theta\, df$ does not exist. All the hypotheses of Theorem 25 are satisfied except C_4, and all the hypotheses of Theorem 27 are satisfied except that no function h can satisfy A_3 and C_2 simultaneously.

5. Let $\theta(x) = 1/x$ for $0 < x \leqq 1$, $\theta(0) = 0$. Let $g_k(x) = 0$ for $0 \leqq x \leqq \frac{1}{2}^k$, $g_k(x) = x - \frac{1}{2}^k$ for $\frac{1}{2}^k \leqq x \leqq \frac{1}{2}^{k-1}$, $g_k(x) = \frac{1}{2}^k$ for $\frac{1}{2}^{k-1} \leqq x \leqq 1$. This example has properties similar to the preceding, except that $\int_0^1 \theta\, dg_k = \ln 2$, $\int_0^1 \theta\, df = 0$.

6. Let $\theta(x) = 1/x$ for $0 < x \leqq 1$, $\theta(0) = 0$. Let $g_k(x) = 0$ for $0 \leqq x < 1/k$, $g_k(x) = 1/k$ for $1/k \leqq x \leqq 1$. This example has properties similar to those for Example 5, except that now A_3 cannot be satisfied.

Some theorems involving uniformity of convergence with respect to a parameter may be obtained from the preceding theorems by means of an indirect proof. Theorem 29 is an extension of Theorem 23, Theorem 30 of Theorem 27, and Theorem 31 of Theorem 28. We shall be concerned with families of functions $g_{k\sigma}(x)$, $f_\sigma(x)$, $\psi_{n\sigma}(x)$, $\theta_\sigma(x)$, and the hypotheses will be chosen from among the following:

$A_{2\sigma}$. The functions $g_{k\sigma}$ and f_σ are of uniformly bounded variation.

$A_{3\sigma}$. There is a nondecreasing function $h(x)$ such that $|\Delta g_{k\sigma}| \leqq \Delta h$, $|\Delta f_\sigma| \leqq \Delta h$ for every subinterval of $[a, b]$ and every k and σ.

$A_{4\sigma}$. The functions $g_{k\sigma}(x)$ and $f_\sigma(x)$ are absolutely continuous uniformly in k and σ.

$B_{1\sigma}$. There is a set E, independent of σ, dense on $[a, b]$ and including the points a and b, such that $\lim_k g_{k\sigma}(x) = f_\sigma(x)$ for x on E, uniformly in σ.

$C_{2\sigma}$. The functions $\psi_{n\sigma}(x)$ are LS-integrable with respect to $h(x)$.

$C_{3\sigma}$. The integrals $\int \psi_{n\sigma}\,dh$ are absolutely continuous with respect to h uniformly in n and σ.

$C_{4\sigma}$. The functions $\psi_{n\sigma}(x)$ and $\theta(x)$ are bounded with respect to x, n, and σ, and θ is independent of σ.

$C_{5\sigma}$. The functions $\psi_{n\sigma}(x)$ and $\theta_\sigma(x)$ are continuous on $[a, b]$ uniformly with respect to σ.

$D_{2\sigma}$. There is a set E_1 independent of σ such that $m_h(E_1) = h(b) - h(a)$ and for x on E_1, $\lim\limits_n \psi_{n\sigma}(x) = \theta(x)$ uniformly with respect to σ, where θ is independent of σ.

$D_{3\sigma}$. $\lim\limits_n \psi_{n\sigma}(x) = \theta_\sigma(x)$ uniformly with respect to x and σ.

The conclusion in each of the next three theorems will be the validity of the statement:

$$\text{(4:6)} \qquad \lim_{\substack{n=\infty \\ k=\infty}} \int_a^b \psi_{n\sigma}\,dg_{k\sigma} = \int_a^b \theta_\sigma\,df_\sigma \text{ uniformly in } \sigma.$$

The existence of the integrals on the right as LS-integrals follows from the preceding theorems.

THEOREM 29. $A_{2\sigma}$, $B_{1\sigma}$, $C_{5\sigma}$, $D_{3\sigma}$ *imply* (4:6).

Proof.—If (4:6) is false, there exist a positive number ϵ and sequences (n_q), (k_q), (σ_q), such that n_q and k_q tend to infinity, and

$$\text{(4:7)} \qquad \left|\int_a^b \psi_{n_q\sigma_q}\,dg_{k_q\sigma_q} - \int_a^b \theta_{\sigma_q}\,df_{\sigma_q}\right| > \epsilon.$$

Let $\psi_q^* = \psi_{n_q\sigma_q}$, $\theta_q^* = \theta_{\sigma_q}$, $g_q^* = g_{k_q\sigma_q} - f_{\sigma_q}$, $f_q^* = f_{\sigma_q}$. From $C_{5\sigma}$ and $D_{3\sigma}$ it follows readily that the functions $\psi_q^*(x)$ are continuous in x uniformly in x and q and that $\lim\limits_q (\psi_q^* - \theta_q^*) = 0$ uniformly in x. From $A_{2\sigma}$ it follows that g_q^* and f_q^* are of uniformly bounded variation, and from $B_{1\sigma}$ that $\lim\limits_q g_q^*(x) = 0$ on E. Then by the proof of Theorem 22, $\lim\limits_q \int_a^b \psi_q^*\,dg_q^* = 0$. By the Corollary of Theorem 16, $\lim\limits_q \int_a^b (\psi_q^* - \theta_q^*)\,df_q^* = 0$. Combining the last two statements leads to a contradiction with (4:7).

THEOREM 30. $A_{3\sigma}$, $B_{1\sigma}$, $C_{2\sigma}$, $C_{3\sigma}$, $D_{2\sigma}$ *imply* (4:6).

Proof.—As in the proof of Theorem 29, we are led to (4:7). Let $\psi_q^* = \psi_{n_q\sigma_q} - \theta$, $g_q^* = g_{k_q\sigma_q}$, $f_q^* = f_{\sigma_q}$. By $D_{2\sigma}$, $\lim_q \psi_q^* = 0$ on E_1, and by $C_{3\sigma}$, the integrals $\int|\psi_q^*|\,dh$ are absolutely continuous with respect to h uniformly in q. Hence $\lim_q \int_a^b |\psi_q^*|\,dh = 0$, and then by Theorem 16,

$$\lim_q \int_a^b \psi_q^*\,dg_q^* = 0. \tag{4:8}$$

By Theorem 27,

$$\lim_q \int_a^b \theta\,d(g_q^* - f_q^*) = 0. \tag{4:9}$$

Combining the last two statements leads to a contradiction with (4:7).

THEOREM 31. *$A_{4\sigma}$, $B_{1\sigma}$, $C_{2\sigma}$, $C_{4\sigma}$, and $D_{2\sigma}$ with $h(x) = x$, imply* (4:6).

Proof.—Let ψ_q^*, g_q^*, f_q^* have the same meanings as in the proof of Theorem 30. By $D_{2\sigma}$, $\lim_q \psi_q^* = 0$ on E_1, and by $C_{4\sigma}$ the functions ψ_q^* are uniformly bounded. By the method used in proving Theorem 28 we are led to (4:8) and, by Theorem 28 itself, to (4:9).

The following example shows that in Theorems 30 and 31 the condition that the function θ is independent of σ cannot be omitted. Let P_j be a partition of the interval $[a, b]$ into 2^j equal intervals, and let the intervals be numbered in order from left to right. Let σ, as well as n and k, range over the positive integers, and let

$$\begin{aligned} \psi_{n\sigma}(x) = \theta_\sigma(x) &= 1 \text{ for } x \text{ on the odd-numbered intervals of } P_\sigma, \\ &= -1 \text{ for } x \text{ on the even-numbered intervals of } P_\sigma, \end{aligned}$$

Let $g_{k\sigma}(x) = \int_a^x \theta_k(x)\,dx$, $f_\sigma(x) = 0$. Then $\int_a^b \psi_{n\sigma}\,dg_{k\sigma} = \int_a^b \theta_\sigma\theta_k\,dx$ and, when $\sigma = k$, this equals $b - a$.

When the functions $g_k(x)$, $f(x)$, $g_{k\sigma}(x)$, $f_\sigma(x)$ are absolutely continuous, we may apply the Corollary of Theorem 20 to obtain from the preceding some interesting theorems on the convergence of sequences of Lebesgue integrals. For example, the "general convergence theorem" of Hobson ([2], Vol. 2, page 422) follows from Theorem 30, if we take $h(x) = Kx$. A theorem useful in existence proofs in the calculus of variations is obtained from Theorem 28.[1]

When the formula for integration by parts of Theorem 8 holds and

$$\lim_{\substack{n=\infty \\ k=\infty}} [\psi_n(b)g_k(b) - \psi_n(a)g_k(a)] = \theta(b)f(b) - \theta(a)f(a),$$

we obtain at once from each of the Theorems 22 to 28 a theorem concerning the validity of

$$\lim_{\substack{n=\infty \\ k=\infty}} \int_a^b g_k\, d\psi_n = \int_a^b f\, d\theta.$$

A corresponding statement may be made for Theorems 29 to 31. Moreover, the remark of the preceding paragraph may again be applied to give some interesting results.

*There is a type of convergence for functions of bounded variation which is still weaker than B_1 and which is analogous to convergence in the mean for L-integrable functions. It is defined as follows:

B_0. $\lim_k g_k(a) = f(a); \lim_k g_k(b) = f(b); \lim_k \int_a^c g_k\, dx = \int_a^c f\, dx$ for each point c on $[a, b]$.

B_0 may replace B_1 in Theorems 22, 23, 27, and 28, and a corresponding $B_{0\sigma}$ may replace $B_{1\sigma}$ in Theorems 29 to 31, as will be shown following the proof of Theorem 34. That the convergence of g_k to f in these theorems cannot be further weakened is shown by the following proposition.

*THEOREM 32. *If* $\lim_k g_k(a) = f(a)$, *and*

$$\lim_k \int_a^b \theta\, dg_k = \int_a^b \theta\, df$$

for every continuous function θ, *then* B_0 *holds.*

To prove this, it is sufficient to take $\theta(x) = 1$ on $[a, b]$, and then to take

$$\begin{aligned} \theta(x) &= (x - a)/(c - a) && \text{on } [a, c], \\ &= 1 && \text{on } [c, b], \end{aligned}$$

and integrate by parts.

[1] Graves, "On the Existence of the Absolute Minimum in Space Problems of the Calculus of Variations," *Annals of Mathematics*, Vol. 28 (1927), p. 162.

That A_2 and B_0 may hold while g_k does not approach f at any point except a and b is shown by the following simple example. Let $g_k(x) = -1$ on the open interval (c_k, d_k), and $g_k(x) = 0$ elsewhere on $[a, b]$. Let the interval (c_k, d_k) wander over $[a, b]$ in suitable fashion, and let $(d_k - c_k)$ tend to zero but not too rapidly.

The following theorem on the compactness of a set of functions of uniformly bounded variation will be useful in studying the relationship between the two types of convergence, B_0 and B_1.

*THEOREM 33. *If the functions $g_k(x)$ are bounded and of bounded variation uniformly in k, then there exist a subsequence (g_{k_q}) and a function $f(x)$ such that* $\lim\limits_{q} g_{k_q}(x) = f(x)$ *everywhere on $[a, b]$. Moreover $t(f) \leqq \liminf\limits_{q=\infty} t(g_{k_q})$.*

Proof.—We suppose at first that each $g_k(x)$ is nondecreasing. Let E be a denumerable set which is dense on $[a, b]$ and includes the end points a and b. By the "diagonal method" used in the proof of Ascoli's theorem (Theorem 28 of Chap. VII), we find a subsequence (g_{k_q}) which converges at the points of E to a nondecreasing function $f(x)$ which is at first defined only on E. But at each point of cE, $f(x)$ has a left-hand limit $f_l(x)$ and a right-hand limit $f_r(x)$. Wherever in cE $f_l(x) = f_r(x)$, we set $f(x)$ equal to this common value. The remaining points where $f(x)$ is still undefined form a denumerable set, and we may select another subsequence, for which we use the same notation (g_{k_q}), and which converges at these points also. We may prove that $g_{k_q}(x)$ converges to $f(x)$ at the points where $f_l(x) = f_r(x)$ as follows. Choose a point z in E such that $x < z$ and $f(x) \leqq f(z) < f(x) + \epsilon$. Then for q sufficiently large we have

$$g_{k_q}(x) \leqq g_{k_q}(z) < f(x) + \epsilon.$$

Similarly we show that $g_{k_q}(x) > f(x) - \epsilon$. The result obtained for nondecreasing functions extends at once to the general case by the usual device. The last statement in the theorem follows from the fact that for each partition P of $[a, b]$,

$$\sum_P |\Delta f| = \lim_q \sum_P |\Delta g_{k_q}| \leqq \liminf_q t(g_{k_q}).$$

The next theorem gives the relations between the two types of convergence B_0 and B_1.

*THEOREM 34. A_2 *and* B_1 *imply* B_0. A_2 *and* B_0 *imply that* B_1 *holds on a subsequence.*

Proof.—The first statement follows from Theorems 22 and 32. It could also be proved by another method. For the second statement, we secure a subsequence (g_{k_q}) approaching a function $f_1(x)$ on $[a, b]$, by Theorem 33, but $f_1(x)$ may differ from the function $f(x)$ given in B_0. However, (g_{k_q}) and f_1 also satisfy B_0, by the first part of the theorem, so $\int_a^c f(x)\,dx = \int_a^c f_1(x)\,dx$ for every point c on $[a, b]$. Hence $f(x) = f_1(x)$ except possibly at their points of discontinuity.

We can now readily verify the statement made above that B_0 may replace B_1 in Theorems 22, 23, 27, and 28. For, if (4:1) does not hold, there are sequences (n_q) and (k_q) such that

$$\lim_q \int_a^b \psi_{n_q}\,dg_{k_q} \tag{4:10}$$

exists but is different from $\int_a^b \theta\,df$. By Theorem 34, B_1 holds for a subsequence of (g_{k_q}). But on this subsequence the value of (4:10) must be $\int_a^b \theta\,df$, which is a contradiction. A similar device in connection with the proofs of Theorems 29 to 31 shows that these theorems may also be extended.

It is interesting to note that Theorems 22, 23, 27, and 28 with B_0 in place of B_1 could have been proved directly, by approximating the functions ψ_n by polygonal functions and integrating by parts.

***5. Linear Continuous Operators on the Space $\mathfrak{C}$.**—In preceding sections we have noted that the S-, GS-, and LS-integrals are bilinear operators, and in particular that $(S)\int\psi\,df$ is defined for every ψ in the space $\mathfrak{C}$ of functions continuous on the interval $[a, b]$ if and only if f is of bounded variation on $[a, b]$. In this section there is given a proof of the theorem of F. Riesz which states that every linear continuous operator on the space $\mathfrak{C}$ is expressible as a Stieltjes integral.[1]

We recall that in the space $\mathfrak{C}$, the norm $\|\psi\| = \text{l.u.b.}\ |\psi(x)|$ on $[a, b]$. Continuity of a real-valued operator L with domain $\mathfrak{C}$ is defined in terms of this norm in the usual way. An operator L is said to be **modular** in case there is a constant μ such that

[1] See Riesz, *Annales scientifiques de l'école normale supérieure*, Vol. 31 (1914), pp. 9–14.

$|L(\psi)| \leqq \mu\|\psi\|$ for every ψ in $\mathfrak{C}$. It is obvious that a linear modular operator L is continuous. Conversely, if a linear operator L is continuous at $\psi = 0$, it is modular. For, suppose $|L(\psi)| \leqq 1$ whenever $\|\psi\| \leqq \delta$. Then

$$|L(\psi)| = \left|L\left(\frac{\delta\psi}{\|\psi\|}\right)\right| \frac{\|\psi\|}{\delta} \leqq \frac{1}{\delta}\|\psi\|$$

for every ψ.

For a linear operator L we set $\|L\| \equiv$ l.u.b. $|L(\psi)|$ for $\|\psi\| = 1$. In case $\|L\|$ is finite, L is modular. A positive linear operator L is always modular, with $\|L\| = L(1)$, as is easily verified. The following theorem gives a decomposition of linear modular operators corresponding to that for functions of bounded variation.

Theorem 35. *If L is linear and modular, there exist unique positive linear operators K, N, M, with the properties:*

1. $L = K - N$,
2. $M = K + N$,
3. *If $L = Q - R$, where Q and R are linear and positive, then $Q - K$ and $R - N$ are positive.*

Moreover, $\|L\| = \|M\| = \|K\| + \|N\|$.

Proof.—If $\psi(x) \geqq 0$, we set

$$K(\psi) = \text{l.u.b. } L(\theta) \qquad \text{for} \qquad 0 \leqq \theta \leqq \psi.$$

Then it is plain that, if $\psi \geqq 0$, $a \geqq 0$, we have

$$0 \leqq K(a\psi) = aK(\psi) < \infty. \tag{5:1}$$

Also if $\psi_1 \geqq 0$, $\psi_2 \geqq 0$, we have

$$K(\psi_1 + \psi_2) = K(\psi_1) + K(\psi_2). \tag{5:2}$$

For, when $0 \leqq \theta_1 \leqq \psi_1$, $0 \leqq \theta_2 \leqq \psi_2$, $L(\theta_1) + L(\theta_2) = L(\theta_1 + \theta_2) \leqq K(\psi_1 + \psi_2)$, and hence $K(\psi_1) + K(\psi_2) \leqq K(\psi_1 + \psi_2)$. On the other hand, if $0 \leqq \theta \leqq \psi_1 + \psi_2$, set $\theta_1 = (\theta - \psi_2) \vee 0$, $\theta_2 = \theta \wedge \psi_2$. Then $\theta_1 + \theta_2 = \theta$, $0 \leqq \theta_1 \leqq \psi_1$, $0 \leqq \theta_2 \leqq \psi_2$, and so $L(\theta_1) \leqq K(\psi_1)$, $L(\theta_2) \leqq K(\psi_2)$, $L(\theta) \leqq K(\psi_1) + K(\psi_2)$, and finally $K(\psi_1 + \psi_2) \leqq K(\psi_1) + K(\psi_2)$.

Every continuous function ψ has infinitely many representations in the form $\psi = \psi_1 - \psi_2$, where $\psi_1 \geqq 0$, $\psi_2 \geqq 0$. But from (5:2) it follows at once that the formula $K(\psi) = K(\psi_1) - K(\psi_2)$ defines K as a single-valued operator on $\mathfrak{C}$, and from (5:2) and (5:1) it follows that K is linear and positive. Then $N \equiv K - L$ and $M \equiv K + N$ are also linear and positive.

Property (3) follows immediately from the definitions of K and N, and the three properties together uniquely determine K, N, and M. We note that for $\psi \geqq 0$, we have

$$M(\psi) = \text{l.u.b. } L(\theta) \qquad \text{for} \qquad -\psi \leqq \theta \leqq \psi,$$

since $M(\psi) = K(2\psi) - L(\psi)$. Hence $\|M\| = M(1) \leqq \|L\|$. But $\|L\| \leqq \|K\| + \|N\| = K(1) + N(1) = M(1) = \|M\|$.

We shall need to extend the domain of definition of the linear operator L. It will be sufficient to consider a positive operator K. If (ψ_n) is a bounded nondecreasing sequence of continuous functions, it has a limit θ, which may, however, be discontinuous. The sequence $(K(\psi_n))$ is also nondecreasing and bounded and so has a limit which we denote by $K(\theta)$. From the following lemma we see that this definition of $K(\theta)$ is consistent and yields a single-valued operator.

LEMMA 4. *Let (ψ_{1n}) and (ψ_{2n}) be nondecreasing bounded sequences in the space $\mathfrak{C}$, such that* $\lim_n \psi_{1n} \geqq \lim_n \psi_{2n}$. *Let K be a positive linear operator. Then* $\lim_n K(\psi_{1n}) \geqq \lim_n K(\psi_{2n})$.

Proof.—Suppose $\lim_n \psi_{1n} \geqq \theta$, where θ is continuous, and set $\psi_{3n} = \psi_{1n} \wedge \theta$. Then $\lim_n \psi_{3n} = \theta$, and in this case the convergence is uniform, by Theorem 26 of Chap. VII. Hence $\lim_n K(\psi_{3n}) = K(\theta)$. But $K(\psi_{1n}) \geqq K(\psi_{3n})$, and so $\lim_n K(\psi_{1n}) \geqq K(\theta)$. But θ may be taken as an arbitrary one of the functions ψ_{2m}.

Let $\mathfrak{D}_1$ denote the class of all limits of bounded nondecreasing sequences (ψ_n) chosen from $\mathfrak{C}$. The enlarged domain $\mathfrak{D}$ of the operators L, K, N, and M is to consist of all functions θ expressible as the difference of two functions chosen from $\mathfrak{D}_1$. It is easily seen that $\mathfrak{D}$ is linear.

THEOREM 36. *The operators K, N, L, and M may have their domain of definition extended to the space $\mathfrak{D}$ in such a way that they remain linear, have the same modulus on $\mathfrak{D}$ as on $\mathfrak{C}$, and continue to satisfy the relations* (1) *and* (2) *of Theorem* 35, *and K, N, and M remain positive on $\mathfrak{D}$.*

Proof.—If $\theta = \theta_1 - \theta_2$ where θ_1 and θ_2 are limits of nondecreasing sequences, set $K(\theta) = K(\theta_1) - K(\theta_2)$, $N(\theta) = N(\theta_1) - N(\theta_2)$, $L(\theta) = K(\theta) - N(\theta)$, $M(\theta) = K(\theta) + N(\theta)$. If θ_1 and θ_4 are limits of nondecreasing sequences, it is readily verified that $K(\theta_1 + \theta_4) = K(\theta_1) + K(\theta_4)$, and hence that $K(\theta)$ is a single-valued positive linear operator on $\mathfrak{D}$. Since K is positive, we still have $\|K\| = K(1)$.

THEOREM 37. **Riesz' Theorem.** *If L is a linear continuous operator on the space $\mathfrak{C}$, there is a function f of bounded variation such that*

$$L(\psi) = \int_a^b \psi \, df, \qquad \|L\| = t(f).$$

Proof.—By virtue of the preceding results, we may restrict attention to a positive operator K. Let

$$\begin{aligned} \theta_y(x) &= 1 \quad \text{for } a \leqq x \leqq y, \qquad a < y \leqq b, \\ &= 0 \quad \text{for } y < x \leqq b, \\ \theta_a(x) &= 0 \quad \text{for } a \leqq x \leqq b, \\ f(y) &= K(\theta_y). \end{aligned}$$

If P is a partition of $[a, b]$ by points y_j, and ψ is continuous,

$$\begin{aligned} S(P; \psi, f) &= \sum_j \psi(z_j)[f(y_j) - f(y_{j-1})], \\ &= K\left[\sum_j \psi(z_j)(\theta_{y_j} - \theta_{y_{j-1}})\right], \end{aligned}$$

and this expression approaches $K(\psi)$ when the norm $N(P)$ tends to zero, since then $\sum \psi(z_j)[\theta_{y_j}(x) - \theta_{y_{j-1}}(x)]$ approaches $\psi(x)$ uniformly on $[a, b]$. The function f is nondecreasing, and $f(a) = 0$, $f(b) = K(1) = \|K\|$. The equation $\|L\| = t(f)$ for the general case follows with the help of the Corollary of Theorem 16.

***6. Remarks on Improper, Multiple, and Repeated Stieltjes Integrals.**—The case when the function f is of bounded variation on every closed subinterval of the open interval (a, b), but is not of bounded variation on (a, b), and the case when the interval of integration is infinite may be handled by the methods of elementary calculus for improper integrals, or by the methods of Sec. 5 in Chap. XI.

Multiple and repeated Stieltjes integrals of various types have been considered by a number of writers. In defining

$$\int_I \psi(x, y) \, d_{xy} f(x, y), \tag{6:1}$$

where I is an interval of the xy-plane, the increment of f over an interval $i = (a, c; b, d)$ is taken to be

$$\Delta(f; i) = f(b, d) - f(b, c) - f(a, d) + f(a, c),$$

as in Sec. 13 of Chap. XI. A function $f(x, y)$ may be of bounded variation in the sense that $\sum |\Delta(f; i)|$ is bounded for all partitions of the fundamental interval, without being of bounded variation in either variable separately. When f is of bounded variation, (6:1) is a linear continuous functional on the space of continuous functions defined on I. The converse theorem of Riesz, given in the preceding section for functions of one variable, extends to the case of functions of two or more variables.[1]

Types of repeated Stieltjes integrals are

$$\int\left(\int\psi(x, y)\, d_x g(x)\right) d_y h(y), \tag{6:2}$$

$$\int\phi(x)\, d_x \int\psi(x, y)\, d_y h(y), \tag{6:3}$$

$$\int\phi(x)\, d_x \int\psi(y)\, d_y f(x, y). \tag{6:4}$$

The general form for a bilinear continuous functional on the space of continuous functions is given by (6:4), where the function f is of bounded variation in a modified sense.[2]

When $f(x, y) = g(x)h(y)$ where g and h are of bounded variation, Fubini's theorem shows the equality of (6:1) and (6:2) as LS-integrals, as was indicated in Chap. XI, Sec. 2. (See also Saks, *Theory of the Integral*, page 77.) A Fubini theorem for (6:4) was given by Cameron and Martin.[3]

REFERENCES

1. McShane, *Integration*, Chap. 7.
2. Hobson, *Theory of Functions of a Real Variable*, Vol. 1, Chaps. 6, 7; Vol. 2, Chap. 7.
3. Lebesgue, *Leçons sur l'intégration*, 2d Ed., 1928, Chap. 11.
4. Hildebrandt, "On Integrals Related to and Extensions of the Lebesgue Integral," *Bulletin of the American Mathematical Society*, Vol. 24 (1917), pp. 177–202.
5. Hildebrandt, "Stieltjes Integrals of the Riemann Type," *American Mathematical Monthly*, Vol. 45 (1938), pp. 265–278.
6. Radon, "Theorie und Anwendung der absolut additiven Mengenfunktionen," *Akademie der Wissenschaften, Wien, Sitzungsberichte*, Vol. 122_{2a} (1913), pp. 1295–1438.

[1] See Fischer, "Linear Functionals of n-spreads," *Annals of Mathematics*, Vol. 19 (1917–1918), pp. 37–43.

[2] See Fréchet, "Sur les fonctionnelles bilineaires," *Transactions of the American Mathematical Society*, Vol. 16 (1915), pp. 215–234; Y. K. Wong, *Representation of Bilinear Functionals in Terms of Stieltjes Integrals*, Master's Dissertation, University of Chicago, 1929.

[3] "An Unsymmetric Fubini Theorem," *Bulletin of the American Mathematical Society*, Vol. 47 (1941), pp. 121–125.

CHAPTER XIII

THE THEORY OF SETS AND TRANSFINITE NUMBERS

1. Introduction.—In this chapter we shall develop the theory of classes somewhat more extensively than was done in Chap. I and shall include a discussion of various propositions equivalent to the axiom of choice. The reader is expected to be familiar with the ideas and notations of Chap. I. A somewhat different notation for the algebra of classes will be introduced in this chapter. It is important for the student to become familiar with both schemes of notation, since both are used extensively in the mathematical literature. On the other hand, we shall continue to use the notations of the previous chapters for the logical connectives and quantifiers.

2. The Algebra of Sets.—The fundamental relation in the theory of classes is the relation of class membership. This is denoted by "$x \epsilon A$"—read "x is a member of A," or "x is an element of A." It is taken as an undefined relation and is understood in the usual sense. Its negation is denoted by "$x \epsilon' A$,"—read "x is not a member of A." We define class inclusion as follows:

$$A \subset B :\equiv: x \epsilon A \cdot \supset \cdot x \epsilon B.$$

The symbol "$A \subset B$" is read "A is a subclass of B." We understand $A = B$ to mean that the classes A and B have the same elements. Thus we may arrive at the same class by many different processes of specifying its elements. In practice, we usually show that $A = B$ by showing $A \subset B$ and $B \subset A$. An example of this is the proof in elementary analytic geometry that when $0 < b < a$, $c^2 = a^2 - b^2$, then

$$x^2/a^2 + y^2/b^2 = 1$$

is the equation of the locus of all points in the xy-plane the sum of whose distances from $(c, 0)$ and $(-c, 0)$ is $2a$. The set A is said to be a **proper subset** of B in case $A \subset B$ and $A \neq B$. This relation is sometimes indicated by the notation $A \subsetneq B$. It is clearly equivalent to the statement

$$x \in A \cdot\supset\cdot x \in B : \exists y \in B \ni \cdot y \,\epsilon'\, A.$$

For an example we may take A as the set of points in the xy-plane given by

$$x = \cos t, \qquad y = 3 \cos t, \qquad (0 < t < \pi),$$

and B as the set of points satisfying $y = 3x$.

A subset of a class B is frequently specified by means of a property P applicable to the members of B. The following forms are frequently used to denote the subset of B whose members have property P (for examples, see Chap. III, page 41):

$$E[x \in B \,.\, x \text{ has property } P],$$
$$B[x \text{ has property } P],$$
$$[x \in B | x \text{ has property } P],$$
$$[x | x \text{ has property } P].$$

We recall that the class whose only member is a is usually denoted by $\{a\}$.

The **union** (or **sum**) of two classes A and B will now be denoted by $A \cup B$, and the **intersection** (or **product**) will now be denoted by $A \cap B$. When subclasses of an algebraic system R are being considered, this notation helps to avoid confusion between these operations of the algebra of sets and the operations denoted by "+" and "×" in the system R. We shall frequently find it convenient to use the symbol "J" for an "index class" of elements i. If W is a fixed class, and $A_i \subset W$ for $i \in J$, then

$$\bigcup_{i \in J} A_i = [\text{all } x \in W \ni : \exists i \in J \ni \cdot x \in A_i],$$
$$\bigcap_{i \in J} A_i = [\text{all } x \in W \ni : i \in J \cdot\supset\cdot x \in A_i].$$

These are the natural extensions of the notions of union and intersection to the case of an arbitrary collection of subclasses of a fixed class.

With respect to a fixed "universal" class W, the **complement** cA of a subset A of W is defined by

$$cA = [x \in W | x \,\epsilon'\, A].$$

The **difference** $A - B$ of two subsets of W may then be defined by the formula $A - B = A \cap cB$. We note that this notation for the logical difference does not avoid the confusion with algebraic subtraction, but it is commonly used because of its convenience. Similarly, the symbols "$+$" and "$\sum$" used in Chap. I for the union of sets are often more convenient than "$\cup$". (Compare, for example, Kuratowski [4].)

We recall that in order to be able always to have a meaning for the intersection and the difference of classes, it is necessary to introduce the **null class**, which is denoted by Λ, or by 0, or sometimes by ϕ. Two sets A and B are termed **disjoint** in case their intersection is the null class, *i.e.*, $A \cap B = 0$.

The distributive laws in terms of the symbols "$\cup$" and "$\cap$" read as follows:

$$(A \cup B) \cap C = (A \cap C) \cup (B \cap C), \tag{2:1}$$
$$A \cup (B \cap C) = (A \cup B) \cap (A \cup C). \tag{2:2}$$

The set in (2:1) is always a subset of the set in (2:2), but examples are readily constructed to show that the two are not always equal. When C is replaced by its complement in (2:1) and (2:2), we obtain

$$(A \cup B) - C = (A - C) \cup (B - C),$$
$$A \cup (B - C) = (A \cup B) - (C - A).$$

The following laws of de Morgan relating to complements of unions and intersections are useful:

$$c(\bigcup_i A_i) = \bigcap_i cA_i,$$
$$c(\bigcap_i A_i) = \bigcup_i cA_i.$$

(Compare formulas (3:8) and (3:9) of Chap. I, page 10.)

We retain the notation $A \times B$ for the **Cartesian product** of the classes A and B, which is defined by the formula

$$A \times B = [(x, y) | x \in A \, . \, y \in B].$$

It is clear that when $A \neq B$, $A \times B \neq B \times A$, although there is an obvious one-to-one correspondence between these classes. A similar remark may be made regarding $A \times (B \times C)$ and $(A \times B) \times C$. The consideration of Cartesian products of arbitrary collections of sets will be postponed to a later section. The Cartesian product is distributive with respect to both unions and intersections, *i.e.*,

$$A \times (\bigcup_i B_i) = \bigcup_i (A \times B_i),$$
$$A \times (\bigcap_i B_i) = \bigcap_i (A \times B_i).$$

There are similar formulas with the order interchanged.

The set $\mathfrak{P}(A) = [\text{all } B \subset A]$ will be very frequently useful. It is called the **power set** of A, for a reason that will become clear later. Note that both A and the null set are members of $\mathfrak{P}(A)$. Thus when A is empty, $\mathfrak{P}(A)$ has just one member.

3. Relations and Functions.—We recall that if A and B are classes, a **binary relation** R on AB is defined as a subset of the Cartesian product $A \times B$. We may write "xRy" as an abbreviation for "(x, y) in R." The relation R may also be referred to as a **function** f (possibly multiple-valued), and the notation $y \in f(x)$ may then be used ($y = f(x)$ when f is a single-valued function). We continue to use the notation "fA_1" for the set

$$[y \in B |\ \exists x \in A_1 \ni\cdot\ y \in f(x)] = \bigcup f(x) \text{ for } x \in A_1,$$

where $A_1 \subset A$. The set $A_0 = [x \in A | f(x) \neq \phi]$ is the **domain** of f, and $B_0 = fA$ is the **range** of f. A function on A to B, *i.e.*, a *single-valued* function f whose domain is A and whose range is a subset of B is sometimes called a **transformation** or a **mapping** of A **into** B. When the range of f is the whole of B, *i.e.*, $fA = B$, such a function is said to map A **onto** B.

If f is a function on A to B, and g is a function on B to C, the **composite** function $g \circ f$ satisfies the condition $(g \circ f)A_1 = g(fA_1)$ for every subset A_1 of A. The same condition holds when f and g are multiple-valued functions. In terms of the notation for relations, (replacing f by R and g by S) we have:

$$(x, z) \in R \circ S :\sim: \exists y \in B \ni\cdot (x, y) \in R\ .\ (y, z) \in S.$$

When no confusion can arise, we may write simply gf in place of $g \circ f$. Note that our notation reverses the order of writing the composite when the function notation is replaced by the notation for relations.

A frequently useful class consists of all mappings of a given set J into another set W. It is denoted by W^J, for a reason that will be clear when we consider exponentiation of cardinal numbers.

It is a subclass of the power set $\mathfrak{P}(J \times W)$. When J is the null class, $J \times W$ is also null, but $\mathfrak{P}(J \times W)$ has one element, namely, the null class, which satisfies the condition of single-valuedness, so it is an element of W^J. Thus W^J has one member when J is null. However, if W is null and J is not, then W^J is null. Note that when $J_1 \cap J_2$ is null, there is a natural isomorphism between $W^{(J_1 \cup J_2)}$ and $W^{J_1} \times W^{J_2}$, which is consistent with the requirement that when J_1 is null, W^{J_1} has exactly one element.

The notion of **characteristic function** of a subset A of W is a useful one. It is a mapping ψ_A of W into the set 2 consisting of the integers 0 and 1, such that

$$\begin{aligned} \psi_A(x) &= 1 \qquad \text{for } x \in A, \\ \psi_A(x) &= 0 \qquad \text{for } x \in W - A. \end{aligned}$$

Thus each ψ_A is an element of 2^W. This determines a mapping ψ of $\mathfrak{P}(W)$ onto 2^W, which is readily seen to be one-to-one. Hence we may use the notations $\mathfrak{P}(W)$ and 2^W interchangeably.

If $A_i \subset W$ for each i in the index set J (*i.e.*, (A_i) is a mapping of J into the power set $\mathfrak{P}(W)$), the general **Cartesian product** $\prod_{i \in J} A_i$ is defined to be the subset of W^J consisting of all those mappings (x_i) such that $x_i \in A_i$ for all $i \in J$. When one A_i is null, then $\prod A_i$ is null. We shall see later that the assumption that whenever every A_i is nonnull, then $\prod A_i$ is also nonnull is equivalent to the axiom of choice.

Since a relation R on AB is merely a subset of $A \times B$, we have an obvious meaning for $R_1 \subset R_2$, $R_1 \cap R_2$, and $R_1 \cup R_2$. If $A_0 \subset A$, then $(A_0 \times B) \cap R$ is a relation $R|A_0$ which is called the restriction of R to A_0. When R determines a single-valued function f mapping A into B, we use the corresponding notation $f|A_0$ for the restriction of f to A_0. If $A = B$, and I is the identity map, then $I|A_0$ is sometimes called the inclusion mapping of A_0 into A. We note that $f|A_0 = f \circ I|A_0$.

Let $J_0 \subset J$, $X = \prod_{i \in J} A_i$, $Y = \prod_{i \in J_0} A_i$, and let $\xi = (x_i)$ denote a member of X. Then $\xi|J_0$ is a member of Y. The **projection** P_Y of X onto Y is defined by $P_Y(\xi) = \xi|J_0$. The **coordinates** x_i of ξ are obtained as special cases by taking $J_0 = \{i\}$.

Let t denote the natural mapping of $A \times B$ onto $B \times A$, which carries the pair (x, y) into (y, x). If R is a relation from A to B, set $R^{-1} = tR$. We note that when R determines a one-to-one mapping, R^{-1} gives the **inverse** mapping.

A relation R on AA (also called a relation on A) is said to be:

(*a*) **symmetric** in case $R \subset R^{-1}$ (hence $R = R^{-1}$);

(*b*) **reflexive** in case $I \subset R$, where I is the identity relation;

(*c*) **transitive** in case $R \circ R \subset R$;

(*d*) **antisymmetric** in case $R \cap R^{-1} \subset I$;

(*e*) **antireflexive** in case $R \cap I = 0$;

(*f*) **exhaustive** in case $R \cup R^{-1} \cup I = A \times A$.

In applying these definitions it is frequently desirable to translate them. Thus (*a*) means

$$aRb \cdot\supset\cdot bRa.$$

For an arbitrary relation R on A, it is obvious that $R \cup I$ is reflexive, and $R - I$ is antireflexive. If R is symmetric (or antisymmetric), this property still holds for $R \cup I$ and $R - I$. If R is transitive, $R \cup I$ is still transitive, but $R - I$ may fail to be so. However, $R - I$ is surely transitive if R is transitive and antisymmetric.

Every relation R on A has an **extension** T_R which is transitive. This extension T_R is defined as the intersection of all transitive relations $S \supset R$. Such transitive relations S exist since the universal relation $U = A \times A$ is transitive, and T_R is transitive since the intersection of transitive relations is transitive. In case R is symmetric, T_R is also symmetric, since, if S is transitive and $S \supset R$, then S^{-1} is transitive and $S^{-1} \supset R$, and so $R \subset S \cap S^{-1}$, which is symmetric. Obviously, when R is reflexive, T_R is also reflexive. But T_R may be reflexive and symmetric when R is antireflexive and antisymmetric. For example, let $A = \{a, b, c\}$, $R = \{(a, b), (b, c), (c, a)\}$. Then $T_R = U = A \times A$.

When we are using the function notation "$y \in f(x)$" or "$y = f(x)$" in place of "xRy," we may replace "xT_Ry" by "$y \in h_f(x)$." The definition of $h_f(x)$ may be phrased directly as follows: Let a subclass B of A be called **hereditary** for f in case $y \in B \cdot\supset\cdot f(y) \subset B$, *i.e.*, $f(B) \subset B$. Then $h_f(x)$ is the intersection of all hereditary subclasses of A containing $f(x)$. To show that when h_f is thus defined, $xT_Ry \cdot\sim\cdot y \in h_f(x)$, we may proceed as follows:

Let $S = [(u,v) | v \epsilon h_f(u)]$. Then $R \subset S$ since $f(u) \subset h_f(u)$, and S is transitive since $v \epsilon h_f(u)$ and $w \epsilon h_f(v)$ imply $w \epsilon h_f(u)$. Hence xT_Ry implies $y \epsilon h_f(x)$. For the converse, let S be a transitive relation containing R, and set $g(x) = [z | (x, z) \epsilon S]$. Then $g(x)$ is hereditary for f and contains $f(x) = [z | (x, z) \epsilon R]$. Thus $y \epsilon h_f(x)$ implies $(x, y) \epsilon S$ for every transitive S containing R, and hence $(x, y) \epsilon T_R$.

An **equivalence** relation R is one that is symmetric, reflexive, and transitive. Important examples of equivalence relations appeared in Chap. II. An equivalence relation determines a **partition** Q of A into mutually exclusive subclasses, such that every pair of elements of a subclass belongs to R. To each element x of A corresponds the subclass $E_x = [y | xRy]$. A partition Q is obviously a subclass of the power set $\mathfrak{P}(A)$. Conversely, to each such partition Q corresponds an equivalence relation R. For convenience let the elements of Q be B_i, where i ranges over an index class J. Then $R = \bigcup_{i \epsilon J} B_i \times B_i$. It is easily seen also that the correspondence between equivalence relations R and partitions Q is one-to-one.

EXERCISES

1. Let W denote the set of all positive integers, A the subset consisting of the even integers, B the subset consisting of the odd integers, and C the subset consisting of the multiples of three. Describe the sets $A \cap C$, $B \cap cC$, $B \cup C$.

2. Verify the relation $A \cap (B \cup C) = (A \cap B) \cup (A \cap C)$ for the sets described in Exercise 1.

3. For arbitrary sets A, B, C, prove that $(A \cap B) \cup C = A \cap (B \cup C)$ if and only if $C \subset A$.

4. Show that a relation R on A which is symmetric and transitive and satisfies the additional condition

$$x \epsilon A \cdot \supset \cdot \exists y \epsilon A \ni \cdot (x, y) \epsilon R$$

is also reflexive.

5. If A is a finite class containing n elements, how many elements has the power set $\mathfrak{P}(A)$?

6. Let n be a positive integer and A be the set of all integers. Define xRy to mean that n divides $x - y$. Show that R is an equivalence relation, and determine the number of equivalence classes.

7. Let R be a relation on AB, S a relation on BC, and T a relation on CD. Prove the associative law

$$(R \circ S) \circ T = R \circ (S \circ T).$$

8. Discuss the properties (a) to (f) listed on page 302 for each of the following relations: (i) brother, (ii) sibling, (iii) friend, (iv) parent, (v) ancestor, (vi) inclusion (between sets), (vii) greater than (for numbers), (viii) xRy means $y > x^2 + 1$, where x and y are real.

9. Let $A = B =$ [all positive integers],

$$R = [\text{all } (x, y) |\ y/x \text{ is an odd integer} > 1],$$
$$S = [\text{all } (x, y) |\ y/x \text{ is an even integer}].$$

Show that $R \circ S = S \circ R$.

10. Let $A = B =$ [all real numbers],

$$R = [\text{all } (x, y) | x^2 + 4y^2 = 4].$$

Determine the domain and the range of the corresponding function $y = f(x)$.

11. Let $f(x) = \sin^{-1} x$, $g(x) = (\pi^2 - 4x^2)^{1/2}$. Determine the domain and range of f, g, and $g \circ f$, assuming that all the variables are real. Show that $g \circ f$ is single-valued.

12. Let $A = B =$ [all real numbers],

$$R = [\text{all } (x, y) |\ y = x^2].$$

Determine the extension T_R of R to be transitive.

13. Show that if R is a relation on AB, and S is a relation on BC, the composite relation $R \circ S$ is the projection on $A \times C$ of $(R \times C) \cap (A \times S)$.

14. Let $A = B =$ [all real numbers],

$$R = [\text{all } (x, y) |\ 5 \leqq x + 1 \leqq y \leqq x + 2 \,.\, y \leqq 10].$$

Show that $T_R = [\text{all } (x, y) |\ 5 \leqq x + 1 \leqq y \leqq 10]$.

4. Partial Ordering.—A relation R on A is called a **partial ordering** of A in case it is transitive and antisymmetric. As was noticed above, we may also require R to be reflexive or anti-reflexive, as is convenient. (A special case is the passage from $<$ to $\leqq$ and vice versa, in the ordering of the real numbers.) If the relation R is merely transitive, it is still sometimes called a partial ordering. There are then always a partition Q of A and a relation S on Q which is transitive and antisymmetric, determined by the relation R as follows. We assume that R is reflexive. Then $R_0 = R \cap R^{-1}$ is an equivalence relation on A, which determines the partition Q. The relation S on Q is defined as follows:

$$B_1SB_2 :\equiv: \exists x_1 \epsilon B_1 . \exists x_2 \epsilon B_2 \ni\cdot x_1Rx_2.$$

A simple example of the process is the following: A is the union of two disjoint classes B_1 and B_2, while $R = (B_1 \times B_1) \cup (B_1 \times B_2) \cup (B_2 \times B_2)$. Then Q has only two members, B_1 and B_2, and S has the three members, (B_1, B_1), (B_1, B_2), (B_2, B_2).

A partial ordering which is exhaustive is called a **simple ordering** or a **linear ordering.** Simple orderings were considered in Chap. II. In case a set A is partially ordered by R, and a subset B of A is simply ordered by R, we shall call B a **chain,** for convenience. For an arbitrary set A the power set $\mathfrak{P}(A)$ is partially ordered by inclusion, but is not simply ordered by this relation when A has more than one element.

Let us assume that the partial ordering R of A is reflexive. Then a member c of A is called an **upper bound** of a subset B of A in case $x \epsilon B \cdot\supset\cdot xRc$, and c is called a **lower bound** of B in case $x \epsilon B \cdot\supset\cdot cRx$. The element c is called the **least upper bound** of B in case it is an upper bound and is a lower bound for the class of all upper bounds of B. The uniqueness of the least upper bound, when it exists, follows at once from the requirement that R be reflexive, antisymmetric, and transitive. The **greatest lower bound** is defined in a corresponding way. These definitions are extensions of those given in Chap. II for linearly ordered sets. The notations "l.u.b. B" and "sup B" are in common use for the least upper bound, and "g.l.b. B" and "inf B" are used for the greatest lower bound. Note that the l.u.b. (g.l.b.) of the null subset of A is the g.l.b. (l.u.b.) of A when existent.

In case every subset of A consisting of two elements has a least upper bound and a greatest lower bound, then the partially ordered set A is called a **lattice.** Clearly every simply ordered set is a lattice. A lattice is called **complete** in case *every* subset has a least upper bound and a greatest lower bound. The power set $\mathfrak{P}(A)$ of an arbitrary set A, when ordered by the inclusion relation, is an important example of a complete lattice. When A is the three-dimensional Euclidean space, the subclass Q of $\mathfrak{P}(A)$ consisting of the points, lines, and planes in A together with A itself and the null set is also a complete lattice. However, Q is not a *sublattice* of $\mathfrak{P}(A)$, since l.u.b. F when F is a subset of Q is usually not the same as l.u.b. F when F is regarded as a subset of $\mathfrak{P}(A)$. For example, let F consist of two distinct points x and y. Then in Q, l.u.b. F is the line joining x and y, while in $\mathfrak{P}(A)$, l.u.b. F is the set $\{x, y\}$. When F consists of two distinct planes, g.l.b. F may be either a line or the null set. This inhomogeneity is removed when the points, lines, and plane "at infinity" are adjoined to Q to form the projective space P.

If A is simply ordered by R, and every nonnull subset B of A has a greatest lower bound belonging to B, *i.e.*, B has a first element, then A is said to be **well-ordered.** Such systems are basic for the theory of ordinal numbers, which is discussed in the next section.

Exercises

1. In the lattice Q described above, determine l.u.b. F and g.l.b. F in each of the following cases:

(*a*) F consists of a line l and a point p not on l;

(*b*) F consists of two intersecting lines l_1 and l_2;

(*c*) F consists of all the lines through a fixed point p.

2. In the usual ordering, each of the following sets is simply ordered, and so is a lattice. Which ones are complete? Which are well-ordered?

A = [the positive integers].

B = [the integers greater than 5, and $+\infty$].

C = [the rational numbers].

D = [the real numbers and $+\infty$ and $-\infty$].

3. In each of the following cases, tell whether R is an equivalence relation, a partial ordering, or neither. Also tell whether (A, R) is a lattice, and if so, whether it is complete.

(*a*) A is the set of lines in the Euclidean plane, and R is the relation of parallelism.

(*b*) A is the set of lines in the plane, and R is the relation of perpendicularity.

(*c*) A is the set of positive integers, and xRy means "x divides y."

(*d*) $A = B \times B$, where B is the set of positive integers, and $(a, b)R(c, d)$ means $ad = bc$.

(*e*) A is the unit square $0 \leqq x \leqq 1$, $0 \leqq y \leqq 1$, in the Cartesian plane, and $(x_1, y_1)R(x_2, y_2)$ means $x_1 \leqq x_2$, $y_1 \leqq y_2$.

(*f*) A consists of the vertices, edges, and faces of a cube in three-space, and R is the relation of point-set inclusion. In this example, what can be adjoined to A to make it a lattice?

4. Let (A, R) be a complete lattice, and let f map A into A, preserving order. Prove that there is at least one fixed element of A under the transformation f.

5. Let f be a single-valued function mapping A into B. Prove that:

(*a*) $f(D \cap E) = (fD) \cap (fE)$ for all D and E contained in A if and only if f^{-1} is single-valued;

(*b*) $f(A - D) \subset B - fD$ for all $D \subset A$ if and only if f^{-1} is single-valued;

(*c*) $f(A - D) \supset B - fD$ for all $D \subset A$ if and only if $fA = B$.

6. Show that for subclasses D and E of A,

$$\psi_D \psi_E = \psi_{(D \cap E)},$$
$$\psi_D + \psi_E = \psi_{(D \cup E)} + \psi_{(D \cap E)},$$

where ψ_D denotes the characteristic function of D.

7. Let $D * E$ denote the symmetric difference

$$D * E = (D - E) \cup (E - D).$$

Consider the values of the characteristic functions ψ_D to be in the system of residue classes of integers modulo 2, so that $1 + 1 = 0$. With this agreement, show that

$$\psi_D + \psi_E = \psi_{(D*E)}.$$

8. From Exercise 7 and the first part of Exercise 6, show that the system $(\mathfrak{P}(A), *, \cap)$ constitutes a commutative ring. What are the units for $*$ and for $\cap$?

9. Show that the following subclasses of the lattice $\mathfrak{P}(A \times A)$, ordered by inclusion, form complete lattices:

(*a*) The class $\mathfrak{S}$ of all symmetric relations on A;

(*b*) The class $\mathfrak{R}$ of all reflexive relations on A;

(*c*) The class $\mathfrak{T}$ of all transitive relations on A;

(*d*) The class $\mathfrak{E}$ of all equivalence relations on A.

Note that the least upper bound in $\mathfrak{T}$ (or $\mathfrak{E}$) of a subclass of $\mathfrak{T}$ (or $\mathfrak{E}$) is not always the same as its least upper bound in $\mathfrak{P}(A \times A)$. Show this by examples.

5. Ordinal and Cardinal Numbers.—Two classes A and B are said to have the same **cardinal number** (or to be **similar**) in case there is a one-to-one correspondence between A and B. If A and B are simply ordered by relations R and S, respectively, they are said to have the same **order type** (or to be **ordinally similar**) in case there exists a one-to-one mapping f of A *onto* B such that $a_1Ra_2 \cdot \supset \cdot f(a_1)Sf(a_2)$. If, in addition, A and B are *well-ordered* by R and S, respectively, then A and B are said to have the same **ordinal number.**

The preceding definitions are adequate for the operations we actually perform in mathematics. However, we naturally prefer that a noun such as "number" should refer to a definite entity. If we are dealing with subsets of a fixed set M and $A \subset M$, the **cardinal** of A, denoted by card A or by $\bar{\bar{A}}$, may be defined as the class of all subsets of M which are similar to A. We may also define the **ordinal** of a well-ordered subset A of M, denoted by ord A, or by $\bar{A}$, as the class of all well-ordered subsets of M which are ordinally similar to A. (No ordering of M is presupposed.) This choice of definitions has the drawback that the cardinal of A is an entity which is not determined by A alone but rather depends also on another set M. If we try defining the cardinal of A as the collection of *all* sets which are similar to A (compare Whitehead and Russell [8], Vol. I, especially pages 331, 347), we soon see that such a definition does not yield a suitable object of thought. For if we let $\mathbf{a}$ denote the cardinal of A thus defined, and set $B = [(x, \mathbf{a})|x \in A]$, we see at once that B is similar to A. But B cannot be a member of $\mathbf{a}$ if we agree that the members of $\mathbf{a}$ must be known entities prior to the formation of the class $\mathbf{a}$ having these members.

If we disregard the preceding objection, we run into contradictions. For example, let S denote the class composed of all classes having just one element, *i.e.*, S is the cardinal usually denoted by "1." Let T be the subclass of S consisting of those elements $x = \{\alpha\}$ such that $x \epsilon' \alpha$, *i.e.*, x is not a member of α. Let $y = \{T\}$. Then $y \in S$, and if $y \in T$, we must have $y \epsilon' T$, while if $y \epsilon' T$, we must have $y \in T$. Whitehead and Russell avoid this contradiction by use of the theory of types. For example, the cardinal 1 is the class of all unit classes of a given type. Then the class $\{1\}$ is a unit class of a higher type. So we again have the situation where similar classes have different cardinals.

These unsatisfactory aspects of this matter can be avoided by selecting one definite class to represent each cardinal number and one definite well-ordered class to represent each ordinal number. It will naturally be convenient to refer to these representations themselves as cardinals and ordinals. In the next section we shall exhibit a simple way in which this selection may be made, first for ordinals, and then for cardinals. The proposition that every cardinal has a representation of this kind is equivalent to the axiom of choice. This relationship will be taken up in Sec. 10.

Before we proceed to this selection, we shall derive some simple consequences of the preceding definition of cardinal number in terms of subclasses of a fixed class M. Since we suppose in the following paragraphs that the classes are all subclasses of M, we may omit further mention of M. An order relation is defined between cardinal numbers by saying that card $A \leqq$ card B in case A is similar to a subset of B, *i.e.*,

$$(5:1) \qquad \bar{\bar{A}} \leqq \bar{\bar{B}} \cdot\equiv\cdot \exists B_1 \subset B \ni\cdot \bar{\bar{A}} = \bar{\bar{B}}_1.$$

This relation is clearly transitive and reflexive. To show that it is antisymmetric, we have the following important result, known as the Schröder-Bernstein theorem, or sometimes simply as the Bernstein theorem.

THEOREM 1. *Let f be a one-to-one mapping of A into B, and let g be a one-to-one mapping of B into A. Then f and g determine a one-to-one mapping F of A onto B.*

Proof.—Let $A' = A - gB$, $\mathfrak{A} = [A'' \subset A \mid A' \subset A'' \,.\, gfA'' \subset A'']$. Obviously $A \in \mathfrak{A}$, so $\mathfrak{A}$ is not null. The intersection A_1 of all the members of $\mathfrak{A}$ clearly belongs to $\mathfrak{A}$, and also

$$(5:2) \qquad A_1 = A' \cup gfA_1,$$

since $A' \cup gfA_1 \subset A_1$, and $gf(A' \cup gfA_1) \subset gfA_1$, so $A' \cup gfA_1$ is a member of $\mathfrak{A}$. Now let $A_2 = A - A_1$, $B_1 = fA_1$, $B_2 = B - B_1$. Then by (5:2), $A_1 = A' \cup gB_1 = (A - gB) \cup gB_1 = A - gB_2$, so $A_2 = gB_2$. Hence we may set $F(x) = f(x)$ on A_1, and $F(x) = g^{-1}(x)$ on A_2.

We note that A_1 is the union of the sequence of sets A', gfA', $(gf)^2A'$, . . . , *i.e.*, A_1 is the least subclass of A which contains A' and is hereditary for the composite function gf in the sense of Sec. 3. In the special case when A and B are real intervals, a sketch showing simple choices of the functions f and g in the Cartesian product $A \times B$ is helpful in indicating how the set A_1 arises.

Since the relation defined by (5:1) is transitive and antisymmetric, it defines a partial ordering. The proposition that this is a linear ordering is equivalent to the axiom of choice, as is shown in Theorems 11 and 12 of Sec. 10.

The ordering defined by (5:1) may be obtained by the process described in the first paragraph of Sec. 4, as follows. In the power set $\mathfrak{P}(M)$, define ARB to mean "A is similar to a subset of B." Then the Bernstein theorem shows that the classes belonging to the partition Q described in Sec. 4 are just the classes of similar subsets of M, and the relation S of Sec. 4 is that defined by (5:1).

Sums, products, and powers for cardinal numbers may be defined as follows. Let $\mathbf{a}$ denote the cardinal of a class A, $\mathbf{b}$ of B, $\mathbf{a}_i$ of A_i, and so on. Then

$$\sum_i \mathbf{a}_i = \text{card } (\cup A_i) \text{ if the sets } A_i \text{ are disjoint,}$$

$$\mathbf{ab} = \text{card } (A \times B),$$
$$\mathbf{a}^{\mathbf{b}} = \text{card } (A^B).$$

It is easy to verify that these definitions give results independent of the representative sets A, B, etc., that the commutative, associative, and distributive laws hold for addition and multiplication, and that $\mathbf{a}^{\mathbf{b}}\mathbf{a}^{\mathbf{c}} = \mathbf{a}^{\mathbf{b}+\mathbf{c}}$, $(\mathbf{a}^{\mathbf{b}})^{\mathbf{c}} = \mathbf{a}^{\mathbf{bc}}$, $(\mathbf{ab})^{\mathbf{c}} = \mathbf{a}^{\mathbf{c}}\mathbf{b}^{\mathbf{c}}$. For example, to see that the last of these three properties of exponents holds, we recall that $A^C \times B^C$ consists of all pairs (f, g) of functions f mapping C into A and g mapping C into B, while $(A \times B)^C$ consists of all functions h mapping C into $A \times B$, and there is a natural isomorphism between these two classes, so that they have the same cardinal. Properties involving infinite products of cardinals will be taken up after we have considered the axiom of choice.

We next consider a fundamental theorm of Cantor which implies that for every cardinal number there is a greater one.

THEOREM 2. *For every class A, the cardinal of the power set $\mathfrak{P}(A)$ is greater than the cardinal of A, i.e.,* $2^{\mathbf{a}} > \mathbf{a}$.

We recall that we may replace $\mathfrak{P}(A)$ by 2^A, and this suggests the final statement in the theorem, which makes the result easy to remember.

Proof.—The function $f(x) = \{x\}$ gives a one-to-one mapping of A into $\mathfrak{P}(A)$, so $\mathbf{a} \leqq 2^{\mathbf{a}}$. Now suppose g maps $\mathfrak{P}(A)$ into A one-to-one, and let $C = [x \in A | x \in' g^{-1}(x)]$. Then $C \in \mathfrak{P}(A)$, so $g(C)$ has a value $y \in A$. The relation $g^{-1}(y) = C$ shows that if $y \in' C$, then $y \in C$, and if $y \in C$, then $y \in' C$.

EXERCISES

1. Prove the distributive law for cardinal numbers.
2. Prove $(\mathbf{a}^{\mathbf{b}})^{\mathbf{c}} = \mathbf{a}^{\mathbf{bc}}$.
3. Determine the function F of Bernstein's theorem in the following cases:

(i) $A = [x \mid 0 \leqq x < 1], B = [y \mid 0 \leqq y \leqq 2], f(x) = x, g(y) = y/4$;

(ii) $A = [x \mid 0 \leqq x \leqq 1],\ B = [y \mid 0 < y < \infty],\ f(x) = x + 1,\ g(y) = y/(y + 1)$.

6. Explicit Definition of Ordinal Numbers.[1]—The definition is suggested by the notion of a class of counters discussed on page 10 of Chap. I, but with a certain modification. The null class is denoted by 0, the class whose only member is the null class by $\{0\}$ or 1, the class $\{0, 1\}$ by 2, the class $\{0, 1, 2\}$ by 3, etc. With this choice of the counter class, each counter is a class whose members are the preceding counters.

Definition.—An ordinal number is a set X with the following properties:

(6:1) X is well-ordered by the relation $\in$ of class membership;

(6:2) $u \in X \cdot\supset\cdot u \subset X$.

In this connection we note the agreement that no set can be a member of itself, *i. e.*, the relation $\in$ is antireflexive, and that it is also antisymmetric. We also note that an arbitrary relation on a set A, when restricted to the null class 0, is a well-ordering of 0. A set Y is called $\in$-complete in case it has property (6:2) above.

THEOREM 3. *Every ordinal number X has the following additional properties:*

[1] Apparently the first published development of a definition of this kind is that of von Neumann [10]. For another discussion, see Bernays [9].

(6:3) *if* $X \neq 0$, *the first member of* X *is* 0;
(6:4) *if* Y *is a proper subset of* X *and is* ϵ-*complete, then* $Y \epsilon X$;
(6:5) *if* Y *is also an ordinal number, then* $Y = X$ *or* $Y \epsilon X$ *or* $X \epsilon Y$;
(6:6) *every member* u *of* X *is an ordinal number.*

Proof.—Let u_0 denote the first member of X. Then by (6:2), if u_0 has an element v, v must precede u_0 in the ordering of X, which contradicts the definition of u_0. This proves (6:3). To prove (6:4), we shall let w denote the first element of $X - Y$, and show that $w = Y$. If $w \epsilon u \epsilon Y$, then $w \epsilon Y$ since Y is ϵ-complete, but this contradicts the definition of w, so $u \epsilon Y \cdot \supset \cdot u \epsilon w$, so $Y \subset w$. It follows at once from the definition of w that $w = Y$. To prove (6:5) let $X \cap Y = Z$. Then Z is ϵ-complete, so by (6:4), if $Z \neq X$, then $Z \epsilon X$, and if $Z \neq Y$, then $Z \epsilon Y$. These two conditions cannot hold simultaneously, since that would imply $Z \epsilon Z$. To prove (6:6), we note that by (6:2), an element u of X is well ordered by ϵ. It is then easily verified that u is ϵ-complete.

THEOREM 4. *Let* $[X_i | i \epsilon J]$ *be a collection of ordinal numbers. Then* $Y = \bigcup_{i \epsilon J} X_i$ *is also an ordinal number, which is* l.u.b. X_i, *and* $Z = \bigcap_{i \epsilon J} X_i$ *is an ordinal number which is the least element of the collection* $[X_i]$.

Proof.—By property (6:6), every element of Y is an ordinal number. We note that the relation ϵ is transitive for ordinals, by (6:2). So by (6:5), Y is ordered by ϵ. Obviously Y is ϵ-complete. So it remains to show that Y is well-ordered. Let $W \subset Y$ and $u \epsilon W$. Then $\exists i \epsilon J \ni \cdot u \epsilon X_i$. The set $W \cap X_i$ is then a nonnull subset of the ordinal number X_i and so has a first element v. If $a \epsilon v$, then $a \epsilon X_i$, so v must also be the first element of W. To see that Y is l.u.b. X_i, we use the property (6:5). Finally, to show that $Z = \bigcap X_i$ is the least element of the collection $[X_i]$, we note that unless all $X_i = Y$, the set of numbers $X_i \epsilon Y$ is a nonnull subset of Y which is well-ordered, and hence has a least member, which is obviously Z.

From the preceding theorem it is clear that a set $W = [X_i]$ of ordinal numbers is well-ordered by the relation ϵ. We observe also that for ordinals the relation of class inclusion is the reflexive version of the relation of membership.

We shall use the notation sX for the set $X \cup \{X\}$. It is verified at once that sX is an ordinal whenever X is, and in this case we may sometimes write $X + 1$ in place of sX. Thus $1 = s(0) = 0 \cup \{0\} = \{0\}$, $2 = s(1) = 1 \cup \{1\}$, etc.

We do not speak of the set of *all* ordinal numbers, since such a set would itself satisfy the definition of an ordinal number and so would be a member of itself. Furthermore, such a set would be the greatest of the ordinals, and we have just seen that for each ordinal X, $X \cup \{X\}$ is a greater ordinal. We may, however, develop theorems about any given set of ordinals. Such a set may be classified into two subclasses: K_{I}, consisting of ordinal numbers of the first kind, *i.e.*, 0 and numbers of the form $X \cup \{X\}$; and K_{II}, consisting of ordinal numbers of the second kind, *i.e.*, not of the first kind. The ordinals of the second kind are also called limit ordinals.

In every well-ordered class, the principle of transfinite induction holds. Let (A, R) be well-ordered, with the relation R antireflexive, and set $\rho(k) = [k_1 \epsilon A | k_1 R k]$ for each $k \epsilon A$. Then the induction principle is as follows.

THEOREM 5. *If A_0 is a subclass of the well-ordered class A such that $\rho(k) \subset A_0 \cdot\supset\cdot k \epsilon A_0$, then $A_0 = A$.*

Proof.—We note that when k_0 is the first element of A, $\rho(k_0)$ is null, so the hypothesis on A_0 includes the condition that $k_0 \epsilon A_0$. If $A_0 \neq A$, let k_2 be the first element of $A - A_0$. Then $\rho(k_2) \subset A_0$, so $k_2 \epsilon A_0$, and we have a contradiction.

THEOREM 6. *Every well-ordered system (A, R) is ordinally similar to a unique ordinal number X, and the correspondence is uniquely determined.*

Proof.—We assume that the relation R is antireflexive. The desired one-to-one mapping g of A onto X is determined by the conditions: (a) $g(k_0) = 0$, where k_0 is the first element of A; (b) $k_1 \epsilon A \,.\, k_0 R k_1 \cdot\supset\cdot g(k_1) = [g(k_2) | k_2 R k_1]$. It will be convenient to let $\sigma(k)$ denote the first element following k in A, $\tau(k) = [k_1 \epsilon A | k_1 R \sigma(k)] = \rho(\sigma(k))$, and to let ($b_k$) denote the condition ($b$) with the set A replaced by $\tau(k)$. Now set

$$A_0 = [k \epsilon A | \exists g_k \text{ satisfying } (a) \text{ and } (b_k)].$$

We note first that $k_0 \epsilon A_0$, and that each functional value $g_k(k_1)$ is an ordinal number. Suppose $k \epsilon A_0$, $l \epsilon A_0$, kRl or $k = l$. Then $g_k(k_1) = g_l(k_1)$ for $k_1 \epsilon \tau(k)$. For if not, let k_2 be the first element of $\tau(k)$ for which $g_k(k_2) \neq g_l(k_2)$. Then $k_0 R k_2$, and $k_3 R k_2 \cdot \supset \cdot g_k(k_3) = g_l(k_3)$. So by (b_k) and (b_l), $g_k(k_2) = g_l(k_2)$. Next we show $A_0 = A$. If $\rho(k) \subset A_0$, we may set $g_k(k_1) = g_{k_1}(k_1)$ for $k_1 R k$, and $g_k(k) = [g_k(k_1) | k_1 R k]$. So $k \in A_0$, and hence $A_0 = A$ by Theorem 5. Thus we may set $g(k) = g_k(k)$ for $k \in A$, and $X = [g(k) | k \in A]$. X is clearly an ordinal number. If $k_2 R k_1$, $g(k_2) \in g(k_1)$, so g^{-1} is single-valued.

COROLLARY. *A subset W of an ordinal Y is well-ordered and is ordinally similar to an ordinal* $X \subset Y$.

Proof.—By the theorem, (W, ϵ) is ordinally similar to a unique ordinal X. Let k_0 be the first member of W. Then $g(k_0) = 0 \in (k_0 + 1)$, and if for fixed $k_1 \in W$, $g(k) \in (k + 1)$ for $k \in k_1 \cap W$, then $g(k_1) = [\text{all } g(k) | k \in k_1 \cap W] \subset k_1 \in (k_1 + 1)$, so $g(k) \in (k + 1)$ for all $k \in W$, by the theorem on transfinite induction. So $X = g(W) \subset \bigcup_{k \in W} (k + 1) \subset Y$.

EXERCISES

1. Show that in the definition of ordinal number, the condition (6:1) may be replaced by the following:

X is simply ordered by ϵ, and every nonnull subset X_0 of X has an element c which has no elements in common with X_0.

2. Show that X is an ordinal number if and only if X is a set such that $X \cup \{X\}$ is well-ordered by inclusion.

7. The Natural Numbers.—We proceed now to the definition of the class of natural numbers and of the ordinal ω. We shall say that a class B of sets x is **hereditary** in case:

$$x \in B \cdot \supset \cdot s(x) = x \cup \{x\} \in B,$$

i.e., B is hereditary for s, in the terminology of Sec. 3. The axiom of infinity may be stated in the following form: There exists a hereditary class B_1 with 0 as a member. Then the class ω of natural numbers may be defined as the intersection of all hereditary subclasses B of B_1, having 0 as a member. This intersection is easily seen to be hereditary. If we start with a different class B_2, we obviously arrive at the same class ω, since we may replace either B_1 or B_2 by $B_1 \cap B_2$. Clearly the system (ω, s) satisfies the Peano postulates listed at the beginning of Chap. II, and in particular the principle of mathematical induction is valid for ω. The following properties also hold.

THEOREM 7. *ω is an ordinal number of the second kind and is the greatest ordinal all of whose members are ordinals of the first kind.*

Proof.—For each $x \epsilon \omega$ we shall find it convenient to let $h(x)$ denote the intersection of all hereditary classes containing x, so that $x \epsilon h(x) \subset \omega$. The proof will be made by means of the following series of properties, (*a*) to (*h*):

(*a*) $x \epsilon y \epsilon \omega \cdot \supset \cdot x \epsilon \omega . x \subset y$;
(*b*) $x \epsilon y \epsilon \omega :\supset: s(x) \epsilon y \cdot \vee \cdot s(x) = y$;
(*c*) ω is ϵ-complete;
(*d*) $y \epsilon \omega \cdot \supset \cdot y$ is ϵ-complete;
(*e*) $x \epsilon \omega . y \epsilon h(x) :\supset: x \epsilon y \cdot \vee \cdot x = y$;
(*f*) $y \epsilon \omega \cdot \supset \cdot y \cup h(y) = \omega$;
(*g*) ω is ordered by ϵ;
(*h*) ω is well-ordered by ϵ.

The properties (*a*) and (*b*) are proved by induction on y, and (*c*) and (*d*) follow at once from (*a*). To obtain (*e*), let $A = [y \epsilon h(x) | x \epsilon y \vee x = y]$. It is easy to see that A is hereditary and $x \epsilon A$, so $A \supset h(x)$. To prove (*f*), we note that $y \subset \omega$ by (*c*), and $h(y) \subset \omega$ by definition of $h(y)$. If $y = 0$, $h(y) = \omega$ by definition. If $y \neq 0$, then $0 \epsilon y$ by (*e*) for $h(0)$. If $x \epsilon y$, then $s(x) \epsilon y \cup h(y)$ by (*b*). If $x \epsilon h(y)$, also $s(x) \epsilon h(y)$. Hence $y \cup h(y)$ is hereditary and contains 0, so $y \cup h(y) \supset \omega$. For (*g*), we note first that the relation ϵ is antireflexive and antisymmetric. If $x \neq y$, then $x \epsilon y$ or $x \epsilon h(y)$ by (*f*). In the second alternative, $y \epsilon x$ by (*e*). So the relation is exhaustive on ω. To show that it is transitive, let $x \epsilon y \epsilon z$. Then $y \subset z$, by (*a*), so $x \epsilon z$. To prove (*h*), let C be a nonnull subclass of ω. If $0 \epsilon C$, then 0 is the first element of C. If $0 \epsilon' C$, the set $B = [x | y \epsilon C \cdot \supset \cdot x \epsilon y]$ contains 0, and $B \cap C = 0$, so B is not hereditary. Hence $\exists x_0 \epsilon B \ni \cdot s(x_0) \epsilon' B$, and so $\exists y_0 \epsilon C \ni \cdot s(x_0) \epsilon' y_0$, and by (*b*), $s(x_0) = y_0$, $s(x_0) \epsilon y$ for $y_0 \neq y \epsilon C$. So C has a first element y_0. From these properties the theorem follows. By (*c*) and (*h*), ω is an ordinal. It cannot be of the first kind, since $x \epsilon \omega \cdot \supset \cdot s(x) \epsilon \omega$. If $\omega \epsilon u$, then u contains an ordinal of the second kind.

A set A is said to be **finite** in case it is similar to a natural number, and A is said to be **denumerably infinite** or **countably infinite** in case it is similar to ω. A is said to be **countable** in case it is finite or countably infinite. Countable sets occupy a position of special importance in mathematics. As was noted in Chap. II, the rational numbers constitute a countable set, while the real numbers constitute an uncountable set. The natural numbers are also called **finite numbers,** and all other ordinals and cardinals are called **infinite** or **transfinite.**

8. Finite Cardinals and the Alephs.—In order to secure specific representatives for the cardinal numbers, we shall select certain specific ones among the ordinal numbers. For convenience we phrase the definition as follows: An ordinal X is a **cardinal number** in case no ordinal $Y \in X$ is similar to X. Thus a cardinal X, regarded as an ordinal, is the first member of the class of ordinals similar to itself, so it may also be called an **initial** ordinal. Such an X is the cardinal number of a class A in case A is similar to X. This definition assigns cardinal numbers only to those classes that can be well-ordered. We shall see in Sec. 10 that the proposition that every class can be well-ordered is equivalent to the axiom of choice. The transfinite cardinals which are found among the ordinals in the above sense are called **alephs.**

THEOREM 8. *ω and all its members are cardinal numbers, but $s(\omega)$ is not a cardinal.*

From this theorem it follows that ω is the least aleph. As a cardinal it is usually denoted by $\aleph_0$.

Proof.—We show first that $s(\omega)$ is similar to ω, by letting x correspond to $s(x)$ and ω to 0. Next, if there exists $x \in y \in \omega$ with x similar to y, let x_0 denote the least such x, and let x_0 be similar to y_0. Obviously $x_0 \neq 0$. Then $s^{-1}(x_0)$ is similar to $s^{-1}(y_0)$ and is a member of $s^{-1}(y_0)$, which is a contradiction. Finally, if there exists $x \in \omega$ with x similar to ω, then $s(x)$ is similar to $s(\omega)$, hence to ω, and hence to x, which contradicts the preceding.

Theorem 8 shows that a finite class A has the property:

D. *A is not similar to a proper part of itself;*

and that if card $A \geqq \aleph_0$, then A cannot have the property D, since ω does not have the property D. Hence if A has property D, then A is finite or else card A is not comparable with $\aleph_0$. Conversely, if A does not have property D, then card $A \geqq \aleph_0$. For, let ϕ be a one-to-one mapping of A onto a proper subset B of A, and choose $x_0 \in (A - B)$. Set $x_{n+1} = \phi(x_n)$ for $n = 0$, $1, 2, \ldots$. This determines a mapping of ω into A. If the terms of the sequence (x_n) are not all distinct, let x_p be the first which is equal to a preceding one, x_q. Since $x_n \in B$ for $n > 0$ and $x_0 \in (A - B)$, we have $0 < q < p$, so $\phi(x_{p-1}) = \phi(x_{q-1})$, and $x_{p-1} = x_{q-1}$, which contradicts the definition of x_p.

The property D was used by Dedekind as the definition of a finite class. It is equivalent to the definition of finite class given at the end of Sec. 7 in case every cardinal is comparable with $\aleph_0$, and this property follows from the axiom of choice, as is shown in Sec. 10.

Another possible definition of "finite" is contained in the following theorem.

THEOREM 9. *A set A is finite if and only if there is an order R in A such that A is well-ordered both by R and by* R^{-1}.

Proof.—The necessity of the condition follows from the fact that every nonnull subset of a finite ordinal α must have a last element. For the sufficiency, we note that if $\omega \subset \alpha = \text{ord } A$, then, since ω has no last element, A cannot be well-ordered by R^{-1}. Hence $\alpha \in \omega$.

COROLLARY. *A descending sequence of ordinal numbers must be finite.*

9. Algebra of Ordinals and Cardinals.—The definitions of sum and product of two ordinal numbers are like those for cardinal numbers as given in Sec. 5, except that attention must be paid to order in the representative classes, and the operations turn out not to be commutative in general. If A and B are disjoint well-ordered sets with ordinals α and β, respectively, we may order $A \cup B$ by agreeing that each element of A precedes each element of B and retaining the original order in A and B. Then we define

$$\alpha + \beta = \text{ord } (A \cup B).$$

In view of the definition of ordinals which we have adopted, we obtain the same result by setting

$$\alpha + 0 = \alpha, \qquad \alpha + 1 = \alpha \cup \{\alpha\}, \qquad \alpha + \beta = \alpha \cup D,$$

where $D = [\text{all } \alpha + \gamma | \gamma \in \beta]$, since D is ordinally similar to β and disjoint from α.

We may well-order the Cartesian product $A \times B$ of well-ordered classes by setting $(x_1, y_1) < (x_2, y_2)$ whenever $y_1 < y_2$, or $y_1 = y_2$ and $x_1 < x_2$. Then we define

$$\alpha\beta = \text{ord } (A \times B).$$

From this point on, we shall for convenience usually denote the order relation for ordinals by the usual sign "$<$" rather than by "ϵ."

The operations of addition and multiplication for ordinal numbers are readily seen to be associative, but not commutative. Thus for $0 < n < \omega$,

$$n + \omega = \omega < \omega + n. \tag{9:1}$$

Also

$$\begin{aligned}\omega 2 &= \text{ord}\,[(0, 0), (1, 0), (2, 0), \ldots, (0, 1), (1, 1), \ldots] \\ &= \omega + \omega > \omega,\end{aligned}$$

while

$$\begin{aligned}2\omega &= \text{ord}\,[(0, 0), (1, 0), (0, 1), (1, 1), (0, 2), \ldots] \\ &= \omega,\end{aligned}$$

and in general, for $1 < n < \omega$,

$$n\omega = \omega < \omega n. \tag{9:2}$$

The distributive law holds on one side, namely,

$$\alpha(\beta + \gamma) = \alpha\beta + \alpha\gamma, \tag{9:3}$$

but if $0 < n < \omega$, $(\omega + n)2 = \omega 2 + n \neq \omega 2 + n2$.

The following additional properties relating to addition, multiplication, and order of ordinals α, β, γ, μ, will be useful.

(9:4) $\mu + \alpha = \mu + \beta \cdot\supset\cdot \alpha = \beta.$
(9:5) $\alpha < \beta \cdot\sim\cdot \exists\gamma > 0 \ni\cdot \alpha + \gamma = \beta.$
(9:6) $\mu :\supset: \alpha < \beta \cdot\sim\cdot \mu + \alpha < \mu + \beta.$
(9:7) $\mu \,.\, \alpha < \beta \cdot\supset\cdot \alpha + \mu \leqq \beta + \mu.$
(9:8) $\alpha + \mu < \beta + \mu \cdot\supset\cdot \alpha < \beta.$
(9:9) $\mu > 0 :\supset: \alpha < \beta \cdot\sim\cdot \mu\alpha < \mu\beta.$
(9:10) $\mu > 0 \,.\, \mu\alpha = \mu\beta \cdot\supset\cdot \alpha = \beta.$
(9:11) $\mu \,.\, \alpha < \beta \cdot\supset\cdot \alpha\mu \leqq \beta\mu.$
(9:12) $\alpha\mu < \beta\mu \cdot\supset\cdot \alpha < \beta.$

(9:4) and (9:5) are obvious from the definitions, and (9:6) follows from (9:4) and (9:5). (9:7) is obtained with the help of the Corollary of Theorem 6 in Sec. 6, and (9:8) follows from (9:7). (9:9) follows from (9:5) and the distributive law (9:3), since $\mu\gamma > 0$ when $\mu > 0$, $\gamma > 0$, and (9:10) follows from (9:9). (9:11) is obtained with the help of the above-mentioned corollary, and (9:12) follows from (9:11). Examples given above show that we cannot obtain a strict inequality in (9:7) and (9:11). By use of (9:1) and (9:6) we see that the sum of finite numbers is finite. That the product of finite numbers is finite may be derived from (9:2) and (9:9). Of course these two properties may also be derived in other ways.

We mention also certain relations between ordinals and their cardinals. If α and β are ordinals, we have

$$\text{(9:13)} \qquad \text{card } (\alpha + \beta) = \text{card } \alpha + \text{card } \beta,$$
$$\text{(9:14)} \qquad \text{card } (\alpha\beta) = \text{card } \alpha \text{ card } \beta,$$

as is obvious from the definitions. Also

$$\text{(9:15)} \qquad \alpha < \beta \cdot\supset\cdot \text{card } \alpha \leqq \text{card } \beta,$$
$$\text{(9:16)} \qquad \text{card } \alpha < \text{card } \beta \cdot\supset\cdot \alpha < \beta.$$

Since multiplication of cardinals is commutative, we may derive from (9:13) and (9:14) that

$$\text{(9:17)} \qquad \aleph_0 + \aleph_0 = \aleph_0,$$

since $\omega + \omega = \omega 2$, and $2\omega = \omega$. Hence for a cardinal $\mathbf{a} \geqq \aleph_0$,

$$\text{(9:18)} \qquad \mathbf{a} + \aleph_0 = \mathbf{a},$$

since $\mathbf{a} = \mathbf{b} + \aleph_0 = \mathbf{b} + \aleph_0 + \aleph_0 = \mathbf{a} + \aleph_0.$

We may show also that

$$\text{(9:19)} \qquad \aleph_0\aleph_0 = \aleph_0,$$

since the formula

$$f(m, n) = m + (m + n)(m + n + 1)/2$$

gives a one-to-one mapping of $\omega \times \omega$ onto ω. Since the union of a countably infinite collection of disjoint countably infinite sets is similar to the Cartesian product of two such sets, we see from (9:19) that the union of a countable collection of countable sets is countable. (Note that there is implicit in this argument a limited use of the axiom of choice, since a denumeration of each set of the collection must be chosen.)

The finite ordinals are sometimes called ordinals of the first class, and ordinals with cardinal $\aleph_0$ are called ordinals of the second class. We have seen that there are many ordinals of the second class. The ordinals of the first and second classes form a well-ordered set which is itself an ordinal number, denoted frequently by Ω, or by ω_1. The cardinal $\mathbf{a}$ of ω_1 cannot be $\aleph_0$, since ω_1 would then be a member of itself, so $\mathbf{a} > \aleph_0$, *i.e.*, there are an uncountable number of countable ordinals. Also ω_1 is the least ordinal with the cardinal $\mathbf{a}$, so it is an aleph and is denoted by $\aleph_1$. We may proceed indefinitely with this notation. Thus the ordinals with cardinal $\aleph_1$ are ordinals of the third class. The cardinal of the aggregate of all the ordinals of the first three classes is denoted by $\aleph_2$. Thus we may consider for each ordinal α a corresponding cardinal $\aleph_\alpha$. Each $\aleph_\alpha$ is the cardinal of the set of ordinals which precede it when $\aleph_\alpha$ is regarded as an ordinal.

If we let $\mathbf{c}$ denote the cardinal of all the reals (also called the cardinal of the continuum), we have $\mathbf{c} = 2^{\aleph_0}$, since each real number has a unique representation in the binary system except for those reals in a certain countable set which have two representations. Since $\aleph_0 < 2^{\aleph_0}$ by the Theorem 2 of Cantor, we have (assuming that $\aleph_1$, and $2^{\aleph_0}$ are comparable)

$$\aleph_0 < \aleph_1 \leqq 2^{\aleph_0}.$$

The proposition that $\aleph_1 = 2^{\aleph_0}$ is called the "continuum hypothesis." A body of equivalent propositions and consequences (many of which are rather startling) has been developed by Sierpinski and others (see Sierpinski [7]), but no proof of its truth or falsity has been discovered. The proposition that $\aleph_{\alpha+1} = 2^{\aleph_\alpha}$ for every α is called the "generalized continuum hypothesis."

Exercises

1. Prove that for all ordinals α, β, γ,

$$(\alpha + \beta) + \gamma = \alpha + (\beta + \gamma),$$
$$(\alpha\beta)\gamma = \alpha(\beta\gamma),$$
$$\alpha(\beta + \gamma) = \alpha\beta + \alpha\gamma.$$

2. A simply ordered set A is called *dense* in case $x < y \cdot\supset\cdot \exists z \in A \ni\cdot x < z < y$. Prove that if A and B are two simply ordered dense sets which are countable and have no first or last elements, then the two systems are isomorphic (*i.e.*, A and B can be put into one-to-one correspondence preserving order).

3. For an arbitrary set S, let P_1 denote the property that

every subclass K of the power set $\mathfrak{P}(S)$ has a minimal element (in the partial ordering by inclusion), and let P_2 denote the property that every such K has a maximal element. Prove that P_1 and P_2 are equivalent.

4. Prove that a set S has the above properties P_1 and P_2 if and only if S is finite. (Hint: When S has the property P_2, take for K the collection of all finite subsets of S.)

5. Prove that the set of all finite subsets of a countable set is countable.

6. Show that ω may be represented as the union of an infinite collection of disjoint infinite sets.

7. Denoting $2^{\aleph_0}$ by $\mathbf{c}$, show that

$$\mathbf{c} + \mathbf{c} = \mathbf{c}\mathbf{c} = \mathbf{c}^{\aleph_0} = \mathbf{c}.$$

8. Show that $\aleph_2^{\aleph_0} > \aleph_1^{\aleph_0}$ if and only if $2^{\aleph_0} = \aleph_1$ (assuming that $2^{\aleph_0}$ is comparable with $\aleph_1$ and $\aleph_2$ is comparable with $\aleph_1^{\aleph_0}$).

10. The Axiom of Choice and Zorn's Lemma.—The preceding section indicates that it would be desirable to know that every set occurring in mathematics can be well-ordered. That this is so follows from an assumption of which special cases have long been commonly used in mathematics. This assumption is called the axiom of choice, or the axiom of Zermelo, after the mathematician who first gave a proof of the well-ordering property. An equivalent proposition, called Zorn's lemma, is very frequently more convenient in applications. Since the axiom of choice is also equivalent to the statement that the Cartesian product of an arbitrary collection of nonnull sets is nonnull, it is sometimes called the multiplicative axiom. The axiom of choice is also equivalent to the proposition that the ordering of cardinals defined by (5:1) is a linear ordering. This proposition is called "the trichotomy of cardinals." Another equivalent statement is that every cardinal is an aleph. In this section we discuss the equivalence of all these propositions, including three forms of Zermelo's axiom and three forms of Zorn's lemma.

The axiom of choice and proofs by transfinite induction have been the subject of serious controversy among mathematicians.[1]

[1] See, for example, Borel, *Leçons sur la théorie des fonctions*, 2d Ed., Paris, 1914, pp. 135–160.

Some mathematicians have made strenuous efforts to avoid use of such logical tools, and some even regard as doubtful all proofs of existence which give no means of identifying an object whose existence is asserted. An existence proof depending on the axiom of choice is necessarily of this character, and such proofs enter into many parts of mathematics. Since the axiom of choice has a way of slipping into proofs without being noticed, it is well for the student to become thoroughly familiar with its various forms. The consistency of this axiom with the other axioms of set theory has been demonstrated by Gödel [11]. Its use in mathematics is now generally regarded as well justified, but some mathematicians make a practice of systematically pointing out the occasions of its use.

In connection with an arbitrary class S (in which no preassigned order is given) we shall wish to consider the set σ of all ordinal numbers of well-ordered subsets of S. The sets S and σ have the following properties.

THEOREM 10. (Hartogs). (1) *σ is an ordinal number;* (2) *card σ is finite or an aleph;* (3) *card S < card σ, or else card S is not comparable with card σ or with any greater aleph.*

Proof.—(1) follows directly from the definition of σ, and (2) is then immediate. If card $\sigma \leqq$ card S, then σ would be the ordinal of a well-ordered subset of S, *i.e.*, $\sigma \in \sigma$, which is impossible. Hence card $S <$ card σ, or else card S and card σ are not comparable. In the latter case we cannot have card $S \leqq \aleph$. On the other hand, card $\sigma \leqq \aleph$, $\aleph <$ card S, cannot hold simultaneously, by the transitivity of order and what has already been proved. Hence (3) holds.

THEOREM 11. *Every class can be well-ordered if and only if every two cardinals are comparable.*

Proof.—From (3) of Theorem 10 we see that if card S is comparable with card σ, then S can be well-ordered. If two sets A and B can be well-ordered then card A and card B are comparable, by Theorem 6, property (6:5) of Sec. 6, and (9:15).

We shall continue to denote the class of all subsets of a set S by $\mathfrak{P}(S)$. A **choice function** for S is a single-valued function ϕ mapping $\mathfrak{P}(S) - \{0\}$ into S such that $\phi(B) \in B$ for each $B \in \mathfrak{P}(S) - \{0\}$. The axiom of choice can be stated in the following three forms, which are readily shown to be equivalent.

ZA1. Zermelo's axiom (first form). *Every set S has a choice function.*

ZA2. Zermelo's axiom (second form; also called the multiplicative axiom). If $[B_i | i \in J]$ *is a family of nonnull sets, then the Cartesian product* $\prod_{i \in J} B_i$ *is nonnull. That is, there is a function* ψ *mapping* J *into* $\bigcup_{i \in J} B_i$, *with* $\psi(i) \in B_i$ *for each* i.

ZA3. Zermelo's axiom (third form). *If* $\mathfrak{F} = [B]$ *is a collection of disjoint nonnull sets, there is a set* C *such that* $B \cap C$ *has exactly one member for each* $B \in \mathfrak{F}$.

We note that ZA2 follows at once from ZA1 by taking $S = \bigcup B_i$, and $\psi(i) = \phi(B_i)$. To see that ZA3 follows from ZA2, we take $J = \mathfrak{F}$. Then $\psi(B) \in B$, and if we set $C = [\psi(B) | B \in \mathfrak{F}]$, we see that $B \cap C = \{\psi(B)\}$ since the sets B are mutually disjoint. To see that ZA1 follows from ZA3, we note that corresponding to each nonnull $B_1 \subset S$, there is a class B consisting of all elements (x, y) of $S \times \mathfrak{P}(S)$, with $x \in B_1$ and $y = B_1$. The classes B constitute a family $\mathfrak{F}$ satisfying the hypothesis of ZA3. The member (x, B_1) of $B \cap C$ determines the value $x = \phi(B_1)$ of the desired choice function ϕ.

THEOREM 12. *A class S can be well-ordered if and only if there is a choice function for S.*

Proof.—The necessity of the condition is obvious from the definition of well-ordering. For the sufficiency, the idea of the proof is to proceed as follows: Let ϕ be a choice function for S, and take $\phi(S)$ for the first element of S, $\phi(S - \{\phi(S)\})$ for the second element, etc. We shall make this procedure precise with the help of Theorem 10. Let σ be the ordinal associated with S in that theorem, and let α and δ be ordinals satisfying $0 \in \alpha \subset \delta \in \sigma$. If f is a function mapping α into S, we shall set

$$B_{f\beta} = [f(\gamma) | \gamma \in \beta]$$

for $0 \in \beta \subset \alpha$. Suppose that f has the properties

(1) $f(0) = \phi(S)$,

(2) $0 \in \beta \in \alpha \cdot \supset \cdot f(\beta) = \phi(S - B_{f\beta})$,

and that g is a function mapping δ into S and having corresponding properties. Then $f(\beta) = g(\beta)$ for $\beta \in \alpha$, by Theorem 5. It is clear that any such function has a single-valued inverse, from the definition of a choice function. If there exists $\alpha \in \sigma$ and a function f with properties (1) and (2) such that $B_{f\alpha} = S$, then S is well ordered by f, and ord $S = \alpha$. In the contrary case, suppose that there is such a function f_β for each β with $0 \in \beta \in \delta$, where $\delta \subset \sigma$. If $\delta = \alpha + 1$, set

$$f_\delta(\beta) = f_\alpha(\beta) \qquad \text{for } \beta \in \alpha,$$
$$f_\delta(\alpha) = \phi(S - B_{f_\alpha\alpha}).$$

If δ is a limit ordinal, set

$$f_\delta(\beta) = f_\alpha(\beta) \qquad \text{for } \beta \in \alpha \in \delta.$$

Thus such a function must exist for $0 \in \alpha \in \sigma$, and so f_σ must exist also, mapping σ into S. But then card $\sigma \leqq$ card S, which contradicts Theorem 10.

Zorn's lemma is a proposition which is equivalent to the axiom of choice but which is in many situations more readily applicable. Consequently a familiarity with Zorn's lemma has become essential for mathematicians. We shall state three forms of it, together with certain modifications of each form, and indicate how the equivalence of all these is proved. Then we shall show the equivalence of Zorn's lemma with Zermelo's axiom.

A simply ordered subset of a partially ordered set S will be called a **chain** in S. The class of all chains in S is a subset $\mathfrak{C}(S)$ of the power set $\mathfrak{P}(S)$ and so is itself partially ordered by inclusion. If we denote the order relation in S by "$\leqq$" (thus indicating that it is assumed to be reflexive), we may define a **maximal element** of S as an element m such that $m \leqq x \cdot\supset\cdot m = x$. A **maximal chain** in S is a maximal element of $\mathfrak{C}(S)$.

ZL1. Zorn's lemma (first form). *Every partially ordered set S contains a maximal chain.*

ZL2. Zorn's lemma (second form). *If S is a nonnull partially ordered set in which every chain has an upper bound, then S has a maximal element.*

ZL3. Zorn's lemma (third form). *If S is a class, and $\mathfrak{F}$ is a nonnull subset of $\mathfrak{P}(S)$, and for every chain $\mathfrak{G} \subset \mathfrak{F}$, the union of the sets $B \in \mathfrak{G}$ is a member of $\mathfrak{F}$, then $\mathfrak{F}$ has a maximal element.*

To show that ZL1 implies ZL2, we observe that S contains a maximal chain C, which must then have an upper bound x, by the hypothesis of ZL2. Since C is a maximal chain, $x \in C$, and so x is a maximal element of S. From the (apparently) weaker form of ZL2 in which all the chains in S are assumed to have *least* upper bounds, we can secure ZL3 by replacing S by $\mathfrak{F}$, since the union of the members of $\mathfrak{G}$ is the least upper bound of $\mathfrak{G}$ in $\mathfrak{F}$. Finally, from the (apparently) weaker form of ZL3 in which the family $\mathfrak{F}$ of sets is assumed to contain a set B if and only if it contains every finite subset of B, we can deduce an (apparently) stronger form of ZL1. In this generalized version of ZL1, the partial ordering of S is replaced by an arbitrary binary relation R on S. A subset B of S is called **R-simple** in case for every pair of distinct elements a and b in B, aRb or bRa. The generalized version of ZL1 states that every R-simple subset of S is contained in a maximal R-simple subset. To derive this, let $\mathfrak{F}$ consist of the R-simple subsets of S. Then clearly $B \in \mathfrak{F}$ if and only if every finite subset of B belongs to $\mathfrak{F}$.[(1)]

We next show that if every set can be well-ordered, then ZL1 holds. Let S be partially ordered by "$<$", and let f be a one-to-one mapping of an ordinal α onto S. For each $\beta \in \alpha$ we define a chain C_β as follows: $C_0 = \{f(0)\}$, $C_\beta = \bigcup_{\gamma\in\beta} C_\gamma \cup \{f(\beta)\}$ if this is a chain, and $C_\beta = \bigcup_{\gamma\in\beta} C_\gamma$ otherwise. It is evident that $\beta \in \delta$ implies $C_\beta \subset C_\delta$, and so that $\bigcup_{\gamma\in\beta} C_\gamma$ is a chain when each C_γ is a chain. Hence $\bigcup_{\beta\in\alpha} C_\beta$ is a chain, and is maximal.

Finally, we prove that ZL2 implies ZA2 (*i.e.*, the multiplicative axiom). Corresponding to a given family $(B_i | i \in J)$ of nonnull

[1] This generalized version of ZL1 was given by A. D. Wallace, *Bulletin of American Mathematical Society*, Vol. 50 (1944), p. 278. ZL1 appears in Hausdorff [1], p. 141, as a consequence of the axiom of choice. ZL3 is the form given by Zorn, *Bulletin of American Mathematical Society*, Vol. 41 (1935), p. 667, and stated by him to be equivalent to the axiom of choice. The "dual" of ZL3, in which "union" is replaced by "intersection" and "maximal" by "minimal," appears in R. L. Moore, "Foundations of Point Set Theory," *American Mathematical Society Colloquium Lectures* (1932), p. 84, in an (apparently) stronger form. ZL2 appears in Tukey, *Convergence and Uniformity in Topology*, Princeton University Press, 1940, p. 7. A note by W. H. Gottschalk, *Proceedings of the American Mathematical Society*, Vol. 3 (1952), p. 631, points out some more variations.

sets, let S denote the collection of all (J_0, ψ_0), where $J_0 \subset J$, and ψ_0 is a function mapping J_0 into $\cup B_i$ with $\psi_0(i) \in B_i$ for $i \in J_0$. The set S is obviously nonnull and is partially ordered by the relation defined by:

$$(J_0, \psi_0) \leqq (J_1, \psi_1) :\equiv: J_0 \subset J_1 \,.\, \psi_0(i) = \psi_1(i) \text{ on } J_0.$$

Also it is seen at once that every chain in S has an upper bound in S. Hence by ZL2, S contains a maximal element (J_2, ψ_2). If there exists $i_3 \in J - J_2$, we could choose $b_3 \in B_{i_3}$, and set $J_3 = J_2 \cup \{i_3\}$, $\psi_3(i) = \psi_2(i)$ on J_2, $\psi_3(i_3) = b_3$, so that (J_2, ψ_2) would not be maximal. Hence $J_2 = J$, and ψ_2 determines an element of the Cartesian product $\prod B_i$.

EXERCISES

NOTE: The axiom of choice may be used in the following.

1. Criticize the following supposed proof without the axiom of choice, that when card $A_i \geqq \aleph_0$ for each i, then the Cartesian product $\prod A_i$ is nonnull:

Let c be a fixed entity, and set $B_i = A_i \cup \{c\}$. Then A_i is similar to B_i for each i, and so $\prod A_i$ is similar to $\prod B_i$. But $\prod B_i$ contains the element f having $f(i) = c$ for each i.

2. Show that every partial ordering R on a set S is contained in a simple ordering.

3. Show that if a set S is simply ordered by R, and every countable subset of S is well-ordered by R, then S is well-ordered by R.

4. If S is simply ordered by R, then S has a subset A which is cofinal and well-ordered by R. (Assume R is reflexive. Then A is, by definition, **cofinal** with S in case: $x \in S \cdot\supset\cdot \exists y \in A \ni\cdot xRy$.)

5. For an arbitrary set S, call a chain Q in $\mathfrak{P}(S)$ **discriminatory** in case:

$$x \in S \,.\, y \in S \,.\, x \neq y :\supset: \exists A \in Q \ni: x \in A \,.\, y \,\epsilon'\, A \cdot \vee \cdot y \in A \,.\, x \,\epsilon'\, A.$$

Prove:

(*a*) Every chain Q in $\mathfrak{P}(S)$ determines a partial ordering of S by the formula

(*) $$x < y \cdot\equiv\cdot \exists A \in Q \ni\cdot x \in A \,.\, y \,\epsilon'\, A.$$

(*b*) If Q is discriminatory, the ordering determined by (*) is a simple ordering.

(*c*) Every maximal chain in $\mathfrak{P}(S)$ is discriminatory.

(*d*) Every simple ordering of S is determined by (*) from a discriminatory chain Q. Q may be required to be maximal, and then it is unique.

(*e*) If S consists of the rational numbers, and Q is the maximal chain determining the usual ordering of S, then Q is ordinally similar to the Cantor set.

6. Let $I = [i]$ and $J = [j]$ be two index classes, and let A_{ij} be a subset of a fixed class W for each i and j. Verify the following extensions of the distributive laws (2:1) and (2:2) for intersection and union:

$$(a) \quad \bigcap\{\bigcup[A_{ij} \mid i \in I] \mid j \in J\} = \bigcup\{\bigcap[A_{f(j),j} \mid j \in J] \mid f \in I^J\},$$
$$(b) \quad \bigcup\{\bigcap[A_{ij} \mid i \in I] \mid j \in J\} = \bigcap\{\bigcup[A_{f(j),j} \mid j \in J] \mid f \in I^J\},$$

where I^J, as usual, denotes the class of all single-valued functions f on J to I.

7. Suppose that $I_j \subset I$ for each $j \in J$, and let K denote the subset of I^J composed of those functions f having $f(j) \in I_j$ for each j. By properly defining A_{ij} for $i \in (I - I_j)$, obtain from (*a*) and (*b*) in Exercise 6 the following more general forms:

$$(c) \quad \bigcap\{\bigcup[A_{ij} \mid i \in I_j] \mid j \in J\} = \bigcup\{\bigcap[A_{f(j),j} \mid j \in J] \mid f \in K\},$$
$$(d) \quad \bigcup\{\bigcap[A_{ij} \mid i \in I_j] \mid j \in J\} = \bigcap\{\bigcup[A_{f(j),j} \mid j \in J] \mid f \in K\}.$$

8. Prove that if f and g are single-valued functions mapping A onto B and B onto A, respectively, then card A = card B.

9. A **Hamel basis** for the real numbers is a set A of real numbers such that every real number b is expressible uniquely as a finite linear combination of the numbers in A, with rational coefficients. Prove the existence of a Hamel basis.

11. Algebra of Ordinals and Cardinals (*Continued*).—In Sec. 5, arbitrary sums, finite products, and powers of cardinal numbers were defined by means of unions, Cartesian products, and function spaces, respectively, associated with corresponding classes. We now consider a few additional relations involving infinite products. As before, set $\mathbf{a}$ = card A, $\mathbf{b}$ = card B, $\mathbf{a}_i$ = card A_i for each i in an index class J. The infinite product $\prod \mathbf{a}_i$ is defined as the cardinal of the Cartesian product $\prod A_i$. If $A_i \subset A$ for each i, then $\prod A_i \subset A^J$, so $\prod \mathbf{a}_i \leqq \mathbf{a}^{\text{card } J}$ (see Sec. 3). The formulas

$$\prod \mathbf{a}_i = \mathbf{a}^{\text{card } J} \qquad \text{when each } \mathbf{a}_i = \mathbf{a},$$

$$\prod \mathbf{b}^{\mathbf{a}_i} = \mathbf{b}^{\sum \mathbf{a}_i},$$

$$\prod \mathbf{a}_i^{\mathbf{b}} = \left(\prod \mathbf{a}_i\right)^{\mathbf{b}}$$

are readily verified.

In Sec. 9, the definitions for finite sums and products of ordinal numbers were introduced in a manner closely related to the corresponding definitions for cardinal numbers, so that the relations (9:13) and (9:14) always hold. Since well-ordering is an essential part of the nature of ordinal numbers, we cannot expect to define arbitrary sums and products of ordinals. Moreover, in order to obtain a useful definition of powers and of infinite products of ordinal numbers, a drastic modification of the definitions used for cardinals is necessary, so that in general, when α_i, α, and β are ordinals, card $(\alpha^\beta) \neq (\text{card } \alpha)^{\text{card } \beta}$, card $\left(\prod \alpha_i\right) \neq \prod \text{card } \alpha_i$.

Let us suppose that J and A are ordered sets, and that A_i is an ordered set for each $i \epsilon J$. Let

$$B = \cup A_i, \qquad \text{(supposing the } A_i \text{ disjoint)},$$

$$C = \prod A_i, \qquad \text{(Cartesian product)},$$

$$D = A^J = [\text{all } f \text{ on } J \text{ to } A].$$

The given orderings of J and the sets A_i determine an ordering of the set B in an obvious way, and this ordering will be a well-ordering if and only if J and A_i are all well-ordered. Since $C \subset D$ when $A = \cup A_i$, it will be sufficient to define the order relation in D, and this is done as follows: $f < g$ in case there exists j such that $f(j) < g(j)$, and $f(i) = g(i)$ for all $i < j$. When A is nonsingular, this ordering is a linear ordering if and only if J is well-ordered, but even when both A and J are well-ordered, the resulting ordering of D may fail to be a well-ordering. For example, if $A = 2 = \{0, 1\}$, and $J = \omega$, the set D is ordinally similar to the Cantor discontinuum. Certain results for the algebra of order types which are not ordinal numbers have been obtained. (See Hausdorff [1], Sierpinski [6].) In the following paragraphs we restrict the discussion to the cases when an ordinal number can be obtained as an infinite product of ordinals or by exponentiation of ordinals. For this we replace the classes C and D defined above by suitable subclasses and choose a different ordering.

Let J, A, and all the A_i be nonnull ordinal numbers. (The exceptional cases are handled by obvious agreements.) Let D_0 be the subclass of D consisting of those functions f having values different from 0 at only a finite number of places, and let C_0 be the corresponding subclass of C. These subclasses C_0 and D_0 may still fail to be well-ordered in the ordering previously defined for D, as is shown by the infinite decreasing sequence (f_n), where $A = 2$, $J = \omega$, $f_n(i) = \delta_{in}$. If the order in D is reversed, the sequence (g_n) is decreasing, where $g_n(i) = 1$ for $i \leqq n$, $g_n(i) = 0$ for $i > n$. But if we define a new order relation $f < g$ by the condition that there exists an index j such that $f(j) < g(j)$, and $f(i) = g(i)$ for $i > j$, then it is easily seen that D_0 is well-ordered. We have reserved lower-case Greek letters to denote ordinal numbers. If we then replace A by α, A_i by α_i, and J by β, we may denote the ordinal number of D_0 by α^β and that of C_0 by $\prod \alpha_i$. But it is important to remember that α^β denotes something quite different from A^J and may in fact have a smaller cardinal. For example, by Exercise 5 of Sec. 9, $2^\omega < \Omega$, while $2^{\aleph_0} \geqq \aleph_1$. Likewise, the formula for cardinals, corresponding to (11:5) below, does not hold.

It is clear that when $\alpha_i = \alpha$ for $i \epsilon \beta$, then

$$\sum_{i \epsilon \beta} \alpha_i = \alpha\beta, \qquad \prod_{i \epsilon \beta} \alpha_i = \alpha^\beta.$$

Moreover, sums, products, and powers are determined uniquely by the following inductive definitions:

$$\alpha + 0 = \alpha, \qquad \alpha + 1 = s(\alpha), \qquad \alpha + \beta = \underset{\gamma < \beta}{\text{l.u.b.}} [\alpha + \gamma + 1];$$

$$\sum_{i \epsilon \beta} \alpha_i = \underset{\gamma < \beta}{\text{l.u.b.}} \left[\sum_{i \epsilon \gamma} \alpha_i + \alpha_\gamma\right];$$

$$\alpha \cdot 0 = 0, \qquad \alpha \cdot 1 = \alpha, \qquad \alpha\beta = \underset{\gamma < \beta}{\text{l.u.b.}} [\alpha\gamma + \alpha];$$

(11:5)
$$\prod_{i\epsilon\beta} \alpha_i = \underset{\gamma<\beta}{\text{l.u.b.}} \left[\prod_{i\epsilon\gamma} \alpha_i \cdot \alpha_\gamma\right];$$
$$\alpha^0 = 1, \qquad \alpha^1 = \alpha, \qquad \alpha^\beta = \underset{\gamma<\beta}{\text{l.u.b.}} [\alpha^\gamma \cdot \alpha].$$

An infinite product of ordinals well-ordered in the reverse order may be defined inductively by the formula

(11:6)
$$\prod_{i\epsilon\beta}^{*} \alpha_i = \underset{\gamma<\beta}{\text{l.u.b.}} \left[\alpha_\gamma \prod_{i\epsilon\gamma}^{*} \alpha_i\right],$$

but as we have already pointed out, the direct definition in terms of the Cartesian product does not work.

If $J = [i]$ is a well-ordered class, it is easily verified that

$$\prod_{i\epsilon J} \alpha^{\beta_i} = \alpha^\gamma, \qquad \text{where } \gamma = \sum_{i\epsilon J} \beta_i.$$

However,

$$\prod_{i\epsilon J} \alpha_i^\beta = \left(\prod_{i\epsilon J} \alpha_i\right)^\beta$$

does not always hold; *e.g.*, $\omega^2 2^2 \neq (\omega 2)^2$. But for cardinal numbers $\mathbf{a}$, $\mathbf{a}_i$, $\mathbf{b}$, $\mathbf{b}_i$, we always have

$$\prod_i \mathbf{a}^{\mathbf{b}_i} = \mathbf{a}^{\mathbf{c}}, \qquad \text{where } \mathbf{c} = \sum_i \mathbf{b}_i,$$
$$\prod_i \mathbf{a}_i^{\mathbf{b}} = \left(\prod_i \mathbf{a}_i\right)^{\mathbf{b}}.$$

From the definitions it is clear that if $\mathbf{a} = \text{card } \alpha$, $\mathbf{b} = \text{card } \beta$, etc., then

$$\text{card}\left(\prod_i \alpha_i\right) \leqq \prod_i \mathbf{a}_i,$$
$$\text{card } (\alpha^\beta) \leqq \mathbf{a}^{\mathbf{b}},$$
$$\text{card}\left(\prod_i \alpha_i^\beta\right) \leqq \prod_i \mathbf{a}_i^{\mathbf{b}},$$

and examples have been indicated where the strict inequality holds.

The next two theorems yield some fundamental results on sums and products of alephs.

THEOREM 13. *When α is an aleph,* $2\alpha = \alpha$.

COROLLARY. $2\aleph = \aleph + \aleph = \aleph$, *and* $\mathbf{a} < \aleph \cdot\supset\cdot \mathbf{a} + \aleph = \aleph$.

Proof.—As was seen in Sec. 9, $2\omega = \omega$, so that the result holds for the first aleph. Suppose that for $\omega \leqq \beta < \alpha$, card $(2\beta) =$ card β. Then there is an ordinal γ such that $2\beta < \gamma < \alpha$. Hence

$$2\alpha = \underset{\beta<\alpha}{\text{l.u.b.}}\,[2\beta + 2] = \underset{\beta<\alpha}{\text{l.u.b.}}\,[2\beta] = \underset{\gamma<\alpha}{\text{l.u.b.}}\,[\gamma] = \alpha.$$

THEOREM 14. *For every* $\aleph$, $\aleph^2 = \aleph$.

COROLLARY. *For every ordinal* $\alpha \geqq \omega$, *card* $\alpha^2 =$ *card* α.

Proof.—Let $\aleph =$ card A, and let

$$\mathfrak{F} = [\text{all } (B, f) \ni \cdot\, B \subset A \cdot f \text{ maps } B \text{ one-to-one onto } B \times B].$$

The family $\mathfrak{F}$ is nonnull, since there is such a mapping f for every countably infinite set B, as was shown in Sec. 9. We partially order $\mathfrak{F}$ by the relation $(B, f) \leqq (C, g)$ defined by: $B \subset C$, and f equals the restriction of g to B. It is easily verified that every simply ordered subset of $\mathfrak{F}$ has a least upper bound in $\mathfrak{F}$, so by Zorn's lemma, $\mathfrak{F}$ contains a maximal element (C, g). If card C = card A, we have our desired result. If card $C <$ card A, then by the preceding corollary, $A - C$ has a subset D such that card D = card C. By the same corollary,

$$\text{card } (C \times D \cup D \times C \cup D \times D) = \text{card } (D \times D) = \text{card } D,$$

so there is a mapping h of D onto $C \times D \cup D \times C \cup D \times D$. Setting $f = g$ on C, $f = h$ on D, we obtain an element $(C \cup D, f) > (C, g)$. But this is a contradiction, since (C, g) is maximal.

In connection with the equation between ordinals,

$$\alpha = \beta + \gamma, \tag{11:7}$$

we recall that for fixed α and β with $\beta < \alpha$, there is always a unique solution γ. On the other hand, with fixed α and γ there may be infinitely many solutions β, just one, or else none at all. For a fixed α, the numbers $\gamma > 0$ which satisfy (11:7) with some $\beta \geqq 0$ are called **remainders** of α. This means that α is a remainder of itself. Ordinals which have no other remainder are called **indecomposable.** Some properties relating to remainders and to indecomposable numbers are listed in the exercises. Additional details are given in Sierpinski [6], Chap. X.

We next consider division and factoring.

THEOREM 15. *For arbitrary ordinals α and β with $\beta > 0$ there exist unique ordinals ξ and ρ with $\rho < \beta$ such that*

$$\alpha = \beta\xi + \rho.$$

Proof.—Since $\beta(\alpha + 1) > \alpha$, there exists a least ordinal η such that $\beta\eta > \alpha$. If η is a limit ordinal, then $\beta\eta = \text{l.u.b.}\ (\beta\gamma)$ for $\gamma < \eta$, so $\beta\eta \leqq \alpha$, which is a contradiction. So $\eta = \xi + 1$, $\beta\xi \leqq \alpha$, $\beta\xi + \beta > \alpha$, so $\beta\xi + \rho = \alpha$ for some $\rho < \beta$. The uniqueness is readily verified.

An ordinal $\alpha > 1$ is called a **prime** in case it is not the product of two ordinals less than itself. We have the following extension of the familiar factorization theorem for finite ordinals.

THEOREM 16. *Every ordinal $\alpha > 1$ which is not itself a prime is a product of a finite number of primes, sometimes in more than one way.*

Proof.—There is a least ordinal $\beta > 1$ such that $\alpha = \alpha_1\beta$, and by (9:9), $1 < \alpha_1 < \alpha$. If α_1 is not a prime, the argument may be repeated on α_1. Since a decreasing sequence of ordinals must be finite, by the Corollary of Theorem 9, Sec. 8, we have the desired result. As an example of nonuniqueness, we may cite

$$\omega^2 = (\omega + 1) \cdot \omega = (\omega + 1) \cdot 2 \cdot \omega$$
$$= (\omega + 1) \cdot 3 \cdot 2 \cdot \omega = 5 \cdot (\omega + 1) \cdot 7 \cdot \omega, \text{ etc.}$$

EXERCISES

1. For two cardinals $\mathbf{a}$ and $\mathbf{b}$ with $0 < \mathbf{a} \leqq \mathbf{b} \geqq \aleph_0$, prove that $\mathbf{a} + \mathbf{b} = \mathbf{ab} = \mathbf{b}$.

2. Give an example of a class S of ordinals α where

$$\text{card}\ (\underset{\alpha\epsilon S}{\text{l.u.b.}}\ \alpha) \neq \underset{\alpha\epsilon S}{\text{l.u.b.}}\ \text{card}\ \alpha.$$

3. If $\mathbf{a}$ is a cardinal such that $\mathbf{a}^2 = \mathbf{a} > 1$, prove that $2^{\mathbf{a}} = \mathbf{a}^{\mathbf{a}}$.

4. Let $\mathbf{c}$ denote the cardinal of the class of real numbers. Determine the number of subsets of the reals which: (i) are finite; (ii) are countably infinite; (iii) have cardinal $\aleph_1$; (iv) have cardinal $\mathbf{c}$.

5. If $\mathbf{a}$, $\mathbf{b}$, $\mathbf{c}$ are cardinals, with $\mathbf{a} \leqq \mathbf{b}$, prove that $\mathbf{a}^{\mathbf{c}} \leqq \mathbf{b}^{\mathbf{c}}$.

6. Show that for infinite cardinals, $\mathbf{a} < \mathbf{b} < \mathbf{c}$ does not imply $\mathbf{b}^{\mathbf{a}} < \mathbf{c}^{\mathbf{b}}$. (HINT: Take $\mathbf{a} = \mathbf{a}_0 = \aleph_0$, $\mathbf{a}_{i+1} = 2^{\mathbf{a}_i}$, $\mathbf{b} = \sum_{i<\omega} \mathbf{a}_i$, $\mathbf{c} = 2^{\mathbf{b}}$.)

7. Show that in the example indicated under Exercise 6, $\mathbf{b}^{\mathbf{b}} = \mathbf{a}^{\mathbf{b}} = \mathbf{b}^{\mathbf{a}}$.

8. Prove that:

(i) $0 < \alpha < \Omega \cdot\supset\cdot \alpha + \Omega = \Omega \,.\, \alpha\Omega = \Omega$;

(ii) $\alpha > 0 \cdot\supset\cdot \Omega + \alpha > \Omega$;
(iii) $\alpha > 1 \cdot\supset\cdot \Omega\alpha > \Omega$.

9. Calculate $(\omega + k)\omega$, $[\omega(\omega + k)]^2$, $\omega^2(\omega + k)^2$, where k is a natural number.

10. Prove that for $\alpha < \Omega$, $\beta < \Omega$, we have $\alpha^\beta < \Omega$. Hence show that $\Omega = \omega^\Omega$.

11. If $\mathbf{a} = \text{card } A$, find the cardinal of the set of all one-to-one mappings of A onto A.

12. Show that an ordinal number can have only a finite number of right-hand divisors.

13. Prove that ω and Ω are primes.

14. Prove that an indecomposable ordinal greater than zero must be a power of ω.

15. Prove that an ordinal α has only a finite number of remainders.

16. Prove that only the least remainder of an ordinal is an indecomposable ordinal.

17. Show that an ordinal α is indecomposable if and only if $\beta < \alpha \cdot\supset\cdot \beta + \alpha = \alpha$.

18. Prove that every ordinal which is an aleph is indecomposable.

19. Show that every ordinal $\alpha > 0$ has a unique representation as a sum of a finite nonincreasing series of indecomposable ordinals.

20. Show that if α is indecomposable and $\alpha > 1$, then $\beta\alpha$ is indecomposable for every ordinal β.

21. Show that if $0 < \beta < \alpha$, and α is indecomposable, then there exists an ordinal γ such that $\alpha = \beta\gamma$, and γ must be indecomposable.

22. Show by applying formulas (11:5) and (11:6) that when $\alpha_0 = \omega$, $\alpha_i = 2$ for $0 < i < \omega$, $\prod_{i<\omega} \alpha_i = \omega^2$, $\prod^*_{i<\omega} \alpha_i = \omega$.

23. Consider the proposition: "card $J < \aleph_\beta$ and card $\alpha_i < \aleph_\beta$ for $i \in J$ implies card $(\text{l.u.b.}_{i \in J}\ \alpha_i) < \aleph_\beta$." Prove that this proposition is true for some values of $\aleph_\beta$ and false for other values.

REFERENCES

1. Hausdorff, *Grundzüge der Mengenlehre*, 1914, Chaps. 1 to 6.
2. Hausdorff, *Mengenlehre*, 3d Ed.
3. Hobson, *The Theory of Functions of a Real Variable*, Vol. 1, Chaps. 1, 4.

4. Kuratowski, *Topologie* I, 1948, Introduction.
5. Pierpont, *The Theory of Functions of Real Variables*, Vol. 2, Chaps. 8, 9.
6. Sierpinski, *Leçons sur les nombres transfinis*, 1950.
7. Sierpinski, *Hypothèse du continu*, 1934.
8. Whitehead and Russell, *Principia Mathematica*, Vol. 1, Part 2; Vol. 2, Parts 3, 4; Vol. 3, Part 5.
9. Bernays, "A System of Axiomatic Set Theory," Part 2, *Journal of Symbolic Logic*, Vol. 6 (1941), pp. 6*ff*.
10. von Neumann, "Zur Einführung der transfiniten Zahlen," *Acta Litterarum ac Scientiarum, Sectio Scientiarum Mathematicarum*, Tom. 1 (1922–1923), pp. 199–208.
11. Gödel, "The Consistency of the Axiom of Choice and of the Generalized Continuum Hypothesis with the Axioms of Set Theory," *Annals of Mathematics Studies*, No. 3, 1951.
12. Birkhoff, *Lattice Theory*, 1949.

CHAPTER XIV

METRIC SPACES

1. Introduction.—The theory of point sets described in Chap. III has an immediate generalization to abstract systems called metric spaces. In addition to the number spaces of Chap. III and the space of continuous functions discussed in Chap. VII, many other useful instances of metric spaces occur in mathematics. Another advantage of the abstract theory is that it brings to light certain concepts, possibilities, and relationships which did not appear in Chap. III. Still more general systems, called topological spaces, are of importance in mathematics. But a knowledge of the special properties of metric spaces remains essential.

2. Definition of Metric Spaces.—Consider a set $\mathfrak{E}$ of elements x (of any nature whatever) and a function ρ mapping the Cartesian product $\mathfrak{E} \times \mathfrak{E}$ into the set $\mathfrak{R}$ of real numbers. The pair $(\mathfrak{E}, \rho)$ is called a metric space in case the following conditions hold for all x, y, z, in $\mathfrak{E}$:

(2:1) $\qquad \rho(x, y) \geqq 0,$

(2:2) $\qquad \rho(x, y) = 0 \cdot\sim\cdot x = y,$

(2:3) $\qquad \rho(x, y) = \rho(y, x),$

(2:4) $\qquad \rho(x, z) \leqq \rho(x, y) + \rho(y, z).$

We shall also say that $\mathfrak{E}$ is a metric space (with metric ρ). The value $\rho(x, y)$ is called the **distance** between x and y. The condition (2:4) on ρ is called the **triangle inequality.**

We note the following examples of metric spaces.

A. $\mathfrak{E}$ is the set $\mathfrak{R}$ of all real numbers, and $\rho(x, y) = |x - y|$.

B1. $\mathfrak{E} = \mathfrak{R} \times \mathfrak{R} \times \cdot \cdot \cdot \times \mathfrak{R} = \mathfrak{R}^k$ (k factors),

$$\rho_1(x, y) = \left[\sum_{i=1}^{k} |x^{(i)} - y^{(i)}|^2 \right]^{1/2}$$

B2. $\mathfrak{E} = \mathfrak{R}^k$, $\rho_2(x, y) = \max |x^{(i)} - y^{(i)}|$.

B3. $\mathfrak{E} = \mathfrak{R}^k$, $\rho_3(x, y) = \sum_{i=1}^{k} |x^{(i)} - y^{(i)}|$.

C. $\mathfrak{E} = \mathfrak{H}$ where $\mathfrak{H}$ consists of all infinite sequences $x = (x^{(i)})$ of real numbers for which

$$\sum_{i=1}^{\infty} |x^{(i)}|^2$$

converges, and

$$\rho(x, y) = \left[\sum_{i=1}^{\infty} |x^{(i)} - y^{(i)}|^2\right]^{1/2}.$$

This is the classical **Hilbert space** and is sometimes also denoted by $\mathfrak{l}_2$.

D. $\mathfrak{E}$ consists of all bounded sequences $x = (x^{(i)})$ of real numbers, and

$$\rho(x, y) = \text{l.u.b. } |x^{(i)} - y^{(i)}|.$$

E. The set $\mathfrak{E}$ consists of all sequences $x = (x^{(i)})$ of real numbers for which

$$\sum_{i=1}^{\infty} |x^{(i)}|$$

converges, and

$$\rho(x, y) = \sum_{i=1}^{\infty} |x^{(i)} - y^{(i)}|.$$

F. Let A be an arbitrary nonnull set. $\mathfrak{E}$ consists of all bounded real-valued functions x defined on A, and

$$\rho(x, y) = \text{l.u.b. } |x(t) - y(t)| \qquad \text{for } t \in A.$$

G. $\mathfrak{E}$ consists of the natural numbers, excluding 0, but with an ideal element ∞ adjoined, and

$$\rho(x, y) = \left|\frac{1}{x} - \frac{1}{y}\right|, \qquad \rho(\infty, x) = \frac{1}{x},$$

H. $\mathfrak{E}$ is an arbitrary nonnull set, and

$$\rho(x, x) = 0, \qquad \rho(x, y) = 1 \qquad \text{if } x \neq y.$$

We note that D and B2 are both special cases of F. The

examples B1, B2, and B3 are grouped together because, while they assign different metrics to $\mathfrak{R}^k$, all these metrics determine the same class of convergent sequences of points in $\mathfrak{R}^k$. We shall discuss the notion of equivalence of metrics in more detail in a later section. The k-dimensional number space of Chap. III, with the points at infinity omitted, is the space $\mathfrak{R}^k$ of example B, with the same class of convergent sequences of points.

We observe also that when we pass from $\mathfrak{R}^k$ to the Cartesian product of a countable infinity of factors $\mathfrak{R}$, none of the metrics ρ_1, ρ_2, ρ_3, remain finite for all pairs of points. The examples C, D, and E are just those subspaces of this Cartesian product for which the metrics ρ_1, ρ_2, ρ_3, respectively, remain finite.

The metric in example H is sometimes called the **discrete** metric. Example G shows that we may regard a convergent sequence of points in a metric space $\mathfrak{S}$ as a continuous mapping of the space $\mathfrak{E}$ of example G into $\mathfrak{S}$.

If A is a subset of a space $\mathfrak{E}$ with metric ρ, then when we restrict the function ρ to $A \times A$, we see at once that A becomes a metric space with this metric, and so we call A a **subspace** of $\mathfrak{E}$. By the selection of subspaces we obtain from each of the examples listed above infinitely many other examples. We may also, in each of these examples, allow complex values for the functions $x \in \mathfrak{E}$. However, it should be noted that the function ρ is required to have real values.

*It is useful to consider also sets $\mathfrak{E}$ with an associated function ρ satisfying the conditions (2:1), (2:3), (2:4), and

$$\rho(x, x) = 0. \tag{2:5}$$

An example of such a system consists of the Lebesgue-integrable functions x defined on a measurable set T, with

$$\rho(x, y) = \int_T |x(t) - y(t)|\, dt. \tag{2:6}$$

In such a system the relation R defined by

$$xRy \cdot\equiv\cdot \rho(x, y) = 0$$

is at once seen to be an equivalence relation. If we let $\mathfrak{E}'$ denote the collection of equivalence classes $\xi, \eta, \ldots$, in $\mathfrak{E}$, and set

$$\rho'(\xi, \eta) = \rho(x, y),$$

where $x \in \xi$, $y \in \eta$, it is easy to verify that $(\mathfrak{E}', \rho')$ is a metric space. In the class of Lebesgue integrable functions with ρ given by (2:6), two functions x and y are equivalent if and only if their values are equal almost everywhere. It is customary to omit separate notations for $\mathfrak{E}'$ and its elements.

*For reference we now list two more examples of metric spaces. In the first we use the practice just mentioned about notations.

I. T is a measurable set with measure $m(T)$ (possibly infinite), and $\mathfrak{E}$ is the class of all measurable functions x on T for which

$$\int_T |x(t)|^p \, dt$$

is finite, where $p \geqq 1$, and

$$\rho(x, y) = \left\{\int_T |x(t) - y(t)|^p \, dt\right\}^{1/p}.$$

These spaces are usually denoted by $\mathfrak{L}_p$ (or $\mathfrak{L}^{(p)}$).

J. $\mathfrak{E}$ is the class of all sequences $x = (x^{(i)})$ of real numbers for which

$$\sum_{i=1}^{\infty} |x^{(i)}|^p$$

converges, where $p \geqq 1$, and

$$\rho(x, y) = \left\{\sum_{i=1}^{\infty} |x^{(i)} - y^{(i)}|^p\right\}^{1/p}.$$

These spaces are sometimes denoted by $\mathfrak{l}_p$ (or $\mathfrak{l}^{(p)}$).

*We note that C and E are special cases of J. It is readily seen that if we use $p < 1$ in J, the function ρ will fail to satisfy the triangle inequality (2:4).

EXERCISES

1. Show that condition (2:1) in the definition of a metric space is a consequence of (2:2), (2:3), and (2:4).

2. Show by examples that conditions (2:2), (2:3), and (2:4) are independent.

3. Show that conditions (2:2) and

$$\rho(x, z) \leqq \rho(x, y) + \rho(z, y) \tag{2:7}$$

imply (2:1), (2:3), and (2:4).

4. Show that if ρ is a metric for a space $\mathfrak{E}$, ρ^2 is not, in general, a metric.

5. Show that if ρ and σ are two metrics for $\mathfrak{E}$, then $\rho + \sigma$ and $(\rho^2 + \sigma^2)^{1/2}$ are also metrics.

6. Show that the metrics in examples B1 and C satisfy the triangle inequality. Start from $|2ab| \leqq a^2 + b^2$, and prove first the Schwarz inequality

$$\left| \sum x^{(i)} y^{(i)} \right|^2 \leqq \sum |x^{(i)}|^2 \sum |y^{(i)}|^2.$$

3. Spheres, Neighborhoods, Open Sets, and Closed Sets.—If b is a point of the metric space $\mathfrak{E}$, and $\epsilon > 0$, the open sphere $N(b; \epsilon)$ with center b and radius ϵ is defined by

$$N(b; \epsilon) = [x \mid \rho(b, x) < \epsilon].$$

For example B2, this coincides with the ϵ-neighborhood defined in Chap. III, Sec. 4. Its shape, in this case, is actually that of a hypercube rather than of a sphere. In the study of a general metric space $\mathfrak{E}$, the shape of a configuration does not enter into our theory. So we use the word "sphere" for convenience.

A subset S of a metric space is said to be **bounded** in case S is contained in some sphere $N(b; \epsilon)$. The **diameter** of a set S is defined by

$$\text{diam } S = \text{l.u.b. } \rho(x_1, x_2) \quad \text{for } x_1, x_2 \text{ in } S.$$

Clearly a set S is bounded if and only if its diameter is finite. If $S \subset N(b; \epsilon)$, then diam $S \leqq 2\epsilon$. However, diam S may also equal the greatest lower bound of numbers ϵ such that $S \subset N(b; \epsilon)$, where $b \in S$.

A set $S \subset \mathfrak{E}$ is called a **neighborhood** of a point $b \in \mathfrak{E}$ in case there exists $N(b; \epsilon) \subset S$, and b is then called an **interior point** of S. If b is interior to $\mathfrak{E} - S$, it is called an **exterior point** of S. All points of $\mathfrak{E}$ which are neither interior to S nor exterior to S are called **boundary points** or **frontier points** of S. A point $b \in \mathfrak{E}$ is an **accumulation point** of S in case every sphere $N(b; \epsilon)$ contains points of S distinct from b. A point $b \in S$ which is not an accumulation point of S is called an **isolated point** of S. In terms of these definitions the following statements hold. (Compare Theorems 1 to 4 of Chap. III.)

1. In every neighborhood of an accumulation point of S there are infinitely many points of S.
2. Every point of S is an accumulation point of S or an isolated point of S.

2'. An isolated point b of the space $\mathfrak{E}$ is interior to every subset S of $\mathfrak{E}$ which contains b.

3. An accumulation point of S is either an interior point of S or a boundary point of S.
4. A boundary point of S is either an accumulation point of S or an isolated point of S.

An **open set** S is one all of whose points are interior to it. Hence it may be represented as a union of spheres $N(b; \epsilon)$ with centers at points b of S. According to this definition, the null set and the whole space $\mathfrak{E}$ are both open sets. If $\mathfrak{E}$ is a subspace of $\mathfrak{E}_1$, and S is open in $\mathfrak{E}$, it may fail to be open in $\mathfrak{E}_1$, unless $\mathfrak{E}$ is open in $\mathfrak{E}_1$, but at any rate it is the intersection of $\mathfrak{E}$ with a set open in $\mathfrak{E}_1$. Also, if S is open in $\mathfrak{E}_1$, then $S \cap \mathfrak{E}$ is open in $\mathfrak{E}$.

A **closed set** S is one which contains all of its points of accumulation. In the last three sentences of the preceding paragraph, the word "open" may be replaced by "closed."

THEOREM 1. *The complement of a closed set is open, and the complement of an open set is closed.*

THEOREM 2. *The union of a family of open sets is open, and the intersection of a family of closed sets is closed. The intersection of a finite number of open sets is open, and the union of a finite number of closed sets is closed.*

The intersection of all the closed sets including a given set S is called the **closure** of S, and denoted by $\bar{S}$. It is closed, by the preceding theorem. It may also be proved that $\bar{S}$ consists of the points of S and the accumulation points of S. A set S is **dense in** a set T in case $\bar{S} \supset T$. Note that this definition differs from the one given in Chap. III. It is a more useful one for general metric spaces. However, we retain the definition that S is **dense-in-itself** in case $S \subset S'$, where S' denotes the set of accumulation points of S.

EXERCISES

1. Show that an arbitrary set A in a metric space $\mathfrak{E}$ is the intersection of a collection of open sets. Hence characterize the

metric spaces in which the intersection of an arbitrary collection of open sets is open.

2. Show that a *closed* set A in a metric space $\mathfrak{E}$ is the intersection of a *countable* collection of open sets.

3. Define a **closed sphere** with center b and radius ϵ as the set $N^c(b; \epsilon) = [x \mid \rho(b, x) \leqq \epsilon]$.

(*a*) Prove that an open sphere is open and a closed sphere is closed.

(*b*) Give an example of a space in which, for suitable b, δ, ϵ, $N(b; \delta) = N^c(b; \delta)$, while $N^c(b; \epsilon)$ is *not* the closure of $N(b; \epsilon)$.

4. When S is a subset of a metric space $(\mathfrak{E}, \rho)$, we may set $\rho(x, S) = \text{g.l.b. } \rho(x, y)$ for $y \epsilon S$. Show that:

(*a*) x is interior to S if and only if $\rho(x, \mathfrak{E} - S) > 0$;

(*b*) x is exterior to S if and only if $\rho(x, S) > 0$;

(*c*) x is a boundary point of S if and only if $\rho(x, S) = 0 = \rho(x, \mathfrak{E} - S)$;

(*d*) x is an accumulation point of S if and only if $\rho(x, S - \{x\}) = 0$;

(*e*) S is dense in $\mathfrak{E}$ if and only if $\rho(x, S) = 0$ for every x in $\mathfrak{E}$.

5. In the space of example D, construct a bounded uncountable set having no point of accumulation.

4. Convergence and Continuity of Functions, Homeomorphisms, and Topological Properties.—We now consider two metric spaces, $\mathfrak{X} = [x]$ with metric ρ, and $\mathfrak{Y} = [y]$ with metric σ, and a function f whose domain S is a subset of $\mathfrak{X}$ and whose range $f(S)$ is a subset of $\mathfrak{Y}$. Let c be a point of the closure $\bar{S}$, and let d be a point of $\mathfrak{Y}$. Then we define $\lim_{x=c} f(x) = d$ in case

$$(4:1) \quad \epsilon > 0 :\supset: \exists \delta > 0 \ni: x \epsilon S \cap N(c; \delta) \cdot\supset\cdot f(x) \subset N(d; \epsilon).$$

We may (when we wish) exclude the point c from the set S. Thus the definition just given has flexibility and convenience. It applies to multiple-valued functions such as occur in the definition of the integral as the limit of a sum. However, whenever the limit exists, it is uniquely determined. Whenever c is an isolated point of S, $\lim_{x=c} f(x)$ exists if and only if f is single-valued at c.

We define f to be **continuous at** c in case c belongs to S, and

$\lim_{x=c} f(x)$ exists. Also f is **continuous on** S in case f is continuous at each point c of S.

As an important special case of the definition of limit, we take $\mathfrak{X}$ to be the space in example G, $c = \infty$, and $S = \mathfrak{X} - \{\infty\}$, and replace the notation $f(x)$ by y_n. Then (4:1) becomes the definition of limit of a sequence of points in $\mathfrak{Y}$. The convergent sequences are those functions defined on S which can be extended to $\mathfrak{X}$ so as to be continuous.

THEOREM 3. *If f is a function with domain S, and $c \in \bar{S}$, then f has a limit at c if and only if, for every sequence (x_n, y_n) with $x_n \in S$, $y_n \in f(x_n)$, and $\lim_{n=\infty} x_n = c$, there exists $\lim_{n=\infty} y_n$.*

Proof.—The necessity of the condition is easily verified. To prove its sufficiency, suppose f does not have a limit at c, and suppose $d \in \mathfrak{Y}$. Then

$$(4{:}2) \quad \exists\epsilon > 0 \ni : n \cdot\supset\cdot \exists(x_n, y_n) \ni\cdot x_n \in S \,.\, y_n \in f(x_n) \,. \\ \rho(x_n, c) < 1/n \,.\, \sigma(y_n, d) > \epsilon.$$

Let $\lim_{n=\infty} y_n = d'$, which exists by hypothesis. Then there is a corresponding sequence (x'_n, y'_n) given by (4:2) for d'. Let (x''_n, y''_n) be the sequence formed by taking terms alternately from (x_n, y_n) and (x'_n, y'_n). Then $\lim_{n=\infty} x''_n = c$, but since $d \neq d'$, $\lim_{n=\infty} y_n = d'$, and (y'_n) does not have the limit d', $\lim_{n=\infty} y''_n$ cannot exist. We note that this proof involves a special case of the axiom of choice.

THEOREM 4. *If f maps $\mathfrak{X}$ into $\mathfrak{Y}$, then f is continuous on $\mathfrak{X}$ if and only if, for every set G open in $\mathfrak{Y}$, the inverse image $f^{-1}(G)$ is open in $\mathfrak{X}$. An equivalent condition is that for every set F closed in $\mathfrak{Y}$, the inverse image $f^{-1}(F)$ is closed in $\mathfrak{X}$.*

Note that in this theorem, f is understood to be single-valued. The proof follows readily from the definitions, with the help of Theorem 1. The condition that the inverse transform of every open set be open is frequently taken as the definition of a continuous function.

Two metric spaces $(\mathfrak{X}, \rho)$ and $(\mathfrak{Y}, \sigma)$ are **homeomorphic** in case there is a mapping f of $\mathfrak{X}$ *onto* $\mathfrak{Y}$ which is one-to-one and bicontinuous, *i.e.*, f, and f^{-1} are both continuous. The mapping f is then called a **homeomorphism** of $\mathfrak{X}$ onto $\mathfrak{Y}$.

In case $\mathfrak{X} = \mathfrak{Y}$, the two metrics ρ and σ for $\mathfrak{X}$ are said to be **equivalent** in case $(\mathfrak{X}, \rho)$ and $(\mathfrak{X}, \sigma)$ are homeomorphic under the identity mapping. This means simply that ρ and σ determine the same open sets in $\mathfrak{X}$. A necessary and sufficient condition for this is the following:

$$(4{:}3) \quad x \in \mathfrak{X} . \epsilon > 0 :\supset: \exists \delta > 0 \ni: \rho(x, x_1) < \delta \cdot\supset\cdot \sigma(x, x_1) < \epsilon . \quad \sigma(x, x_1) < \delta \cdot\supset\cdot \rho(x, x_1) < \epsilon.$$

Another necessary and sufficient condition is that for every sequence (x_n), and every x, $\rho(x, x_n)$ tends to zero if and only if $\sigma(x, x_n)$ tends to zero.

From either of these conditions it is easy to see that the three metrics B1, B2, B3 given above for Euclidean space are all equivalent. The space $\mathfrak{X}$ given in example E is a subset of that in C, which in turn is a subset of that in D, so any one of the three metrics may be applied in $\mathfrak{X}$, but they are not equivalent.

If ρ is a metric for a space $\mathfrak{X}$, we may obtain an equivalent metric σ by the formula $\sigma = \rho/(1 + \rho)$. Then $\sigma(x_1, x_2) < 1$ for all pairs of points, so we see that the property of boundedness for a metric space is not particularly significant. Every homeomorphism f between $(\mathfrak{X}, \rho)$ and $(\mathfrak{Y}, \sigma)$ determines a metric ρ' equivalent to ρ by the formula

$$\rho'(x_1, x_2) = \sigma(f(x_1), f(x_2)).$$

A property of a space $\mathfrak{X}$ is called a **topological property** in case it is invariant under homeomorphisms, *i.e.*, whenever the property is possessed by $\mathfrak{X}$, it is possessed by every space $\mathfrak{Y}$ homeomorphic to $\mathfrak{X}$. Likewise, a property of a subset A relative to a space $\mathfrak{X}$ is a topological property in case it is possessed by the image $B = fA$ relative to the space $\mathfrak{Y} = f\mathfrak{X}$ whenever f is a homeomorphic mapping of $\mathfrak{X}$ onto $\mathfrak{Y}$. In the preceding paragraphs we have observed that the distance of a pair of points is *not* a topological property, and also that a homeomorphism can be defined as a one-to-one mapping that preserves open sets. This suggests that the collection of open subsets of $\mathfrak{X}$ might well be taken as the basis for the study of the topological properties of $\mathfrak{X}$, rather than the distance function ρ, and this is usually done in general topology. Many important examples exist where the collection of open sets *cannot* be defined by a metric. Most, but not all, of the properties of metric spaces considered in the following sections are topological properties. Some of these properties are absent in more general topological spaces where the open sets cannot be defined by a metric.

A metric may be defined for the Cartesian product of two metric spaces in many ways. Three of these have been indicated in example B of Sec. 2. In general, given $(\mathfrak{X}, \rho)$ and $(\mathfrak{Y}, \sigma)$, we may define a distance τ for $\mathfrak{X} \times \mathfrak{Y}$ by

$$(4\text{:}4)\qquad \tau[(x_1, y_1), (x_2, y_2)] = \{[\rho(x_1, x_2)]^p + [\sigma(y_1, y_2)]^p\}^{1/p},$$

where $p \geqq 1$, or by

$$(4\text{:}5)\qquad \tau[(x_1, y_1), (x_2, y_2)] = \max \{\rho(x_1, x_2), \sigma(y_1, y_2)\}.$$

We note that the second formula is obtained as a limiting case of the first when p tends to infinity. There are obvious extensions of these definitions to the case of any finite number of factor spaces. For Cartesian products of infinitely many spaces, these definitions lead to finite values for the distance only for subsets, in general. We may avoid this limitation by choosing other metrics. For example, if $(\mathfrak{X}^i, \rho^i)$, where i ranges over the index class J, is an infinite system of metric spaces, we may set

$$(4\text{:}6)\qquad \tau(\xi_1, \xi_2) = \underset{i}{\text{l.u.b.}}\ \frac{\rho^i(x_1^i, x_2^i)}{1 + \rho^i(x_1^i, x_2^i)},$$

where $\xi_1 = (x_1^i)$, $\xi_2 = (x_2^i)$. If J is countable, we may choose instead to set

$$\tau(\xi_1, \xi_2) = \sum_i \frac{\rho^i(x_1^i, x_2^i)}{2^i[1 + \rho^i(x_1^i, x_2^i)]}.$$

Note that the last metric is not equivalent to (4:6) in case there is a positive number δ such that infinitely many of the spaces $\mathfrak{X}^i$ contain pairs of points x_1^i, x_2^i with $\rho^i(x_1^i, x_2^i) > \delta$. When $(\mathfrak{X}^i, \rho^i)$ is the same for all i, we obtain the **function space $\mathfrak{X}^J$** consisting of all functions ξ on J to $\mathfrak{X}$. If J is also a metric space, we may consider the subspace of all *continuous* functions on J to $\mathfrak{X}$. With the metric (4:6) we shall denote this space by $\mathfrak{C}(J, \mathfrak{X})$. In the subspace of $\mathfrak{X}^J$ consisting of all the *bounded* functions, the metric

$$(4\text{:}7)\qquad \tau_1(\xi_1, \xi_2) = \underset{i}{\text{l.u.b.}}\ \rho(x_1^i, x_2^i)$$

is equivalent to (4:6) and is frequently more convenient.

A function f mapping a metric space $\mathfrak{X}$ into a metric space $\mathfrak{Y}$ is called **uniformly continuous** in case:

$$\epsilon > 0 :\supset: \exists \delta > 0 \ni: x_1 \in \mathfrak{X} . x_2 \in \mathfrak{X} . \rho(x_1, x_2) < \delta \cdot\supset\cdot \sigma(f(x_1), f(x_2)) < \epsilon.$$

A first example of a function which is uniformly continuous is the distance function ρ, which maps the Cartesian product $\mathfrak{X} \times \mathfrak{X}$ into the reals. Two metrics ρ and σ for a space $\mathfrak{X}$ will be called **uniformly equivalent** in case the identity mapping is uniformly continuous when regarded as a function on $(\mathfrak{X}, \rho)$ to $(\mathfrak{X}, \sigma)$, and also when regarded as a function on $(\mathfrak{X}, \sigma)$ to $(\mathfrak{X}, \rho)$. A condition for this to hold is like (4:3) except that δ is independent of x, depending only on ϵ.

*The metric spaces $\mathfrak{L}_p$ and $\mathfrak{l}_q$ described in Sec. 2 have been the object of special study. In Chap. XI, Sec. 11, it was shown that a one-to-one correspondence between $\mathfrak{L}_2$ and $\mathfrak{l}_2$ may be set up which is linear and isometric (*i.e.*, it preserves distances). Hence $\mathfrak{L}_2$ and $\mathfrak{l}_2$ are indistinguishable by properties involving only distance, addition, and multiplication by scalars. It may be shown that the function f defined by

$$(4{:}8) \qquad f(x) = (|x^i|^{1/p} \operatorname{sgn} x^i \mid i = 1, 2, \ldots)$$

maps $\mathfrak{l}_1$ onto $\mathfrak{l}_p$ one-to-one, and that if ρ is the metric in $\mathfrak{l}_1$, and σ the metric in $\mathfrak{l}_p$,

$$(4{:}9) \qquad \sigma(f(x), f(y)) \leqq 2\rho(x, y)^{1/p},$$

$$(4{:}10) \qquad \rho(x, y) \leqq p\sigma(f(x), f(y))\{\sigma(f(x), 0) + \sigma(f(y), 0)\}^{p-1}.$$

A similar formula may be used to show that $\mathfrak{L}$ is homeomorphic to $\mathfrak{L}_q$ for every $q > 1$, so that $\mathfrak{l}_p$ and $\mathfrak{L}_q$ are homeomorphic for $p \geqq 1, q \geqq 1$.[1] However, the inequality (4:10) leads us to suspect that f^{-1} is *not* uniformly continuous, and this may be verified by taking $y = ax$, where $a > 1$ and $x^i = 1$ for $i = 1, \ldots, n$, $x^i = 0$ for $i > n$. Then $f(x) = x$, $f(y) = a^{1/p}x$, $\rho(x, y) = n(a - 1)$, $\sigma(f(x), f(y)) = n^{1/p}(a^{1/p} - 1)$. By taking $a = (1 + n^k)^p$ with $-1 < k < -1/p$, we find that $\rho(x, y)$ tends to infinity with n, while $\sigma(f(x), f(y))$ approaches zero. Questions of the existence

[1] See Mazur, "Une remarque sur l'homéomorphie des champs fonctionnels," *Studia Mathematica*, Vol. 1 (1929), pp. 83–85. With a suitable modification of the formula (4:8) the result may be extended to the case when the values of x are complex.

of *linear* and continuous mappings between $\mathfrak{l}_p$, $\mathfrak{l}_q$, $\mathfrak{L}_p$ and $\mathfrak{L}_q$ are discussed in Banach [7], Chap. XII.

5. Complete Spaces.—A sequence (x_m) of points in a metric space $(\mathfrak{X}, \rho)$ is called a **Cauchy sequence** in case

$$\lim_{\substack{m=\infty \\ n=\infty}} \rho(x_m, x_n) = 0.$$

Every sequence having a limit in $\mathfrak{X}$ is a Cauchy sequence. When we pass to a *uniformly* equivalent metric, a Cauchy sequence clearly remains a Cauchy sequence. But this may fail to be so when the two metrics are not uniformly equivalent. For example, if $\mathfrak{X}$ is the class of real numbers (or the rationals), and we set $\rho(x_1, x_2) = |\tanh x_1 - \tanh x_2|$, we see that the sequence with $x_n = n$ is a Cauchy sequence, although it is not one under the usual metric.

A metric space $(\mathfrak{X}, \rho)$ is called **complete** in case every Cauchy sequence in $\mathfrak{X}$ has a limit in $\mathfrak{X}$. In case this property of completeness holds for one metric, it holds for all uniformly equivalent metrics, but it does not always hold for all equivalent metrics, as the example of the preceding paragraph indicates. The following theorem is an obvious consequence of the definition of completeness.

THEOREM 5. *A subset A of a complete space $\mathfrak{X}$ is complete if and only if A is closed in $\mathfrak{X}$.*

The Cauchy condition for the existence of a limit may be generalized from the case of sequences, as is indicated in the following theorem.

THEOREM 6. *Let $(\mathfrak{X}, \rho)$ and $(\mathfrak{Y}, \sigma)$ be metric spaces, with $\mathfrak{Y}$ complete, and let f be a function on S to $\mathfrak{Y}$, where $S \subset \mathfrak{X}$. If $c \in \bar{S}$, then $\lim_{x=c} f(x)$ exists if and only if*

$$\epsilon > 0 :\supset: \exists \delta > 0 \ni: \rho(x_1, c) < \delta \; . \; \rho(x_2, c) < \delta \cdot\supset\cdot \sigma(f(x_1), f(x_2)) < \epsilon.$$

The necessity of this condition follows readily from the triangle inequality, and the sufficiency may be obtained with the help of Theorem 3. The theorem holds also for multiple-valued functions f if we interpret $\sigma(f(x_1), f(x_2)) < \epsilon$ to mean $\sigma(y_1, y_2) < \epsilon$ for every $y_1 \in f(x_1)$, $y_2 \in f(x_2)$. The condition in this case may be conveniently rewritten as follows:

$$\epsilon > 0 \cdot\supset\cdot \exists \delta > 0 \ni\cdot \operatorname{diam} (f(N(c; \delta))) < \epsilon.$$

A corollary of the last theorem is the following fundamental result.

THEOREM 7. *Let* $(\mathfrak{Y}, \sigma)$ *be a complete metric space, and let* (A_n) *be a decreasing sequence of closed sets in* $\mathfrak{Y}$ *with* $\lim_{n=\infty} \text{diam } A_n = 0$. *Then the sets* A_n *have exactly one point in common.*

Proof.—We take the space of example G, Sec. 2, for the space $\mathfrak{X}$, and take $f(n) = A_n$, *i.e.*, f is a multiple-valued function. Then by the condition of the last theorem, f has a limit y_0, and $y_0 \in A_n$ since A_n is closed. There cannot be more than one point in $\bigcap A_n$, since $\lim \text{diam } A_n = 0$.

A mapping f on $\mathfrak{X}$ to $\mathfrak{Y}$, where $(\mathfrak{X}, \rho)$ and $(\mathfrak{Y}, \sigma)$ are metric spaces, is called an **isometric mapping,** or an **isometry,** in case

$$\sigma(f(x_1), f(x_2)) = \rho(x_1, x_2) \qquad \text{for all } x_1, x_2.$$

An isometry is clearly one-to-one, and so is a homeomorphism between $\mathfrak{X}$ and $f(\mathfrak{X})$. A result frequently useful is the following.

THEOREM 8. *Suppose* $(\mathfrak{X}, \rho)$ *and* $(\mathfrak{Y}, \sigma)$ *are metric spaces, with* $\mathfrak{Y}$ *complete, and let* g *be a uniformly continuous mapping of* A *into* $\mathfrak{Y}$, *where* A *is dense in* $\mathfrak{X}$. *Then there exists a unique continuous mapping* g^* *of* $\mathfrak{X}$ *into* $\mathfrak{Y}$ *such that* g^*, *when restricted to* A, *coincides with* g. *Moreover,* g^* *is uniformly continuous, and if* g *is an isometry, so is* g^*.

Proof.—Corresponding to a point $x \in \mathfrak{X}$ we may choose a sequence (x_n) from A with $\lim x_n = x$. Then $g(x_n)$ is a Cauchy sequence in $\mathfrak{Y}$ and so has a limit $y \in \mathfrak{Y}$. The limit y is independent of the sequence (x_n) with limit x, since from two such sequences (x'_n) and (x''_n) we may form a single sequence by setting $x_{2n} = x'_n$, $x_{2n+1} = x''_n$. Thus we may define $g^*(x) = y$, and g^* is uniquely determined. Obviously $g^*|A = g$. To show g^* uniformly continuous, suppose that

$$(5{:}1) \qquad x \in A \,.\, x' \in A \,.\, \rho(x, x') < \delta \cdot\!\supset\!\cdot\, \sigma(g(x), g(x')) \leqq \epsilon.$$

Then if $x_1 \in \mathfrak{X}$, $x_2 \in \mathfrak{X}$, and $\rho(x_1, x_2) < \delta$, there are sequences (x_{1n}) and (x_{2n}) from A such that $\lim x_{1n} = x_1$, $\lim x_{2n} = x_2$, and so $\rho(x_{1n}, x_{2n}) < \delta$ for $n > n_0$, sufficiently large. Thus by (5:1), $\sigma(g(x_{1n}), g(x_{2n})) \leqq \epsilon$ for $n > n_0$, and so $\sigma(g^*(x_1), g^*(x_2)) \leqq \epsilon$, by the continuity of σ. That g^* is an isometry when g is follows from the continuity of ρ and of σ.

The mapping g^* of the preceding theorem is naturally called an **extension** of g, just as g is called a restriction of g^*. The uniqueness of an extension is readily seen to hold under weaker hypotheses, as stated in the following theorem.

Theorem 9. *If* $(\mathfrak{X}, \rho)$ *and* $(\mathfrak{Y}, \sigma)$ *are metric spaces, A is dense in* $\mathfrak{X}$, *and f and g are continuous functions mapping* $\mathfrak{X}$ *into* $\mathfrak{Y}$, *such that* $f|A = g|A$, *then* $f = g$.

It was indicated in Chap. VII how a space of continuous functions becomes a metric space by a suitable choice of distance. In the preceding section the metric (4:6) was defined for the space of all mappings of a set J into a metric space $\mathfrak{X}$. The following useful theorem on the completeness of such spaces is readily verified.

Theorem 10. *If J is an arbitrary set and* $(\mathfrak{X}, \rho)$ *is a complete metric space, the space* $\mathfrak{X}^J$ *of all functions* ξ *on J to* $\mathfrak{X}$ *is a complete metric space with the metric* (4:6). *When J is also a metric space, the subset* $\mathfrak{C}(J, \mathfrak{X})$ *of* $\mathfrak{X}^J$ *consisting of the continuous functions is closed, and so is also complete. For the subspace of* $\mathfrak{X}^J$ *consisting of the bounded functions, the metric* (4:7) *is uniformly equivalent to* (4:6).

Every metric space is embedded in a complete metric space. The sense in which a minimal completion is unique is made explicit in the following theorem.

Theorem 11. *For every metric space* $(\mathfrak{X}, \rho)$ *there exists a complete metric space* $(\mathfrak{Y}, \sigma)$ *and an isometry f of* $\mathfrak{X}$ *into* $\mathfrak{Y}$. *If g is an isometry of* $\mathfrak{X}$ *into another complete metric space* $\mathfrak{Z}$, *then there is a unique isometry h mapping* $\overline{f(\mathfrak{X})}$ *onto* $\overline{g(\mathfrak{X})}$ *such that* $h \circ f = g$.

The set $\overline{f(\mathfrak{X})}$ (where $\overline{f(\mathfrak{X})}$ denotes the closure of $f(\mathfrak{X})$) is called a **completion** of $\mathfrak{X}$. The last sentence of the theorem states that any two completions of a given space are isometric. The existence of a completion may be established in a manner quite analogous to the Cantor process for constructing the real numbers from the rationals. However, since we already have the real number system which is complete, Theorem 11 follows almost immediately from Theorem 10. Let $\mathfrak{R}$ denote the real numbers with the usual metric, and let $\mathfrak{Y}$ denote the set of all bounded functions η mapping $\mathfrak{X}$ into $\mathfrak{R}$, with the metric $\sigma(\eta_1, \eta_2) = \text{l.u.b.} |\eta_1(x) - \eta_2(x)|$. Then $\mathfrak{Y}$ is complete. To obtain an isometry f of $\mathfrak{X}$ into $\mathfrak{Y}$, select a point x_0 in $\mathfrak{X}$, and set $f(x) = \eta$, where $\eta(x_1) = \rho(x_1, x) - \rho(x_1, x_0)$. That each such η is bounded, and that f is an isometry, follow from the triangle inequality for ρ. So the closure $\overline{f(\mathfrak{X})}$ of $f(\mathfrak{X})$ is a completion of $\mathfrak{X}$. We note that $\overline{f(\mathfrak{X})}$ consists of continuous functions in $\mathfrak{Y}$. If $\overline{g(\mathfrak{X})}$ is another completion, where $g(\mathfrak{X}) \subset \mathfrak{Z}$, then the composite mapping $g \circ f^{-1}$ is an isometry of $f(\mathfrak{X})$ onto $g(\mathfrak{X})$. By Theorem 8, there exists a unique extension h of $g \circ f^{-1}$, which is an isometry of $\overline{f(\mathfrak{X})}$ into $\mathfrak{Z}$, and $h \circ f = g$. Since h is an isometry, $h(\overline{f(\mathfrak{X})})$ is complete, so it contains $\overline{g(\mathfrak{X})}$. Also h^{-1} is an isometry, $h^{-1} \circ g = f$, $h^{-1}(\overline{g(\mathfrak{X})})$ is complete, and so $h^{-1}(\overline{g(\mathfrak{X})}) \supset \overline{f(\mathfrak{X})}$. Hence h maps $\overline{f(\mathfrak{X})}$ onto $\overline{g(\mathfrak{X})}$.

All the examples given at the beginning of Sec. 2 are complete spaces.

*It is instructive to consider some equivalent metrics in the space of example B (*i.e.*, the k-dimensional space $\mathfrak{R}^k$), for which the space ceases to be complete, and to construct the completions. Every point x in $\mathfrak{R}^k$ may be represented in the form $x = ru$, where u is a unit vector, *i.e.*, $\rho_1(u, 0) = 1$, and $r \geqq 0$. The representation is uniquely determined except when $r = \rho_1(x, 0) = 0$. Let the points of $\mathfrak{R}^{k+1}$ be denoted by ξ, and the (Euclidean) distance in $\mathfrak{R}^{k+1}$ by ρ_1' (corresponding to ρ_1 for $\mathfrak{R}^k$). Define a mapping f of $\mathfrak{R}^k$ into $\mathfrak{R}^{k+1}$ by the formula $f(x) = \xi$, where

$$\xi^{(i)} = \frac{2ru^{(i)}}{r^2 + 1}, \qquad \xi^{(k+1)} = \frac{r^2 - 1}{r^2 + 1}.$$

This mapping is one-to-one and bicontinuous, so we may take

$$(5{:}2) \qquad \rho_4(x_1, x_2) = \rho_1'(f(x_1), f(x_2)).$$

Thus $(\mathfrak{R}^k, \rho_4)$ is isometric to $(f(\mathfrak{R}^k), \rho_1')$, but $f(\mathfrak{R}^k)$ is the unit sphere in $\mathfrak{R}^{k+1}$ with one point omitted. Thus the completion of $(\mathfrak{R}^k, \rho_4)$ is equivalent to the adjunction of one point "at infinity." It is easily verified that any sequence with r_n tending to infinity is a Cauchy sequence in $(\mathfrak{R}^k, \rho_4)$.

*Next, define a mapping g of $\mathfrak{R}^k$ into $\mathfrak{R}^{k+1}$ by setting $g(x) = \xi$, where

$$\xi^{(i)} = \frac{2ru^{(i)}}{(r^2 + 1)^{1/2}}, \qquad \xi^{(k+1)} = \frac{1}{(r^2 + 1)^{1/2}},$$

and take

$$(5{:}3) \quad \rho_5(x_1, x_2) = \min \{\rho_1'(g(x_1), g(x_2)), \rho_1'(-g(x_1), g(x_2))\}.$$

In this case $g(\mathfrak{R}^k)$ is a unit hemisphere in $\mathfrak{R}^{k+1}$ with the equator omitted. A Cauchy sequence (x_n) in $(\mathfrak{R}^k, \rho_5)$ must have r_n convergent, or else r_n tending to infinity. In the first case, the sequence is also a Cauchy sequence in $(\mathfrak{R}^k, \rho_1)$ and so converges in $(\mathfrak{R}^k, \rho_1)$, and hence in $(\mathfrak{R}^k, \rho_5)$. In the second case, the sequence (u_n) has either one limit point u or two limit points $\pm u$. The completion of $(\mathfrak{R}^k, \rho_5)$ is then projective k-dimensional space, since it adjoins one point at infinity on each bundle of parallel lines.

*We may also define a one-to-one and bicontinuous mapping h of $\mathfrak{R}^k$ into $\mathfrak{R}^k$ by setting $h(x) = y$, where $y^{(i)} = \tanh x^{(i)}$, and take

$$\rho_6(x_1, x_2) = \rho_1(h(x_1), h(x_2)). \tag{5:4}$$

Then $h(\mathfrak{R}^k)$ is the interior of a k-dimensional cube and its completion adds the $2k$ bounding faces, *i e.*, the completion of $\mathfrak{R}^k$ in the metric ρ_6 adjoins $2k$ hyperplanes at infinity.

EXERCISES

1. Prove that a point y is in the closure $\bar{A}$ of a set A in a metric space if and only if there is a sequence (x_n) of points of A such that $\lim x_n = y$.

2. Let (x_n), (y_n) be two Cauchy sequences in a metric space. Prove that $(\rho(x_n, y_n))$ is a Cauchy sequence of numbers.

3. Prove that a Cauchy sequence in a metric space is bounded.

4. Let f be a uniformly continuous function mapping $\mathfrak{X}$ into $\mathfrak{Y}$. Show that $(f(x_n))$ is a Cauchy sequence whenever (x_n) is.

5. Show by an example that the converse of Exercise 4 does not hold, even when f is one-to-one.

6. Prove that the composite of two uniformly continuous functions is uniformly continuous.

7. Let $\mathfrak{Y} = \mathfrak{X}_1 \times \mathfrak{X}_2$, with one of the metrics indicated by (4:4) or (4:5). Let π_i denote the projection of $\mathfrak{Y}$ onto $\mathfrak{X}_i$. Prove that a function f mapping $\mathfrak{Z}$ into $\mathfrak{Y}$ is uniformly continuous on $\mathfrak{Z}$ if and only if each $\pi_i \circ f$ is uniformly continuous.

8. Prove that the spaces listed under examples A to J in Sec. 2 are complete.

9. Prove that if U and V are subsets of a metric space $\mathfrak{E}$ and $\bar{U} \cap V = 0 = U \cap \bar{V}$, then there exists a pair of open disjoint sets A and B such that $U \subset A$, $V \subset B$.

10. Let p be a prime number, and let $0 < b < 1$. Show that a metric ρ for the class of rational numbers is given by the formula $\rho(x, x) = 0$, $\rho(x, y) = b^m$, where $x - y = p^m r/s$ and r and s are

integers not divisible by p. (NOTE: The completion of this space yields the so-called p-adic numbers.)

11. Let $\mathfrak{E}$ be the class of all sequences $x = (\xi_n)$, $y = (\eta_n)$, . . . , whose elements are chosen from a fixed class A. Prove that $\mathfrak{E}$ is a metric space with the metric: $\rho(x, x) = 0$, $\rho(x, y) = 1/m(x, y)$, where $m(x, y)$ is the first integer m such that $\xi_m \neq \eta_m$.

12. Let A be a set partially ordered by a relation R, let B be another set, and define a partial order S in the function space A^B = [all f on B to A] by the formula:

$$f_1 S f_2 \text{ in case } f_1(b) R f_2(b) \quad \text{for every } b \in B.$$

(*a*) When A is a lattice, is A^B also a lattice?

(*b*) When A is a complete lattice, is A^B also a complete lattice?

(*c*) When A consists of the interval $0 \leqq a \leqq 1$ of the real numbers in the usual ordering, and B is a metric space, is the set $\mathfrak{C}(B, A)$ of all continuous functions on B to A a lattice? A complete lattice?

(*d*) Formulate a generalization of (*c*) to the case when A is a metric space and a lattice.

(*e*) When A consists of the real numbers, and $B = A$, and M consists of all the measurable functions on B to A, is M a lattice? A complete lattice? Is there any difference in the answer in case A is the interval [0, 1]?

(In each of the preceding cases, justify your conclusions.)

6. Connected Sets.—A **separation** of a space $\mathfrak{E}$ is a partition of $\mathfrak{E}$ into two disjoint nonnull open sets A and B. In case such a separation exists, $\mathfrak{E}$ is said to be **disconnected**; otherwise $\mathfrak{E}$ is said to be **connected.** The property of connectedness is an absolute property, *i.e.*, it has nothing to do with any embedding of $\mathfrak{E}$ in a larger space. Since the sets A and B constituting a separation are complementary, they are also closed sets. We apply the definition of connectedness to a subset C of $\mathfrak{E}$ by regarding C as a space. When this definition is interpreted relative to $\mathfrak{E}$, it takes the following form: C is connected in case there exists no separation of C into disjoint nonnull sets A and B, both open relative to C, *i.e.*,

$$C = A \cup B \,.\, (A \cap \bar{B}) \cup (\bar{A} \cap B) = 0 :\supset: A = 0 \cdot \vee \cdot B = 0.$$

A fundamental theorem is the following.

THEOREM 12. *A continuous transform of a connected space is connected.*

An indirect proof is readily made. Theorem 21 of Chap. IV is a frequently used special case. Theorem 12 shows that the property of being connected is a topological property.

THEOREM 13. *If* $A \subset \mathfrak{E}$, $C \subset \mathfrak{E}$, *and* C *is connected and has points in* A *and in* $\mathfrak{E} - A$, *then* C *intersects the boundary of* A.

Proof.—If not, then C is separated into the sets $C \cap A$ and $C \cap (\mathfrak{E} - A)$, which are open in C.

A closed connected set is called a **continuum.** Thus the property of being a continuum is a relative property. A **component** of a space $\mathfrak{E}$ is defined to be a maximal connected subset of $\mathfrak{E}$. That every point of $\mathfrak{E}$ belongs to a component of $\mathfrak{E}$ follows at once from Exercise 1, below, and the third form of Zorn's lemma, applied to the family $\mathfrak{F}$ of connected subsets of $\mathfrak{E}$. By Exercise 4, below, no two components of $\mathfrak{E}$ can have a point in common. Also each component of a space $\mathfrak{E}$ is a continuum. Every set consisting of just one point is connected and so is a continuum. In case every component of $\mathfrak{E}$ consists of a single point, $\mathfrak{E}$ is called **totally disconnected.** Obviously a discrete space is totally disconnected.

THEOREM 14. *A connected space* $\mathfrak{E}$ *containing more than one point is dense-in-itself, and* card $\mathfrak{E} \geqq 2^{\aleph_0}$, *i e.,* $\mathfrak{E}$ *has at least the power of the continuum.*

Proof.—In Theorem 13, let $A = N(a; \epsilon)$, where $a \in \mathfrak{E}$, $b \in (\mathfrak{E} - A)$. A point x on the boundary of A must have

$$\rho(a, x) = \epsilon. \tag{6:1}$$

So $\mathfrak{E}$ has a point x satisfying (6:1) for every ϵ in the interval I defined by $0 < \epsilon < \rho(a, b)$. Hence a is an accumulation point of $\mathfrak{E}$. Since points satisfying (6:1) for different values of ϵ must be distinct, card $\mathfrak{E} \geqq$ card $I = 2^{\aleph_0}$.

A useful example of a connected set in the xy-plane is composed of the points on the graph of $y = \sin(1/x)$ for $x \neq 0$ and of the interval $-1 \leqq y \leqq 1$ of the y-axis. This example fails to have another property of some interest which we now define. A space $\mathfrak{E}$ is **locally connected at a point** x in case every neighborhood of x contains a connected neighborhood of x. $\mathfrak{E}$ is said to be **locally connected** in case it is locally connected at each of its points. Note that a space may be locally connected without being connected.

THEOREM 15. *The following conditions on a metric space* $\mathfrak{E}$ *are equivalent:* (i) $\mathfrak{E}$ *is locally connected;* (ii) *the components of every open set in* $\mathfrak{E}$ *are open;* (iii) *for each* $x \in \mathfrak{E}$, *every neighborhood of* x *contains a connected open neighborhood of* x.

Proof.—To show that (i) implies (ii), let S be open, S_1 be one of the components of S, and $x \in S_1$. Then S contains a connected neighborhood T of x. Hence $T \subset S_1$, so x is interior to S_1, and S_1 is open. To show that (ii) implies (iii), let S be a neighborhood of x. S contains an open neighborhood S_0 of x, and the component of S_0 containing x is a neighborhood of the required kind. It is obvious that (iii) implies (i).

THEOREM 16. *A space homeomorphic to a locally connected space is locally connected.*

This is easy to verify with the help of (ii) of the preceding theorem. However, the statement analogous to Theorem 12, *i.e.*, that a continuous transform of a locally connected space is locally connected, is false, as the following example shows. In this example, the mapping is one-to-one. Let $\mathfrak{E}$ be the subset of $\mathfrak{R}^2$ consisting of the points $(x, 0)$ with $0 < x \leqq 2\pi$ and the points $(2\pi/n, y)$ for $n = 1, 2, 3, \ldots$, and $0 \leqq y < 1$, and set $f(x, y) = (\cos x, y, \sin x)$ on $\mathfrak{E}$.

EXERCISES

Prove the following:

1. A space $\mathfrak{E}$ is connected in case every pair of its points lies in a connected subspace.
2. The connected subsets of the real line are the intervals.
3. The Cartesian product of two connected spaces is connected.
4. If S and T are connected subspaces of a space $\mathfrak{E}$, and $(S \cap \bar{T}) \cup (\bar{S} \cap T) \neq 0$, then $S \cup T$ is connected.
5. The set B is totally disconnected in case:

(*a*) B consists of all points in $\mathfrak{R}^k$ with rational coordinates;

(*b*) B consists of all points in $\mathfrak{R}^k$ with irrational coordinates.

(HINT: Apply Theorem 13.)

6. If $k \geqq 2$, the set C consisting of all points in $\mathfrak{R}^k$ with at least one irrational coordinate is connected. (HINT: The set of rays issuing from a point x of C and containing a point not in C is countable. Use also Exercises 2, 4, and 1.)

7. If A and B are closed, and $A \cap B$ and $A \cup B$ are each connected, then A is connected.

8. If $A \subset B \subset \bar{A}$, and A is connected, B is connected.

7. Separable Spaces.—From the definition of neighborhoods for metric spaces, it follows that every point x has a *countable* family $\mathfrak{F}$ of neighborhoods such that every neighborhood of x includes a neighborhood from the family $\mathfrak{F}$. For example, we may take the family $\mathfrak{F}$ to consist of the neighborhoods $N(x; 1/n)$ for $n = 1, 2, \ldots$. In general topology, spaces are considered which do not have this property. Its possession by metric spaces accounts for the prominence of sequences of points in the preceding sections. We now consider a stronger property, which is not possessed by some metric spaces. In Theorem 17, we shall see five ways of stating this stronger property, which are all equivalent for metric spaces. As a preliminary, we define some new terms.

A **base** for the open sets in a space $\mathfrak{E}$ is a family $\mathfrak{F}$ of open sets such that every open set in $\mathfrak{E}$ is a union of sets chosen from $\mathfrak{F}$. We observe that if $\mathfrak{E}$ has a countable base (for its open sets), every subspace also has that property.

A space $\mathfrak{E}$ is said to be **separable** in case there is a countable subset S of $\mathfrak{E}$ which is dense in $\mathfrak{E}$, *i.e.*, $\bar{S} = \mathfrak{E}$.

An **open covering** of $\mathfrak{E}$ is a family $\mathfrak{F}$ of open sets such that $\mathfrak{E}$ is the union of the sets in $\mathfrak{F}$. A subfamily of $\mathfrak{F}$ which is still a covering of $\mathfrak{E}$ is called a **subcovering** of the covering $\mathfrak{F}$. A space $\mathfrak{E}$ is said to have the **Lindelöf property** in case every open covering of $\mathfrak{E}$ has a *countable* subcovering.

The accumulation points x of a subset S of a metric space $\mathfrak{E}$ may be classified according to the minimum cardinal number of the intersection of S with a neighborhood of x. We shall not study such a classification in detail but simply note that if that minimum cardinal is greater than $\aleph_0$, x is called a condensation point of S. That is, x is a **condensation point** of S in case every neighborhood of x contains uncountably many points of S.

Theorem 17. *For a metric space $\mathfrak{E}$ the following five statements are all equivalent;* (i) *$\mathfrak{E}$ is separable;* (ii) *$\mathfrak{E}$ has a countable base;* (iii) *$\mathfrak{E}$ has the Lindelöf property;* (iv) *every uncountable subset A of $\mathfrak{E}$ has a point of condensation in A;* (v) *every uncountable subset of $\mathfrak{E}$ has a point of accumulation.*

Proof.—To show that (i) implies (ii), let (x_n) be a countable dense subset of $\mathfrak{E}$. Let $\mathfrak{F}$ consist of the open neighborhoods $N(x_n; 1/k)$. Then $\mathfrak{F}$ is countable. Let A be open in $\mathfrak{E}$, and $x \in A$. Then $\exists k \ni\cdot N(x; 1/k) \subset A$. Also $\exists n \ni\cdot \rho(x_n, x) < 1/2k$. Then $x \in N(x_n; 1/2k) \in \mathfrak{F}$. So A is the union of the elements of $\mathfrak{F}$ contained in A. To show that (ii) implies (iii), let $\mathfrak{F}$ denote any countable base, and let $\mathfrak{G}$ be an open covering of $\mathfrak{E}$. Drop out of $\mathfrak{F}$ any set A which is not a subset of some set $B \in \mathfrak{G}$, and denote the remaining subfamily of $\mathfrak{F}$ by $\mathfrak{F}_0$. Then $\mathfrak{F}_0$ covers $\mathfrak{E}$. To each $A \in \mathfrak{F}_0$ there corresponds $B \in \mathfrak{G}$ such that $A \subset B$. The subfamily $\mathfrak{G}_0$ of $\mathfrak{G}$ thus selected is a countable subcovering. We show next that (iii) implies the (apparently weaker) property (iv′): Every uncountable subset A of $\mathfrak{E}$ has a point of condensation in $\mathfrak{E}$. If A has no point of condensation in $\mathfrak{E}$, then each point x in $\mathfrak{E}$ has a neighborhood U containing only countably many points of A. By the Lindelöf property, a countable subset of these neighborhoods covers $\mathfrak{E}$, so A must be countable, which contradicts the hypothesis. It is obvious that (iv′) implies (v). To see that (v) implies (i), let $\epsilon > 0$, and consider the family $\mathfrak{F}$ of all subsets A of $\mathfrak{E}$ such that for distinct points x and y in A, $\rho(x, y) \geqq \epsilon$. Using the partial ordering of the sets A by inclusion, we readily verify that the union of the elements of a chain $\mathfrak{G}$ contained in $\mathfrak{F}$ is again a member of $\mathfrak{F}$. Hence by Zorn's lemma, the family $\mathfrak{F}$ has a maximal element B_ϵ, which then has the property that

$$\rho(x, B_\epsilon) < \epsilon \qquad \text{for all } x \in \mathfrak{E}. \tag{7:1}$$

We next show that each B_ϵ is countable. For if it were uncountable, it would have a point x of accumulation, by the assumption (v). Then there would exist distinct points y and z in B_ϵ with $\rho(x, y) < \epsilon/2$, $\rho(x, z) < \epsilon/2$, and hence $\rho(y, z) < \epsilon$, but this would contradict the definition of the family $\mathfrak{F}$. So each B_ϵ is countable, and the union of a countable collection of sets B_ϵ is also countable. If we let ϵ range over a countable set whose greatest lower bound is zero, then $\bigcup B_\epsilon$ is a countable dense set, by (7:1), and so $\mathfrak{E}$ is separable. Finally, since the property (ii) of having a countable base is inherited by subspaces of $\mathfrak{E}$, the same is true for the properties (i), (iii), (iv′), (v), and this shows that (iv′) implies (iv).

THEOREM 18. *The cardinal number of a separable metric space is not greater than* $2^{\aleph_0}$.

This result follows from the fact that if A is dense in $\mathfrak{E}$, then we may make correspond to each point $x \epsilon (\mathfrak{E} - A)$ a subset of A having x for its only accumulation point, and to each $x \epsilon A$, the subset $\{x\}$ of A. This gives a one-to-one mapping of $\mathfrak{E}$ into the power set $\mathfrak{P}(A)$.

From this theorem and Theorem 14 we obtain the following

COROLLARY. *The cardinal number of a connected separable space is either* 0, 1, *or* $2^{\aleph_0}$.

Important examples of separable spaces are the spaces $\mathfrak{R}^k$ of k dimensions, in each of which the set of points with rational coordinates is a countable dense subset. The Hilbert space of Sec. 2, example C, is a separable space of infinitely many dimensions, as is the space $\mathfrak{C}$ of all continuous functions on a bounded closed subset of $\mathfrak{R}^k$, discussed in Chap. VII, Sec. 4.

Any space with the discrete metric and containing uncountably many points is nonseparable. A more interesting example of a nonseparable space is the space of all bounded sequences of real numbers, with the metric given in example D of Sec. 2. Still another example may be formed by considering an uncountable index set J, and the set $\mathfrak{E}$ of all real-valued functions x on J such that

$$\sum_{i \epsilon J} |x^{(i)}|^2 < \infty.$$

Such a space is usually called a nonseparable Hilbert space when the metric is defined in an obvious way. For a function $x \epsilon \mathfrak{E}$, only a countable set of its values can be different from zero. It is easily seen that these spaces do not possess property (v) of Theorem 17.

That the property of being separable is invariant under homeomorphisms is a corollary of the following theorem, which is readily verified.

THEOREM 19. *If f is a continuous function on $\mathfrak{X}$ to $\mathfrak{Y}$, and $\mathfrak{X}$ is separable, then the range $f(\mathfrak{X})$ is separable.*

8. Compact Spaces and Sets.—According to the definition in general use for many years, a subset S of a metric space $\mathfrak{E}$ is called **compact** in case every infinite subset of S has a point of accumulation (in $\mathfrak{E}$), and S is called **compact-in-itself** or **self-**

compact in case every infinite subset of S has a point of accumulation in S. When $S = \mathfrak{E}$, the two concepts coincide. In recent years many mathematicians have found it more convenient to reserve the term "compact" for this latter case, and to say "S is compact in $\mathfrak{E}$," or "S is relatively compact in $\mathfrak{E}$" in the first case. Since the student will meet both usages in the mathematical literature, it is important that he should be familiar with both. The earlier definition was the one used in Chap. VII, Sec. 4. The second definition is gaining in acceptance, and will be used in this chapter. That is, we shall say that a *space* $\mathfrak{E}$ is **compact** in case every infinite subset of $\mathfrak{E}$ has a point of accumulation (in $\mathfrak{E}$). A subset S of $\mathfrak{E}$ is **compact** in case S as a space is compact. For general topological spaces, still another definition of "compact" is frequently used, but for metric spaces it is equivalent to the above, as we shall show in Theorem 25.

THEOREM 20. *Every compact space is bounded. A necessary condition for a subset S of a metric space $\mathfrak{E}$ to be compact is that S is closed in $\mathfrak{E}$. In case $\mathfrak{E}$ is compact, this condition is also sufficient.*

Proof.—If a compact space $\mathfrak{E}$ is unbounded, there is a sequence of points (x_n) such that $\rho(x_0, x_n) \geqq n$ for all n. The set S consisting of the points of this sequence is infinite, and so has a point x of accumulation. Let $\epsilon = \rho(x, x_0)$. Then $N(x; \epsilon)$ contains infinitely many points of S, and so must contain points x_n with $n > 2\epsilon$. Then $\rho(x_0, x_n) \leqq \rho(x_0, x) + \rho(x, x_n) < 2\epsilon < n$, which contradicts the assumption about x_n. Hence $\mathfrak{E}$ is bounded. If b is an accumulation point of the subset S of $\mathfrak{E}$, there exists an infinite subset T of S such that b is the only accumulation point of T, as we see by selecting from S a point $x_n \neq b$ from each of the neighborhoods $N(b; 1/n)$. Hence if S is compact, b must belong to S, and S is closed in $\mathfrak{E}$. The sufficiency of the condition of closure on S when $\mathfrak{E}$ is compact is obvious.

The space $\mathfrak{R}^k$ is not compact, but a subset S of $\mathfrak{R}^k$ which is bounded (in terms of the usual metric) and closed is compact. This follows from the Weierstrass-Bolzano theorem, which was discussed in Chap. III, Sec. 5. That section and Sec. 5 of this chapter show also that if $\mathfrak{R}^k$ is completed in terms of the metric ρ_6 defined in (5:4), then the completion $\bar{\mathfrak{R}}^k$ is compact, and so every closed subset of $\bar{\mathfrak{R}}^k$ is compact. A similar result holds for the completion of $\mathfrak{R}^k$ in terms of the metric ρ_4 defined in (5:2) or the metric ρ_5 defined in (5:3).

THEOREM 21. *A space $\mathfrak{E}$ is compact if and only if every sequence of points in $\mathfrak{E}$ has a convergent subsequence.*

THEOREM 22. *The Cartesian product of a finite number of compact metric spaces is compact.*

Proof.—It is sufficient to consider the product of two spaces $\mathfrak{X}$ and $\mathfrak{Y}$. We understand that a metric equivalent to (4:4) or (4:5) is used for the Cartesian product. Let (x_i, y_i) be a sequence in $\mathfrak{X} \times \mathfrak{Y}$. Then by the preceding theorem, (x_i) has a convergent subsequence (x_{i_k}). The corresponding subsequence (y_{i_k}) in turn has a convergent subsequence $(y_{i_{k_l}})$, so (x_i, y_i) has the convergent subsequence $(x_{i_{k_l}}, y_{i_{k_l}})$, and, again by the preceding theorem, $\mathfrak{X} \times \mathfrak{Y}$ is compact.

We shall now need to consider some concepts related to compactness. If A is a subset of a metric space $\mathfrak{E}$, and x is a point of $\mathfrak{E}$, it will be convenient to set

$$\rho(x, A) = \text{g.l.b. } \rho(x, y) \qquad \text{for } y \in A.$$

Then an **ϵ-net** in $\mathfrak{E}$ is defined to be a finite subset A of $\mathfrak{E}$ such that $\rho(x, A) < \epsilon$ for every $x \in \mathfrak{E}$. Note that an ϵ-net A determines a finite open covering of $\mathfrak{E}$ by the spheres $N(y; \epsilon)$ with centers $y \in A$. The space $\mathfrak{E}$ is called **totally bounded** in case: for every $\epsilon > 0$, $\mathfrak{E}$ contains an ϵ-net.

THEOREM 23. *A totally bounded metric space $\mathfrak{E}$ is separable.*

Proof.—The union of the ϵ-nets A_n corresponding to $\epsilon = 1/n$ is a countable set which is clearly dense in $\mathfrak{E}$.

THEOREM 24. *A metric space $\mathfrak{E}$ is totally bounded if and only if every sequence (x_n) in $\mathfrak{E}$ has a Cauchy subsequence.*

Proof.—Assume that $\mathfrak{E}$ is totally bounded, and let (x_n) be an arbitrary sequence of points of $\mathfrak{E}$. Let ϵ_k tend to zero, and let A_k be an ϵ_k-net. The finite covering of $\mathfrak{E}$ by the spheres $N(y; \epsilon_1)$ for $y \in A_1$ then has the property that x_n is in some one of these spheres, say $N(y_1; \epsilon_1)$, for infinitely many values of n. Let (x_{n1}) denote the subsequence of (x_n) whose terms lie in $N(y_1; \epsilon_1)$. Suppose now that sequences $(x_{n1}), \ldots, (x_{np})$ and points $y_k \in A_k$ for $k = 1, \ldots, p$ have been determined in such a way that (x_{nk}) is a subsequence of (x_{nj}) for $k > j$, and $x_{nk} \in N(y_k; \epsilon_k)$ for all n and for $k = 1, \ldots, p$. Then x_{np} lies in some sphere $N(y_{p+1}; \epsilon_{p+1})$ for infinitely many values of n, and we may let $(x_{n,p+1})$ denote the subsequence of (x_{np}) whose terms lie in $N(y_{p+1}; \epsilon_{p+1})$. In this way an infinite sequence of subsequences is selected.

Now set $z_n = x_{nn}$. Then (z_n) is a subsequence of (x_n), and for $m > p$, $n > p$, we have $\rho(z_m, z_n) < 2\epsilon_p$, since z_m and z_n are both in $N(y_p; \epsilon_p)$. So (z_n) is a Cauchy sequence.

For the converse, let us suppose there is a positive ϵ for which no ϵ-net exists. Then if points $x_1, \ldots, x_p$ of $\mathfrak{E}$ have been found such that

$$\rho(x_i, x_j) \geqq \epsilon \qquad \text{for } i \neq j, \tag{8:1}$$

there must exist also a point x_{p+1} with $\rho(x_{p+1}, x_j) \geqq \epsilon$ for $j = 1, \ldots, p$. Hence there exists an infinite sequence (x_n) with the property (8:1). Evidently no subsequence of (x_n) can be a Cauchy sequence.

A space is said to have the **Borel property** in case every open covering has a finite subcovering. This property is obviously stronger than the Lindelöf property of Sec. 7. A family $\mathfrak{F}$ of sets B is said to have the **finite intersection property** in case every finite subfamily $\mathfrak{F}_0$ of $\mathfrak{F}$ has a nonnull intersection, *i.e.*, $\cap B$ for $B \in \mathfrak{F}_0$ is not empty.

THEOREM 25. *For a metric space* $\mathfrak{E}$ *the following properties are equivalent:* (i) $\mathfrak{E}$ *is compact;* (ii) $\mathfrak{E}$ *has the Borel property;* (iii) *every family* $\mathfrak{F}$ *of closed sets in* $\mathfrak{E}$ *with the finite intersection property has a nonnull intersection;* (iv) $\mathfrak{E}$ *is complete and totally bounded.*

Proof.—To show that (i) implies (ii), we note that by Theorems 21, 24, 23, and 17, every open covering $\mathfrak{G}$ has a countable subcovering $\mathfrak{G}_0$ composed of sets $A_1, A_2, \ldots$. If no finite subcollection of $\mathfrak{G}_0$ covers $\mathfrak{E}$, there exists $x_n \in (\mathfrak{E} - \bigcup_{i=1}^{n} A_i)$ for every n. By Theorem 21, the sequence (x_n) has a subsequence converging to some point y, and y must be in some A_j of $\mathfrak{G}_0$. Then since A_j is open, infinitely many terms of the sequence (x_n) must lie in A_j. But this contradicts the definition of (x_n). To show that (ii) implies (i), let A be an arbitrary subset of $\mathfrak{E}$ with no accumulation point. Then

$$x \in \mathfrak{E} \cdot\supset\cdot \exists \epsilon > 0 \ni\cdot A \cap N(x; \epsilon) \subset \{x\}.$$

A finite subcollection of these neighborhoods $N(x; \epsilon)$ covers $\mathfrak{E}$, and each contains at most one point of A. Hence A is finite. To show that (ii) is equivalent to (iii), it suffices to note that the complement of a closed set is open, and that a family of sets has a null intersection if and only if the family composed of the complementary sets covers $\mathfrak{C}$. To show that (i) is equivalent to (iv), we use Theorems 21 and 24 and the readily verified fact that if a subsequence of a Cauchy sequence has a limit x, then the whole sequence converges to x.

A totally bounded metric space is sometimes called **conditionally compact.** In view of the last theorem and the fact that the completion of a totally bounded space is totally bounded, we see that the completion of a totally bounded space is compact.

*When topological spaces more general than metric spaces are considered, the Borel property still implies compactness, but the converse no longer holds. Such spaces having the Borel property were called **bicompact** by Fréchet and others (see Fréchet [5], Alexandroff and Hopf [6], Sierpinski [4]). On account of the important place in mathematics held by the Borel covering property, many mathematicians have preferred to take that property as the definition for "compact." This confusion of terms is unfortunate but is too well established in the mathematical literature to be repaired now.

An important property of continuous transformations of compact spaces is the following, which is readily proved with the help of the Borel covering property or by an indirect proof.

THEOREM 26. *If $\mathfrak{X}$ and $\mathfrak{Y}$ are metric spaces, with $\mathfrak{X}$ compact, and f is continuous on $\mathfrak{X}$ to $\mathfrak{Y}$, then f is uniformly continuous.*

THEOREM 27. *Under the hypotheses of the preceding theorem, the image $f(\mathfrak{X})$ is compact.*

Proof.—Let (y_n) be an infinite sequence of points in $f(\mathfrak{X})$, *i.e.*, $y_n = f(x_n)$. Then by Theorem 21, (x_n) has a subsequence (x_{n_i}) converging to a point $x_0 \in \mathfrak{X}$. Then $f(x_{n_i})$ converges to $f(x_0)$, and hence $f(\mathfrak{X})$ is compact by Theorem 21.

COROLLARY 1. *Under the same hypotheses, the image $f(A)$ of a closed subset A of $\mathfrak{X}$ is closed in $\mathfrak{Y}$.*

COROLLARY 2. *A real-valued continuous function defined on a compact metric space is bounded and attains its upper and lower bounds.*

COROLLARY 3. *If in additon to the hypotheses of Theorem 26 it is assumed that the mapping f is one-to-one, then f is a homeomorphism.*

Proof.—Since f is one-to-one, we have $f(\mathfrak{X} - A) = f(\mathfrak{X}) - f(A)$, so by Corollary 1, the image of an open subset A of $\mathfrak{X}$ is open in $f(\mathfrak{X})$. Hence f^{-1} is continuous.

COROLLARY 4. *Equivalent metrics for a compact space are uniformly equivalent.*

*It was noted at the end of Sec. 6 that a continuous transform of a locally connected space need not be locally connected. However, we can now derive the following result.

*THEOREM 28. *If $\mathfrak{X}$ and $\mathfrak{Y}$ are metric spaces, $\mathfrak{X}$ is compact and locally connected, and f is continuous on $\mathfrak{X}$ to $\mathfrak{Y}$, then the image $f(\mathfrak{X})$ is locally connected.*

Proof.—Let U be open in $f(\mathfrak{X})$, and let G be one of its components. Then $f^{-1}(U)$ is open in $\mathfrak{X}$, and so its components are open, by Theorem 15. By Theorem 12, a component of $f^{-1}(U)$ having a point in common with $f^{-1}(G)$ is a subset of $f^{-1}(G)$. So $f^{-1}(G)$, being a union of components of $f^{-1}(U)$, is open, and thus $\mathfrak{X} - f^{-1}(G)$ is closed, and so by Corollary 1 of the preceding theorem, $f(\mathfrak{X}) - G$ is closed. Hence G is open in $f(\mathfrak{X})$, and so $f(\mathfrak{X})$ is locally connected, by Theorem 15.

*A metric space which is compact, connected, and locally connected is frequently called a **Peano space.** A bounded closed interval I of the real axis is an example of a Peano space. Hence the image of I under any continuous mapping into a metric space is always a Peano space, as follows from Theorems 27, 12, and 28. Conversely, every Peano space is the image of I under such a mapping, but we shall not prove this here. (See Hausdorff [2], page 207.)

At times it is useful to consider a weaker property than compactness. A metric space $\mathfrak{E}$ is said to be **locally compact** in case every point of $\mathfrak{E}$ has a compact neighborhood. Since every neighborhood contains a closed neighborhood, we see that an equivalent definition would say that $\mathfrak{E}$ is locally compact in case every neighborhood of each point x in $\mathfrak{E}$ contains a compact neighborhood of x. The property of local compactness is preserved under homeomorphisms, but it is not always preserved by one-to-one and continuous transformations, as the following example shows. Let the space $\mathfrak{E}$ be the set of the example following Theorem 16 of Sec. 6, and take $f(x, y) = (\cos x, xy, \sin x)$ on $\mathfrak{E}$. The examples A, B, G, and H listed in Sec. 2 are locally compact spaces (in fact, G is compact), but the other examples are not locally compact.

*Since a totally bounded subset S of a complete space $\mathfrak{E}$ is relatively compact in $\mathfrak{C}$ (by Theorem 24), and the examples C, D, E, I, and J of Sec. 2 are complete spaces, it is interesting to have conditions for total boundedness of subsets of these spaces. For the space $\mathfrak{C}$ of all continuous functions on a bounded closed interval of $\mathfrak{R}^k$ (which was discussed in Chap. VII, Sec. 4), a subset S is totally bounded if and only if it is bounded and equicontinuous, *i.e.*, composed of equicontinuous functions. This follows from Theorems 27 and 28 (Ascoli's Theorem) of Chap. VII and the results of this section. We shall indicate a direct verification of this relation in a more general situation, embodied in the following theorem.

*THEOREM 29. *Let* $(\mathfrak{D}, \tau)$ *be a compact metric space of points* t, $(\mathfrak{X}, \sigma)$ *a metric space of points* x, *and let* $\mathfrak{C} =$ [*all continuous* f *on* $\mathfrak{D}$ *to* $\mathfrak{X}$], *with* $\rho(f_1, f_2) = \text{l.u.b. } \sigma(f_1(t), f_2(t))$ *on* $\mathfrak{D}$. *If* $S \subset \mathfrak{C}$, *let* $R(S) = \bigcup f(\mathfrak{D})$ *for* $f \in S$. *Then* S *is totally bounded if and only if* S *is equicontinuous and* $R(S)$ *is totally bounded.*

Proof.—If S is totally bounded, and $\epsilon > 0$, there exist functions $f_1, \ldots, f_m$ such that

$$S \subset \bigcup_{i=1}^{m} N(f_i; \epsilon). \tag{8:2}$$

Since each $f \in \mathfrak{C}$ is uniformly continuous, by Theorem 26,

$$\exists \delta > 0 \ni: \tau(t, \bar{t}) < \delta \cdot\supset\cdot \sigma(f_i(t), f_i(\bar{t})) < \epsilon \qquad \text{for } i = 1, \ldots, m. \tag{8:3}$$

By combining (8:2) and (8:3), we find that

$$\tau(t, \bar{t}) < \delta \cdot\supset\cdot \sigma(f(t), f(\bar{t})) < 3\epsilon \quad \text{for all } f \in S,$$

and so S is equicontinuous. Now choose $t_1, \ldots, t_n$ so that $\mathfrak{D} \subset \bigcup_j N(t_j; \delta)$. Then $R(S) \subset \bigcup_{i,j} N(f_i(t_j); 2\epsilon)$, so $R(S)$ is totally bounded.

For the converse, suppose $\delta > 0$ chosen so that

$$\tau(t, \bar{t}) < \delta \cdot\supset\cdot \sigma(f(t), f(\bar{t})) < \epsilon \quad \text{for all } f \in S, \tag{8:4}$$

and $t_1, \ldots, t_n, x_1, \ldots, x_m$ chosen so that

$$\mathfrak{D} \subset \bigcup_j N(t_j; \delta), \qquad R(S) \subset \bigcup_i N(x_i; \epsilon). \tag{8:5}$$

Then the Cartesian product $R(S) \times \cdots \times R(S) = [R(S)]^n$ is covered by the collection of m^n sets

(8:6) $N(x_{i_1}; \epsilon) \times N(x_{i_2}; \epsilon) \times \cdots \times N(x_{i_n}; \epsilon),$
$$i_j = 1, \ldots, m, \qquad j = 1, \ldots, n,$$

and for each $f \in S$ the point

$$\phi_f = (f(t_1), f(t_2), \ldots, f(t_n))$$

lies in at least one of the sets (8:6). For each set (8:6) select a function $f_k \in S$ such that ϕ_{f_k} is in that set (if such an f_k exists). Then from (8:4) and (8:5) we readily find that the neighborhoods $N(f_k; 4\epsilon)$ cover S.

*In the Lebesgue space $\mathfrak{L}_p$ $(p \geqq 1)$ of example I in Sec. 2, let us suppose that the domain of integration T is a bounded measurable set in a finite-dimensional space. Choose a sequence of partitions π_n (with norm tending to zero) of an interval containing T, and let $\sum_n$ denote the class of all step functions ξ which are constant on each interval of π_n, take values which are multiples of $1/2^n$, and satisfy $|\xi(t)| \leqq n$. With these notations we can state the following result.

*THEOREM 30. *A set $S \subset \mathfrak{L}_p$ is totally bounded if and only if*

$$\epsilon > 0 :\supset: \exists n \ni: x \in S \cdot\supset\cdot \exists \xi \in \textstyle\sum_n \ni\cdot \int_T |x - \xi|^p \, dt < \epsilon.$$

To prove this we recall that every $x \in \mathfrak{L}_p$ may be approximated by a step function (see the first part of the proof of Theorem 28, Chap. XI), and then observe that every step function may be approximated by a function from $\sum_n$ for n sufficiently large. Also note that each $\sum_n$ contains only a finite number of functions.

*For the sequence spaces $\mathfrak{l}_p$ of example J, the situation is even simpler. Let the mapping $u = P_n(x)$ be defined by

$$\begin{aligned} u^{(i)} &= x^{(i)} && \text{for } i \leqq n, \\ &= 0 && \text{for } i > n, \end{aligned}$$

i.e., P_n projects the space $\mathfrak{l}_p$ on an n-dimensional subspace.

*THEOREM 31. *A set $S \subset \mathfrak{l}_p$ is totally bounded if and only if it is bounded and satisfies the condition*

$$\epsilon > 0 :\supset: \exists n \ni: x \in S \cdot\supset\cdot \rho(x, P_n(x)) < \epsilon.$$

For the proof, we recall that in a finite-dimensional space, bounded sets are totally bounded.

*In the Hilbert space $\mathfrak{H} = \mathfrak{l}_2$, the fundamental "cube" $\mathfrak{H}_0$

consists of all x such that $0 \leqq x^{(i)} \leqq 1/i$ for every i. By the preceding theorem, $\mathfrak{H}_0$ is totally bounded, and it is obviously closed, so since $\mathfrak{H}$ is complete, $\mathfrak{H}_0$ is compact. $\mathfrak{H}_0$ is also a "universal" space, in the sense of the following theorem.

*THEOREM 32. *Every separable metric space $\mathfrak{X}$ is homeomorphic to a subset of $\mathfrak{H}_0$.*

Proof.—The mapping f of $\mathfrak{X}$ into $\mathfrak{H}_0$ will be specified in terms of a sequence (q_n) dense on $\mathfrak{X}$. We suppose the metric ρ in $\mathfrak{X}$ chosen so that $\rho(p, q) \leqq 1$ for every pair of points, and set $f(p) = x$ where $x^{(n)} = \rho(p, q_n)/n$. This mapping is clearly one-to-one. From the triangle inequalities

$$|\rho(p, q_n) - \rho(\bar{p}, q_n)| \leqq \rho(p, \bar{p}) \leqq \rho(p, q_n) + \rho(\bar{p}, q_n)$$

and the inequality $|\rho(p, q_n) - \rho(\bar{p}, q_n)| \leqq n\sigma(f(p), f(\bar{p}))$, where σ is the usual metric in Hilbert space, we see that

$$\sigma(f(p), f(\bar{p})) \leqq \rho(p, \bar{p})[\Sigma 1/n^2]^{1/2},$$

and

$$\rho(p, \bar{p}) \leqq 2\rho(p, q_n) + n\sigma(f(p), f(\bar{p})) < \epsilon,$$

provided n is chosen so that $\rho(p, q_n) < \epsilon/4$ and $\bar{p}$ is chosen so that $\sigma(f(p), f(\bar{p})) < \epsilon/2n$. Thus the mapping is bicontinuous.

*The metric σ in $\mathfrak{H}$ and the mapping f induce a metric ρ_1 in $\mathfrak{X}$ which is equivalent to ρ but not in general uniformly equivalent. In terms of ρ_1, the mapping f is an isometry. Thus the closure C of $f(\mathfrak{X})$ is a completion of $(\mathfrak{X}, \rho_1)$ in the sense of Theorem 11. We observe that C is also compact. From these remarks we see that a separable metric space which is complete in every equivalent metric is compact.

EXERCISES

1. If A is a compact set and B is a closed set in a metric space, and A and B are disjoint, prove that the greatest lower bound $\rho(A, B)$ of the distances $\rho(x, y)$ between points x of A and points y of B is positive.

2. Prove that the Cartesian product of a finite number of locally compact metric spaces is locally compact.

3. Show that every discrete space is locally compact.

4. Give examples of the following:

(*a*) A locally compact space which is not separable;

(*b*) A complete space which is not locally compact;

(*c*) A locally compact subspace of a complete space which is not closed;

(*d*) A space which is not locally compact but which is a one-to-one continuous image of a locally compact space.

5. An ϵ-chain is defined to be a finite sequence of points, $(x_0, x_1, \ldots, x_n)$ such that $\rho(x_{i-1}, x_i) < \epsilon$ for $i = 1, \ldots, n$. Prove that if a space $\mathfrak{E}$ is connected, then for every $\epsilon > 0$, every pair of its points belongs to an ϵ-chain.

6. Prove that when $\mathfrak{E}$ is a compact space, the converse of the statement of Exercise 5 holds. Give an example where the converse fails.

7. A Lebesgue number for an open covering $\mathfrak{F}$ of a metric space $\mathfrak{E}$ is a positive number η such that if A is a subset of $\mathfrak{E}$ with diameter less than η, then A is contained in one of the sets of $\mathfrak{F}$. Prove that every open covering of a compact space has a Lebesgue number.

8. Let (A_n) be a decreasing sequence of compact nonnull continua. Show that $A = \bigcap A_n$ is a nonnull continuum. Generalize this result, using the finite intersection property.

9. Prove that each compact continuum containing two fixed points x and y has a minimal subcontinuum containing x and y.

10. Show that if $\mathfrak{X}$ and $\mathfrak{Y}$ are metric spaces and $\mathfrak{X}$ is totally bounded, and f maps $\mathfrak{X}$ into $\mathfrak{Y}$ in such a way that $(f(x_n))$ is a Cauchy sequence whenever (x_n) is, then f is uniformly continuous. (Compare Exercises 4 and 5 of Sec. 5.)

9. Category of Sets.—Subsets of a metric space are classified into sets of the first category and sets of the second category, according to definitions which we shall give below. Theorems on the category of sets are useful in proving some important results in functional analysis.

As in Sec. 3, we say that a set A is **dense in** a set B in case $B \subset \bar{A}$. A set A is **nowhere dense in** B in case the set $B - \bar{A}$ is dense in B. This is obviously equivalent to the following condition:

$$(9{:}1) \quad x \in B \,.\, \epsilon > 0 \cdot\supset\cdot \exists y \in B \,.\, \exists \delta > 0 \ni\cdot N(y; \delta) \subset N(x; \epsilon) \,.\, N(y; \delta) \cap A = 0,$$

i.e., every sphere in B contains a sphere having no points in common with A. A set A is of the **first category in** B in case A is the union of a countable family of sets each of which is nowhere dense in B. A set A is said to be of the **second category in** B in case it is not of the first category in B. The following lemma will be useful.

LEMMA. *If $A \subset B \subset C \subset D$, and B is nowhere dense in C, then A is nowhere dense in C, and B is nowhere dense in D.*

Proof.—From $A \subset B$ we have $(C - \bar{A}) \supset (C - \bar{B})$, and so

$$\overline{C - \bar{A}} \supset \overline{C - \bar{B}} \supset C,$$

and A is nowhere dense in C. Also we have $(D - \bar{B}) = (C - \bar{B}) \cup (D - C)$, and so

$$\overline{D - \bar{B}} \supset [(\overline{C - \bar{B}}) \cup (D - C)] \supset [C \cup (D - C)] = D,$$

and B is nowhere dense in D.

COROLLARY. *If $A \subset B \subset C \subset D$, and B is of the first category in C , then A is of the first category in C, and B is of the first category in D. On the other hand, if A is of the second category in C, then A is of the second category in B, and B is of the second category in C.*

THEOREM 33. *Let $\mathfrak{X}$ be a complete metric space, and let A_i be nowhere dense in $\mathfrak{X}$ for $i = 1, 2, \ldots$. Then $\mathfrak{X} - \cup A_i$ is dense in $\mathfrak{X}$.*

Proof.—In the condition (9:1) we may clearly require δ to be arbitrarily small, and hence may also require

$$\overline{N(y; \delta)} \subset N(x; \epsilon), \qquad \overline{N(y; \delta)} \cap A = 0.$$

So let y_1, δ_1, correspond to A_1, and suppose $\delta_1 < 1$. Let us use the abbreviation $S_i = N_i(y; \delta_i)$, and suppose that $S_1, \ldots, S_{p-1}$ have been determined so that

$$(9:2) \qquad \bar{S}_i \subset S_{i-1}, \qquad \bar{S}_i \cap A_i = 0, \qquad \delta_i \leqq 1/i$$

for $i < p$. Then since A_p is nowhere dense, S_p may be determined to satisfy (9:2) for $i = p$. Since $\mathfrak{X}$ is complete, the intersection of the sets $\bar{S}_i$ consists of exactly one point z in $N(x; \epsilon)$, by Theorem 7. By construction, z lies in $\mathfrak{X} - \cup A_i$, and since this process can be carried through for arbitrary x and $\epsilon > 0$, $\mathfrak{X} - \cup A_i$ is dense in $\mathfrak{X}$.

An immediate corollary of the preceding is the following fundamental result.

THEOREM 34. *A complete metric space is of the second category (in itself).*

As examples of nowhere dense sets in the reals, we may cite the Cantor set (example F of Chap. III, page 41) and examples C and D of the same chapter. A set nowhere dense in $\mathfrak{R}^2$ is composed of the rays from the origin with integral slopes. However, each of these examples is of the second category (in itself). By the last theorem, each $\mathfrak{R}^k$ is a space of the second category. The subset A of $\mathfrak{R}^k$ composed of points with rational coordinates is of the first category in A, and so also in $\mathfrak{R}^k$. However, the subset B composed of points with integral coordinates is of the second category in B, although it is nowhere dense in $\mathfrak{R}^k$. The subset C of $\mathfrak{R}^2$ composed of the rays from the origin with rational slopes is of the first category in C, while its complement in $\mathfrak{R}^2$ is of the second category in $\mathfrak{R}^2$.

If the part of a set A near a point x is of the first category in B, *i.e.*, if there is a neighborhood $N(x)$ such that $A \cap N(x)$ is of the first category in B, we say that A is of the **first category in** B **at** x. Otherwise A is of the **second category in** B **at** x.

THEOREM 35. *If every nonnull open set in the metric space* $\mathfrak{X}$ *contains a point* x *at which the set* A *is of the first category in* $\mathfrak{X}$, *then* A *is of the first category in* $\mathfrak{X}$.

Proof.—The hypothesis implies that every nonnull open set U contains a nonnull open set V such that

(9:3) $$V \cap A \text{ is of the first category in } \mathfrak{X}.$$

Hence there exist collections of mutually disjoint open sets V satisfying (9:3). By Zorn's lemma, there is a maximal collection $\mathfrak{F} = [V_\alpha]$ of this kind, which then has the property that for every nonnull open set U

(9:4) $$\exists V_\alpha \in \mathfrak{F} \ni \cdot V_\alpha \cap U \neq 0.$$

By (9:3), $V_\alpha \cap A = \bigcup_k N_{\alpha k}$, where each $N_{\alpha k}$ is nowhere dense. Let $M_k = \bigcup_\alpha N_{\alpha k}$. Then

(9:5) $$\bar{M}_k \cap V_\alpha = \bar{N}_{\alpha k} \cap V_\alpha.$$

Suppose M_k is dense in U, and let V_α correspond to U, as in (9:4). Then by (9:5), $0 \neq U \cap V_\alpha \subset \bar{N}_{\alpha k} \cap V_\alpha$, which contradicts the supposition that $N_{\alpha k}$ is nowhere dense. Hence M_k is nowhere dense. Also $C = \mathfrak{X} - \bigcup V_\alpha$ is closed and has no interior points by (9:4), and so is nowhere dense. But $A \subset \bigcup_k M_k \cup C$, so A is of the first category in $\mathfrak{X}$.

COROLLARY. *Let A consist of the points x at which the space $\mathfrak{X}$ is of the first category. Then the closure $\bar{A}$ of A is of the first category in $\mathfrak{X}$.*

Proof.—If $\mathfrak{X}$ is of the first category at x, then $\bar{A}$ is of the first category at x. If U is open, and $U \cap \bar{A} \neq 0$, then $U \cap A \neq 0$, while if $U \cap \bar{A} = 0$, $\bar{A}$ is trivially of the first category in $\mathfrak{X}$ at each point of U, so the theorem applies to $\bar{A}$.

The next theorem states an intrinsic restriction on the possible discontinuities of the limit of a sequence of continuous functions.

THEOREM 36. *Suppose $\mathfrak{X}$ and $\mathfrak{Y}$ are metric spaces, and (f_n) is a sequence of continuous functions on $\mathfrak{X}$ to $\mathfrak{Y}$ converging to a function g at each point of $\mathfrak{X}$. Then the set D composed of the points of discontinuity of g is of the first category in $\mathfrak{X}$.*

Proof.—Let σ denote the metric in $\mathfrak{Y}$, and let

$$C_q = [x | \exists N(x) \,.\, \exists p \ni : x' \in N(x) \,.\, n > p \cdot\!\supset\!\cdot \sigma(f_n(x'), g(x')) < 1/q].$$

Obviously each C_q is open, and by the usual elementary proof, g is continuous at the points x common to all the sets C_q. Now let A be defined as in the Corollary to Theorem 35, so that $\bar{A}$ is of the first category in $\mathfrak{X}$, and set $B_q = \mathfrak{X} - \bar{A} - C_q$. If B_q is dense in an open set U, then $U \cap C_q = 0$, since C_q is open, so $U \cap B_q = U \cap (\mathfrak{X} - \bar{A})$, which is open and nonnull, *i.e.*, B_q must contain an open set. Since $D \subset \bigcup_q B_q \cup \bar{A}$, it remains to show that the assumption that some B_q contains a nonnull open set U leads to a contradiction. Let

$$B_{qk} = [x \in U \mid n > k \cdot\!\supset\!\cdot \sigma(f_n(x), g(x)) < 1/5q].$$

Then $U = \bigcup_k B_{qk}$. Since U is open and $U \cap A = 0$, U is of the second category in $\mathfrak{X}$ at each of its points, so that there is an open set $W \subset U$ and an integer k such that B_{qk} is dense in W. Since $B_{qk} \subset U \subset B_q$, we have

$$(9{:}6) \qquad p > k \cdot\!\supset\!\cdot \exists n > p \,.\, \exists x \in W \ni\cdot \sigma(f_n(x), g(x)) \geqq 1/q,$$

and since the sequence (f_n) converges to g at the point x,

$$(9{:}7) \qquad \exists h > k \ni\cdot \sigma(f_h(x), g(x)) < 1/5q.$$

But f_n and f_h are continuous at x, and B_{qk} is dense in W, so we can select a point z in B_{qk} such that

$$(9{:}8) \qquad \sigma(f_n(x), f_n(z)) < 1/5q, \qquad \sigma(f_h(x), f_h(z)) < 1/5q.$$

By combining (9:7) and (9:8) with the definition of B_{qk}, we arrive at a contradiction with (9:6).

Theorems 34 and 36 are readily applied to show the existence of continuous nowhere differentiable functions of a single real variable. Explicit examples of such functions have been exhibited by various mathematicians, beginning with Weierstrass. (Compare Chap. VII, page 125.) Proofs like the following, which depend on the category of metric spaces, are nonconstructive proofs.

Let $\mathfrak{C}$ denote the space of all real-valued continuous functions f on the interval $[0 \leqq x \leqq 1]$, with the metric

$$\rho(f_1, f_2) = \text{l.u.b. } |f_1(x) - f_2(x)|.$$

This is a complete metric space, and so is of the second category, by Theorem 34. Let $0 \leqq x_0 < x_n \leqq 1$, $\lim x_n = x_0$, and set

$$\Delta_n(f) = \frac{f(x_n) - f(x_0)}{x_n - x_0}.$$

Then each Δ_n is a continuous function on $\mathfrak{C}$. Let $\mathfrak{C}_0$ denote the subset of $\mathfrak{C}$ composed of all those functions f for which $\Delta_n(f)$ has a limit $\phi(f)$, finite or $+\infty$ or $-\infty$. Thus ϕ (as well as each Δ_n) takes values in the space $\mathfrak{Y} = [-\infty \leqq y \leqq +\infty]$, which can be metrized, as was indicated at the end of Sec. 5. By Theorem 36, the subset of $\mathfrak{C}_0$ where ϕ is discontinuous is a set of the first category in $\mathfrak{C}_0$, and hence in $\mathfrak{C}$. We now show that ϕ is discontinuous at every $f \in \mathfrak{C}_0$. Corresponding to arbitrary $f \in \mathfrak{C}_0$, $\alpha > 0$ and q, set

$$\begin{aligned} f_{q\alpha}(x) &= f(x) && \text{for } 0 \leqq x \leqq x_0, \\ &= f(x_0) + q(x - x_0) && \text{for } x_0 < x < x_0 + \alpha, \\ &= f(x) - f(x_0 + \alpha) + f(x_0) + q\alpha && \text{for } x_0 + \alpha \leqq x \leqq 1. \end{aligned}$$

Then $f_{q\alpha}$ is in $\mathfrak{C}_0$, $\phi(f_{q\alpha}) = q$, and $\rho(f_{q\alpha}, f)$ tends to zero with α. We can always choose $q \neq \phi(f)$. Since the space $\mathfrak{C}$ is of the second category and $\mathfrak{C}_0$ is of the first category in $\mathfrak{C}$, we have the following result.

THEOREM 37. *The set of all functions in $\mathfrak{C}$ which have a right-hand derivative at no point is a set of the second category in $\mathfrak{C}$.*

EXERCISES

1. Using Theorem 34, show that the set A of irrational points on the real line is not an F_σ, *i.e.*, is not the union of a countable collection of closed sets.

2. If the sets A and B are nowhere dense in $\mathfrak{X}$, show that their union is nowhere dense in $\mathfrak{X}$.

3. If $\mathfrak{X}$ and $\mathfrak{Y}$ are metric spaces and A is nowhere dense in $\mathfrak{X}$, show that $A \times \mathfrak{Y}$ is nowhere dense in $\mathfrak{X} \times \mathfrak{Y}$; and that if $\mathfrak{X}$ is of the first category, so is $\mathfrak{X} \times \mathfrak{Y}$.

4. Prove that a space of the first category has no isolated points.

5. Prove that a complete metric space with cardinal $\aleph_0$ has $\aleph_0$ isolated points. Show by an example that it may also have $\aleph_0$ accumulation points.

6. Let $\mathfrak{X}$ be a complete metric space. For $n = 1, 2, 3, \ldots$ let G_n be an open set dense in $\mathfrak{X}$. Prove that $\cap G_n$ is a set dense in $\mathfrak{X}$. (HINT: Apply Theorem 33.)

REFERENCES

1. Hausdorff, *Grundzüge der Mengenlehre*, 1914.
2. Hausdorff, *Mengenlehre*, 3d Ed.
3. Kuratowski, *Topologie* I.
4. Sierpinski, *Topology*.
5. Fréchet, *Les espaces abstraits*, 1928.
6. Alexandroff and Hopf, *Topologie*, Chaps. 1, 2.
7. Banach, *Théorie des opérations linéaires*, 1932.

INDEX

A

Abelian group, 24
Absolute continuity, 187, 203, 257
  in the sense of Tonelli, 257
Absolute convergence, 108
Absolutely-uniform convergence, 110
Accumulation point, of a sequence, 49, 50
  of a set, 44, 49, 339
    of functions, 119, 246
Additive classes, 195
Additive function, 174, 196–197
Aggregate, 7, 42
  (*See also* Set)
Alephs, 316
Almost everywhere, 182
Almost uniform convergence, 183
Alternation of propositions, 2
Antiderivative, 90
Approximate convergence, 236–237
Archimedean property, 27, 34
Ascoli's theorem, 122, 362
Asymptotic series, 115
Axiom, of choice, 10, 321–323
  of infinity, 10, 314

B

Baire's classification of discontinuous functions, 127, 200
Base for open sets, 354
Bernstein theorem, 309
Bessel's inequality, 249
Bicompact space, 360
Biconditional of propositions, 4
Bilinear functions, 76
Bilinear operator, 262
Binary relation, 11, 300
Bolzano, 49
Borel-measurable functions, 200
Borel-measurable sets, 196
Borel property, 359
Borel theorem, 51, 359
Boundary point, 44, 339
  of a sheet, 142
Bounded set, 49, 339
Bounded variation, 202, 267

C

Cantor, 38, 310
Cantor discontinuum, 41, 48
Cardinal number, 308, 316
Cartesian product, 9, 40, 299, 301
Categorical set of postulates, 17
Category of sets, 365
Cauchy condition, for convergence in the mean, 243
  for existence of a limit, 36, 60
  for uniform convergence, 99
Cauchy sequence, 36, 346
Characteristic function, 60, 181, 301
Choice function, 322
Class $C^{(m)}$, function of, 78
Class calculus, 7–10, 297–300
Classes $\mathfrak{A}$ and $\mathfrak{C}$ of sets, 175
Closed sequences in $\mathfrak{L}_2$, 248
Closed set, 45, 340
Closed sphere, 341
Closure of a set, 45, 340
Cofinal sets, 326
Compact sets, 119, 356
Complement of a set, 8, 42
Complete linearly ordered sets, 28

Complete metric space, 346
Complete sequences in $\mathfrak{L}_2$, 248
Completion of a space, 348
Component of a space, 352
Concave function, 116
Condensation point, 354
Conditional of propositions, 2
Conditionally compact sets, 360
Conjunction of propositions, 2
Connected set, 47, 351
Continuous function, 63, 341
  of two variables, 102
Continuum, 47, 352
Continuum hypothesis, 320
Convergence, absolute, 108
  absolutely-uniform, 110
  almost uniform, 183
  in the mean, 237
  in measure, 236–237
  by rows, 113
  unconditional, 108
  uniform, 98
Convergent series, 107
Convex set, 47
Countable sets, 315
Counter class, 10, 18, 311
Curves, 48, 211

D

Decimal sequence, 38
Dedekind cuts, 28
Dedekind property, 28, 37
Degenerate interval, 174
de Morgan's laws, 4, 10, 299
Dense linearly ordered set, 28
Denumerable, 38
Derivate, 73, 204
Derivative, 69, 72, 205, 252–253
  of limit functions, 103, 252
Derived set, 45
Diameter of a set, 339
Differential of a function of several variables, 76
Dini's theorem, 121
Discrete metric, 337
Discriminatory chains, 326
Disjoint sets, 42, 174, 299
Distance, 335
Divergent series, 107, 115
Domain of a function, 11, 54, 300

E

Egoroff's theorem, 184, 239
ϵ-neighborhood, of a function, 119
  of a point, 43
  of a set, 44
Equicontinuous functions, 119, 362
Equivalence relation, 24, 303
Equivalent metrics, 343
Equivalent sequences, 38
Essentially bounded functions, 183, 186
Exceptional points, 142, 170
Existential quantifier, 6
Extension of a function, 116, 347
Extensionally attainable properties, 180
Exterior measure, 88, 197
Exterior point, 44, 339

F

Field, 33
Finite intersection property, 359
Finite sets, 315, 317
Fixed point, 146, 149
Frontier point, 44, 339
Fubini's theorem, 218
Function, 11, 54, 300
  of accumulation, 119
  additive, 174, 196–197
  bilinear, 76
  characteristic, 60, 181, 301
  choice, 322
  of class $C^{(m)}$, 78
  concave, 116
  continuous, 63, 341–342
    norm of, 119
  derivate of, 73, 204
  differential of, 76
  domain of, 11, 54, 300
  equicontinuous, 119, 362
  essentially bounded, 183, 186
  extension of, 116, 347

Function, integrable, 85, 189, 260, 261, 269, 271
  of intervals, 174
  jump, 268
  limit of, 56
  linear, 75
  maximum and minimum of, 65
  measurable, 183
  of measurable sets, 197
  nondifferentiable, 125, 369
  oscillation of, 88
  range of, 11, 54, 300
  restriction of, 56, 301
  semicontinuous, 63
  of singularities, 269
  space, 344
  step, 181
  summable, 189
  uniformly continuous, 66
  variation of, 202
Fundamental set of solutions, 161

G

Greatest lower bound, 28, 57, 62, 305

H

Hamel basis, 327
Hartogs theorem, 322
Heine-Borel theorem, 51
Hereditary classes, 302, 314
Hilbert space, 336
Hölder condition, 118
Hölder's inequality, 233
Homeomorphism, 342

I

Identity, **7**
Implication, **7**
Indecomposable ordinals, 331
Indefinite integral, 90, 187
Infinity, axiom of, 10, 314
  points at, 40, 349–350
Integrable functions in the sense, of Lebesgue, 189
  of Riemann, 85, 194
  of Stieltjes, 260–261, 269, 271
Integral of differential equations, 168
Integration, of limit functions, 103, 185, 190, 193, 240–241, 281–292
  by parts, 94, 220, 265
  by substitution, 94, 221–227
Interchange of order, of differentiation, 80
  of repeated limits, 100
Interior point, 44, 339
Interval, 41, 174
Interval function, 174
Isolated point, 44, 339
Isometry, 347
Isomorphism, 17, 23

J

Jordan content, 88
Jump function, 268

L

$\mathfrak{L}_p$, l_p, 232, 247–251, 338
Lattice, 305
Least upper bound, 28, 57, 62, 305
Lebesgue measure, 88, 195
Lebesgue number of a covering, 365
Length of a curve, 212
Limit ordinals, 313
Limit point, 44
Limited variation, 202, 267
Limits, 36, 49, 56, 236
  lower and upper, 57, 58, 62, 98
  of a sequence of sets, 42, 43
Lindelöf property, 354
Linear class of functions, 119, 181
Linear differential equations, matrix solution of, 161
Linear function, 75
Linear operator, 182, 262, 292
Linear order, 21, 27, 28, 305
Linear space, 119
Lipschitz condition, 118, 136, 203
Locally compact space, 361
Locally connected sets, 352
Logical addition and multiplication, 181

Logical connectives, 2–7, 12–13
Logical laws, 4–7
Lower bound, 28, 57, 62, 305
Lower integral, 86, 269
Lower limit, 58, 62, 98
Lower semicontinuity, 63

M

Mapping, 300
Mathematical induction, 18, 19
Matrix solution of linear differential equations, 161
Maximum of a function, 65
Mean-value theorems, for derivatives, 71, 72, 81
  for integrals, 96, 231
Measurable function, 183
Measure, exterior, 88, 197
  Lebesgue, 195
  zero, 88, 178
Metric density, 210
Minimum of a function, 65
Minkowski's inequality, 234
Modulus of continuity, 116
Monotonic functions, 56
Monotonic sequences, 37
Moore theorem, 100
Morgan, de, laws of, 4, 10, 299
Multiplicative axiom, 321, 323

N

Natural numbers, 18–23, 314–316
Negation of a proposition, 2
Neighborhood, 43, 44, 119, 339
Nondifferentiable functions, 125, 369
Norm, of a continuous function, 119
  of a function in $\mathfrak{L}_p$, 246
  of a point, 76
Nowhere-dense set, 46, 365
Null class, 8, 42, 299

O

Open covering, 354
Open set, 45, 177, 340, 354
Open sphere, 339
Operations on classes, 8, 42, 45, 298–300
Order type, 308
Ordered field, 33
Ordinal number, 308, 311
  of first and second kinds, 313, 315
Ordinary point, 142, 170
Oscillation of a function, 88
Oscillatory series, 107, 114

P

Parseval's theorem, 251
Partial ordering, 304
Partition, 85, 201, 260, 303
  simplicial, 146
Peano postulates for the natural numbers, 18, 19
Peano space, 361
Perfect set, 46
Point, 40
  of accumulation (*see* Accumulation point)
  exceptional, 142
  fixed, 146, 149
  frontier, 44, 339
  ordinary, 142
Power set, 300
Prime ordinals, 332
Primitive, 90
Projection, 301

R

Range of a function, 11, 54, 300
Reflexive relation, 25, 302
Regular sequences, 36
Relative closure, 46
Riesz' theorem, 295
Riesz-Fischer theorem, 250
Rolle's theorem, 70

S

Schwarz inequality, 234
Self-compact sets, 356
Semi-group, 24
Separable sets, 123, 354
Sequences, decimal, 38
  equivalent, 38
  in $\mathfrak{L}_2$, closed, 248

Sequences, in $\mathfrak{L}_2$, complete, 248
  limits of, 36, 49
  monotonic, 37
  of numbers, 36
  of points, 49
  regular, 36
  of sets, 42, 43
Series, 107
  asymptotic, 115
  summability of, 114
Sets, bounded, 49, 339
  category of, 365
  classes $\mathfrak{A}$ and $\mathfrak{C}$ of, 175
  closed, 45, 340
  cofinal, 326
  compact, 119, 356
    conditionally, 360
  complete linearly ordered, 28
  connected, 47, 351
    locally, 352
  convex, 47
  countable, 315
  dense, in another set, 46, 340, 365
    in itself, 46, 340
  derivative, 45
  disjoint, 42, 174, 299
  finite, 315, 317
  measurable, 195
  nowhere-dense, 46, 365
  open, 45, 340
    base for, 354
  perfect, 46
  power, 300
  relatively closed, 46
  separable, 123, 354
  sequences of, 42, 43
  totally disconnected, 352
  well-ordered, 306
Sheet of points, 141, 142
Similar classes, 308
Simple ordering, 305
Simplex, 146
Simplicial partition, 146
Solution of a differential equation, 152
Step functions, 181
Successive substitutions, 134–136, 152
Summability of series, 114
Summable functions, 189
Symmetric relations, 25, 302

T

Taylor's theorem, 72, 80, 95
Theorem of the mean, 71, 72, 81
  for integrals, 96, 231
Tonelli, absolute continuity in the sense of, 257
Topological property, 343
Total differential, 76
Total variation, 202, 209
Totally bounded space, 358, 362
Totally disconnected sets, 352
Transfinite induction, 313
Transformation, 300
Transitive relations, 21, 25, 302
Trichotomy of cardinals, 321–322
Truth table, 5

U

Unconditional convergence, 108
Uniform approach to upper and lower limits, 98
Uniform continuity, 66, 345
Uniform convergence, 98
Uniformly equivalent metrics, 345
Universal quantifier, 3, 6
Universal space, 364
Upper bound, 28, 57, 62, 305
Upper integral, 86, 269
Upper limit, 57, 62, 98
Upper semicontinuity, 63, 64

V

Variation of a function, 202

W

Weierstrass, 49
  approximation theorem of, 123
Well-ordered sets, 306

Z

Zermelo's axion, 10, 321–323
Zorn's lemma, 324–326